Elonka Dunin is an award-winning cryptographer and game developer. She led the team that cracked the decade-old Cyrillic Projector cipher, and is an internationally recognized expert on the codes of the CIA's Kryptos sculpture. She is also a founding member of the International Game Developer Association's Online Games Special Interest Group. When not cracking codes, she lives and works in St. Louis, Missouri, managing online communities at Simutronics (play.net).

Also available

THE MAMMOTH BOOK OF
SECRET CODE
PUZZLES

Elonka Dunin

ROBINSON

ROBINSON

First published in the UK by Robinson, an imprint of Constable & Robinson Ltd, 2006

Reprinted by Robinson in 2017

5 7 9 10 8 6

A CIP catalogue record for this book
is available from the British Library.

UK ISBN: 978-1-84529-325-3

Robinson
An imprint of
Little, Brown Book Group
Carmelite House
50 Victoria Embankment
London EC4Y 0DZ

An Hachette UK Company
www.hachette.co.uk

www.littlebrown.co.uk

First published in the United States in 2007 by Running Press Book Publishers
A member of the Perseus Books Group

Books published by Running Press are available at special discounts for bulk purchases in the
United States by corporations, institutions and other organizations. For more information, please
contact the Special Markets Department at the Perseus Books Group, 2300 Chestnut Street, Suite 200,
Philadelphia, PA 19103, or call (800) 810-4145, ext. 5000, or email special.markets@perseusbooks.com.

US Library of Congress data available on file
US ISBN 978-0-7624-1726-2

10 9 8 7 6 5 4 3 2 1
Digit on the right indicates the number of this printing

Running Press Book Publishers
2300 Chestnut Street
Philadelphia, PA 19103-4371
Visit us on the web!
www.runningpress.com

Printed and bound in Great Britain by CPI Group (UK) Ltd., Croydon CR0 4YY

Papers used by Robinson are from well-managed forests and other responsible sources

MIX
Paper from
responsible sources
FSC® C104740

CONTENTS

CONTENTS (continued)

INTRODUCTION

You have in your hands the largest ever collection of secret code puzzles, enough to satisfy any Robert Langdon, Sophie Neveu, Marian Rejewski or Sherlock Holmes. The puzzles range from easy cryptograms – over half the book falls into this category – to fiendish ciphers used in actual wartime conditions. All are designed to be solved with pencil and paper.

If you have never solved a cryptogram before, don't worry! This book follows a 'desert island' rule. All the basic information that you need to reach the solutions is contained inside the book. So if you find yourself stranded on an island, or an extended plane ride, any tables and reference charts you'll need to solve the puzzles are right here in your hand.

I am often asked why people are so fascinated by puzzles and codes. My guess is that it stems from our nature, as humans, to want to improve ourselves – to gain advantage of some type. Knowledge is power, and the desire to solve puzzles could have been that tiny edge that gave our Stone Age ancestors the ability to survive. Whether it was to bury a cache of water in a dry desert, or to understand the language of another tribe so as to trade goods, our species has always loved to take on challenges and discover new ways of doing things.

That desire is encapsulated in a single encrypted message. You look at it, you know you cannot read it (yet), but you also know that if you just set your mind to it, it will surrender its secrets, and you'll gain control over it. The final realization of having solved it – that brilliant moment when everything clicks – is often more gratifying than reading the final message!

And even if you manage to solve every cipher in this book, you'll still find a further 'metapuzzle' mystery remaining, for those sharp enough to figure it out *(hint: scrutinize the Hidden Key Puzzles for a clue. Remember to look both for things that are there, and things that are not).*

I hope you'll find the puzzles in this book as much fun to solve as they were to make. Good luck!

P.S. 64:

T W V 0 Y X B 1 e n p s Z T o g U m V t Z W 1 i Z X I g Z W F j a C B j a X B o Z X I g a G
F z I D M g c G F y d H M 6 I C B D a X B o Z X I s I G t I e S w g J i B h b n N 3 Z X I u

CRYPTOGRAPHY 101

The word 'cryptography' literally means *hidden writing*. There are many ways to hide a message, but they all boil down to three types of systems: substitution; transposition; and concealment. The puzzles in this book make use of one or more of these methods.

Like for like – *substitution*
When most people think about secret codes, the first thought is of a simple substitution method, where each letter in a message is replaced with a different letter. For example, if each letter is replaced with the letter immediately following it in the alphabet:

```
A = B
B = C
C = D
D = E
E = F
(etc.)
```

This could be described as saying that the letters ABCDE were enciphered as BCDEF. Simple substitution ciphers like this form the easiest kind to crack (and all the puzzles in the first Part of this book are like this.)

Substitution ciphers can be as simple as that one-to-one swap for each letter, or as complicated as encrypting each letter of a message via an entirely different set of rules, called 'polyalphabetic'.

Other substitution methods might swap a single plaintext letter with multiple letters or symbols. Morse code is a classic example of such a system, where each letter is replaced with a variable-length group of dots and/or dashes.

Mixing it up – *transposition*
In the transposition method, the letters of the message are not changed into something else, but instead scrambled by some predefined method. An extremely simple transposition method would be to spell something backwards, so CAT would become TAC. More complicated transposition systems may involve for example

arranging the letters of a message into rows of set length, and then reading off the letters vertically by column to arrive at the encrypted message.

Sheep's clothing – *concealment*

In substitution and transposition systems, it's usually clear there is something there which has been encrypted. But with a concealment cipher, the message is hidden in such a way that it is not even clear that there is a hidden message.

For example, examine the sentence: 'Carrie adores Theodore.' Taking the first letter of each word, there is a hidden word inside: CAT. Another example of a concealment cipher would be using invisible ink to put a secret message on an otherwise normal looking piece of paper. The secret message might not be encrypted with a substitution or a transposition cipher, but it would still definitely be hidden!

Concealment ciphers usually piggyback on top of (or inside of) some other message, like a letter from a prisoner which has a secret message concealed by using the first letter of each sentence. Computers can also be used to come up with sophisticated ways of concealing messages, such as hiding information inside digital images by making small changes to the binary code that makes up the graphic file.

Modern concealment ciphers are often referred to as 'steganography', meaning 'covered writing'. For the puzzles in this book, the best way to solve concealment ciphers is to be extra vigilant and to look out for anything that may seem out of place, such as odd punctuation, or elements of a list that are not numbered in an expected way. It may also be worth looking at the typical length of certain messages – for example, comparing what appears to be the answer of a cipher, with the length of its ciphertext. If it looks like the cipher is longer than the answer, it may be because the cipher contains more information than expected! There are dozens of concealment ciphers in this book, which give clues towards a larger metapuzzle. (For a hint as to where to start, check the Introduction)

PART ONE: SIMPLE CRYPTOGRAMS

Part One contains over 400 simple cryptogram puzzles for you to enjoy. Hidden in the puzzles are famous quotations and secret messages. They all use what's known as the simple substitution method – where each letter of the alphabet stands for another – so the only skill required is a little trial-and-error and everyday logic. The puzzles start easy and then get slightly harder, but even the more difficult ones are still within the capabilities of a casual solver. To get things started, there's an explanation of the simple substitution cipher, and tips for solving.

FIRST STEPS

The simple substitution cipher is where it all begins.

In one form of the simple substitution cipher – the form most commonly used in cryptogram puzzle books – each letter of the alphabet is replaced by a corresponding letter from a randomly scrambled cipher alphabet.

The best way to visualize this method is to line up a cipher alphabet underneath a normal plaintext alphabet. Encipherment is then a matter of looking for the appropriate letter in the plain alphabet, and seeing what it lines up against in the cipher alphabet. For example:

```
Plaintext:   ABCDEFGHIJKLMNOPQRSTUVWXYZ
Ciphertext:  EDRJHISFCBZYXTLVWNAPQGOMKU
```

```
PT:     Great    spirits    have    encountered
CT:     SNHEP    AVCNCPA    FEGH    HTRLQTPHNHJ

        violent  opposition  from  weak
        GCLYHTP  LVVLACPCLT  INLX  OHEZ

        minds.  - Albert  Einstein
        XCTJA.  - EYDHNP  HCTAPHCT
```

Notice how the word breaks are still intact, making it what is known as an 'Aristocrat' cipher.

In a 'Patristocrat' cipher, the advantage of seeing the word breaks is removed, by forcing the letters into blocks of 5. If there aren't enough letters to make a message evenly divisible by 5, then null characters (such as Q, X, Y, or Z) may be added to fill out the blocks.

```
Plaintext:   ABCDEFGHIJKLMNOPQRSTUVWXYZ
Ciphertext:  KDABHTWPZCMLUNXYVOSEQGPRIJ
```

```
CT:     EXUKM    HKNKY    YLHYZ    HTOXU    SAOKE
PT:     Tomak    eanap    plepi    efrom    scrat
```

```
APIXQ   UQSET   ZOSEA   OHKEH   EPHQN
chyou   mustf   irstc   reate   theun

ZGHOS   HQAKO   LSKWK   NWXYZ
ivers   e.Car   lSaga   n....
```

(To make an apple pie from scratch, you must first
create the universe. — Carl Sagan)

Basic tips

The good news if you are starting out is that, whilst there are
various types of simple substitution ciphers, they all share exactly
the same weakness: the letter distribution remains the same. Any
time an A is encrypted, it is always encrypted to the same
ciphertext equivalent throughout the message. Any place that the
letters TH are encrypted, there will be the same ciphertext pair of
letters. By recognizing patterns in these ciphers, you can guess
what the letters are and decipher the message.

Check the sentence structure

You can tell a lot simply by examining how the letters are arranged
in the various words. For example, in English, there are only two
words that are one letter long: 'A', and 'I'.

If the puzzle is a quote, and includes the name of the person
quoted at the end, this may be another possible place to start. For
example, try common first names. There are also some people
who get quoted often, such as Benjamin Franklin, so if you see a
name that has two words of similar length, he may be worth trying
as a guess.

Letter frequency analysis

Once you've got a feel for the overall sentence structure, look
carefully at the frequency of the letters used. Frequency analysis
is the single most powerful tool in your cryptanalysis arsenal.

Languages tend to have certain patterns. In English, the most
common letter is E. Taken in order, the most commonly used
letters are: ETAOINSHRDLU. One way to remember these is to

split them into words, or even a name. When I took a typesetting class at school, I was taught to remember the name 'Etaoin Shrdlu' (pronounced 'Ay'-Toe-In Shoord'-loo'), as someone who could be useful when dealing with the English language!

Count all the letters in the puzzle, look for the most common ones, and then compare them with the most common letters in the language. For example, if you discover that the most common letter in a particular puzzle is Q, then it's very likely that that Q is there in place of either E, T, A, O, I, or N!

Vowels and spaces are going to be the most frequent. Consonants S, T, N, and R are more common than others. The most common doubled letters are LL, EE, and SS.

You can also carry out frequency analysis on letter groups, especially for small words and repeated letters. For example, compare two-letter words for common starting or ending letters. If there are three two-letter words that all start with the same letter but end with a different one, they may be words such as IT, IN, or IS.

If there's no clue as to the lengths of the words, a cryptogram becomes more difficult to break, but repeated groups of letters will still form common words. For example, if DQM is repeated several places throughout the text, you could hazard a guess that those letters are a common word such as THE or AND.

For a detailed list of common letters, digrams, trigrams, and words in the English language, flip to the appendix on page 573.

FIRST STEP PUZZLES

Here are five easy starter puzzles to get you going, that are quotations by famous historical figures. They are all simple substitution ciphers, where each letter of the alphabet stands for another. Can you work out who the people are and what they said? If you need it, a helpful tip is given for each puzzle.

DIFFICULTY RATING: 1

SOLUTIONS: PAGE 528

1

Uatnatl xhq nabgd napn xhq spg, hl

napn xhq spg'n, xhq plt qmqpeex

lbyan. Atglx Vhli (1863 – 1947)

Hint: contains the word 'whether'

Solution:

_____

_____

_____

_____

2

Vcsj eckkpdjb asqvssj qvk sudhp,

D mhvmyp hdgs qk qoy qcs kjs D'us

jsuso qodsw astkos.

— Ims Vspq (1892-1980)

Hint: contains the word 'between'

Solution:

_____

_____

_____

_____

_____

<u>3</u>

D wi jks ndqoktpwbgn, rgowtqg

gugpy vpkjb wssgils ndqowpngn dq

wjkscgp qsgl akpvwpn.

Sckiwq W. Gndqkj

Hint: contains the word 'attempt'

Solution:

_____

_____

_____

_____

_____

4

Wbvp co v wuut? V lgvjp wbkou

scnpquo bvsu jkp iuuj tcorksunut. -

Nvglb Wvgtk Uhunokj

Hint: contains the word 'virtues'

Solution:
_____

_____

_____

_____

_____

5

F julb refq ibrrbp imkdbp reuk
tqtui sbautqb F iuah reb rfjb rm
juhb fr qempr. — Siufqb Nuqaui

Hint: contains the word 'letter'

Solution:
_____
_____
_____
_____
_____

EASY 100

Try these 100 encrypted sayings by well known names past and present. They all use simple letter substitution, so look out for telltale patterns in the words and letters, and you'll soon be able to decipher the message. If you need a hand, a clue is given for each puzzle on page 16.

(You may also find the occasional 'metapuzzle' clue as you work through these ciphers. If you find one, make a note of it, as it may come in handy later! Dozens of metapuzzle hints are scattered throughout the book.)

DIFFICULTY RATING: 2
SOLUTIONS: PAGE 528

Hints
Here's a tip for each of the puzzles in this section. The letter on the left is a letter from the ciphertext, and the letter on the right is its plaintext equivalent.

1.	W=A	21.	F=S	41.	H=O	61.	E=C	81.	L=P
2.	R=H	22.	H=M	42.	S=C	62.	S=P	82.	L=O
3.	N=I	23.	V=T	43.	I=M	63.	Y=Y	83.	A=G
4.	I=A	24.	N=E	44.	S=T	64.	E=B	84.	T=B
5.	F=L	25.	M=S	45.	S=T	65.	H=L	85.	O=G
6.	R=T	26.	Q=T	46.	I=L	66.	T=E	86.	N=Q
7.	N=C	27.	O=E	47.	R=S	67.	T=U	87.	T=D
8.	J=O	28.	Q=S	48.	K=N	68.	A=N	88.	N=A
9.	H=E	29.	Q=T	49.	Z=Z	69.	H=K	89.	I=M
10.	R=C	30.	C=E	50.	R=T	70.	W=W	90.	H=I
11.	G=R	31.	K=O	51.	N=E	71.	E=S	91.	E=K
12.	B=G	32.	R=T	52.	P=S	72.	R=U	92.	L=E
13.	I=H	33.	O=T	53.	G=A	73.	A=C	93.	Z=Z
14.	J=M	34.	Z=A	54.	O=T	74.	S=U	94.	Z=Z
15.	N=E	35.	E=B	55.	K=S	75.	Y=Y	95.	U=V
16.	B=H	36.	R=E	56.	S=T	76.	E=D	96.	P=W
17.	Q=T	37.	Q=T	57.	L=O	77.	K=P	97.	A=I
18.	D=I	38.	H=F	58.	Q=S	78.	E=J	98.	T=T
19.	F=N	39.	A=G	59.	M=A	79.	H=L	99.	E=C
20.	N=T	40.	C=H	60.	E=T	80.	T=U	100.	M=O

<u>1</u>

WXFML LBH LTCH PH LBTDV PH

YWD CWVH HDZK CHHL, KFCHXFZS

CFNHK LBH HDZK. – BHJXHJL

BFFNHJ, 31KL MK GJHKTZHDL

Solution:
_____

_____

_____

_____

_____

2

RH GHPHOVHP MLOLGBPH WRK
ILDHP RBP UKIMLJBKJP FLSER. –
QRH DKOLJ. IHQLMSZZFH RBJQ:
QRH PHVHJQR BP TOKI PUKQQ LJG
GKSEFLP.

Solution:
_____
_____
_____
_____
_____

<u>3</u>

Wonga kja lapqkj oaqnreraq dauesqa oa taagq njtapnkp; roa kroap nq dsqy hefnji hnqrefaq ejc daukhnji qslapnkp. — Oajpy U. Gnjf

Solution:
_____
_____
_____
_____
_____

4

I CIWQND GL I YNRROU UFO

RNWXL BOA FGL AECDNRRI UFNW

KFN LAW GL LFGWGWH, CAK

UIWKL GK CIMQ KFN EGWAKN GK

CNHGWL KO DIGW. — EIDQ KUIGW

Hint: contains the word 'Umbrella'

Solution:
_____

_____

_____

_____

_____

5

CFF NILQN IT MIGJSQUL ULLILN
CLU HIW QSLHAHE SJ. YIS'P OU
NSLJLANUP QI DHIW QRU HSGOUL
IT PIMQILN WRI MFCAG QRUY CLU
QLUCQAHE JLUEHCHQ GUH. –
ANCCM CNAGIV

Solution:
_____
_____
_____
_____
_____

6

JR RWMIRY YMJPQ KE JNM RTM
WAFF PMANIQ; JR RTAPRY, RTM
WAR; JIG JR EKPRY, RTM
BSGNHMIR. – UMIBJHAI EPJICFAI

Solution:
_____
_____
_____
_____
_____

7

NJEFL YMUQ RCLAEQ IERMQE YMU

OMCLT FT KY SOMTS. – IELDFKCL

RQFLHJCL

Hint: Ben

Solution:
_____

_____

_____

_____

_____

8

NJQS SBJT GJUK GCLK? SBKI NJ

IJS QOTFINKP SCHK, LJP SBFS CQ

SBK QSTLL GCLK CQ HFNK JL. –

RKIDFHCI LPFIEGCI

Solution:
_____
_____
_____
_____
_____

9

Hqjlqhhuv olnh wr vroyh sureohpv.
Li wkhuh duh qr sureohpv kdqglob
dydlodeoh, wkhb zloo fuhdwh wkhlu
rzq sureohpv. — Vfrww Dgdpv

Solution:
_____

_____

_____

_____

_____

<u>10</u>

lviqy rdtdzil wdjj ai eaji, dl cds
oqmnurtdvi yieqs wcil ci ds
ieqldlb, tm dlsuqi cdksijg ebedlst
tci qevebis mg djjliss dl cds mjn
ebi. — Jylnml A. Fmclsml

Solution:
_____
_____
_____
_____
_____

<u>11</u>

VLVGO TQH'I AZWV VHUI JYV IQTV

MQO. ZJ ZI BHAO JYV UVJQZAI BW

YBM YV AZLVU QHU YBM YV UZVU

JYQJ UZIJZHXKZIY BHV TQH WGBT

QHBJYVG. VGHVIJ YVTZHXMQO

Solution:
_____
_____
_____
_____
_____

<u>12</u>

BEDJ IEY XS RSILKOEOY EJN

TJPSOREDJ; XTR SUSO VCDHS YKT

HDUS, SWLSJQS DQ PKJQREJR EJN

PSOREDJ: EJN DR DQ SEQDSO RK

XTDHN RVK PCDIJSYQ RCEJ RK

GSSL KJS DJ ATSH. — XSJFEIDJ

AOEJGHDJ

Solution:

_____

_____

_____

_____

_____

<u>13</u>

IYKKLHDPP LH LHQDFFLSDHQ

KDJKFD LP QID NYNDPQ QILHS L

CHJU. - DNHDPQ IDGLHSUYW

Solution:

_____

_____

_____

_____

_____

14

ASJFK TCHBLBRX BQ NPMISLCI

KMR FQ JSLA EX YPCFR NBCLCQ

MT YMMI TMPRSKC RAFR QCHIMJ

AFNNCK FQ EX HBRRHC

FIUFKRFYCQ RAFR MLLSP CUCPX

IFX. – ECKDFJBK TPFKGHBK

Solution:
_____

_____

_____

_____

_____

15

B cnhbnvn rasr s qibnkrbqr hllgbkf

sr klkqibnkrbtbi mplchnjq bq duqr

sq eujc sq ran knxr fuy. – Pbiaspe

Tnykjsk

Solution:

_____

_____

_____

_____

_____

16

C bnvi klsbcka sl lggiq ous ofllh,
slcf, sinqr nkh rwins. — Wckrslk
Tbuqtbcff

Solution:
_____
_____
_____
_____
_____

17

A DACW QJ NWDAWUW QISQ
KWJKDW, AG QIW DJGE MTG, SMW
EJAGE QJ OJ FJMW QJ KMJFJQW
KWSHW QISG JTM EJUWMGFWGQP.
AGOWWO, A QIAGC QISQ KWJKDW
VSGQ KWSHW PJ FTHI QISQ JGW
JR QIWPW OSYP EJUWMGFWGQP
ISO NWQQWM EWQ JTQ JR QIW
VSY SGO DWQ QIWF ISUW AQ.

Solution:
_____

_____

_____

18

DS YKR WKRHU GJKW QCE TVHRE

KS IKJEY, BK VJU QOY QK

AKOOKW PKIE. – AEJFVIDJ

SOVJGHDJ

Solution:
_____
_____
_____
_____
_____

<u>19</u>

Tf hsm ehdo reomo wuq ubwuyq
jmuyom-ubhsp, jmhsp ufp
sfujhbhgorta. — Byfphf N. lhefqhf

Solution:
_____
_____
_____
_____
_____

20

BN BM V SLVGT FBMNVDU NH
NABGD HO IUBGS SLUVN WBNAHPN
SHHTGUMM VGT B JLHGHPGRU BN
VM RULNVBG NAVN NAULU WVM
GUQUL V NLPEY SLUVN FVG NAVN
WVM GHN VN NAU MVFU NBFU
NLPEY QBLNPHPM. — IUGCVFBG
OLVGDEBG

Solution:
_____
_____
_____
_____
_____

21

Vg'f fgevxvat gung Angvir

Nzrevpnaf ribyirq ab qrinfgngvat

rcvqrzvp qvfrnfrf gb tvir gb

Rhebcrnaf, va erghea sbe gur znal

qrinfgngvat rcvqrzvp qvfrnfrf gung

Vaqvnaf erprvirq sebz gur Byq

Jbeyq. — Wnerq Qvnzbaq

Solution:

_____

_____

_____

_____

_____

22

HFQOSLRE: RJE JLRREQR MGDNEQ
FI JEGG DPE PEQEPUET BLP
RJLQE VJL FI RFHEQ LB YPEDR
HLPDG NPFQFQ HDFIRDFI RJEFP
IESRPDGFRX. NLPPENR OSLRE:
'RJE TDPCEQR MGDNEQ FI JEGG
DPE PEQEPUET BLP RJLQE VJL
HDFIRDFI RJEFP IESRPDGFRX FI
RFHEQ LB HLPDG NPFQFQ.'

Solution:
_____
_____
_____
_____
_____

23

HYVNTDJ HB E DHI, E WHHA TN
FEU'N WJNV BLTJUD. TUNTDJ HB E
DHI TV'N VHH DELA VH LJED.
ILHYXSH FELG

Solution:
_____
_____
_____
_____
_____

24

Mnsin iskklr cn gnmr cx zlpin. Dr isk lkhx cn sibdnune cx tkenpqrskedka. — Shcnpr Ndkqrndk

Solution:
_____
_____
_____
_____
_____

<u>25</u>

Mrofgrf rpg jslocy lfdoaohg clhe fllhl pgi msjflmqoqohg. Lfdoaohg rpg jslocy mrofgrf clhe oihdpqly pgi cpdmf pumhdsqfm.

– Jhjf Nhtg Jpsd

Solution:

_____

_____

_____

_____

_____

26

QCT ATYDJDQDKJ KY DJPIJDQX DP

AKDJB QCT PIHT QCDJB KUTO IJA

KUTO IJA TWLTSQDJB ADYYTOTJQ

OTPRGQP. — NTJEIHDJ YOIJFGDJ

Solution:
_____
_____
_____
_____
_____

27

Rbo bcaboqr mkph km vcqdkh cq

fcjdjoqq. — Rbo Rwghtd

Solution:

_____

_____

_____

_____

_____

28

SDA JMQS AXRFSFLC NDPEQA SM

DAEP FL QRFALRA, SDA MLA SDES

DAPEIKQ LAW KFQRMVAPFAQ, FQ

LMS 'ATPAHE!' UTS 'SDES'Q

BTLLY...' – FQEER EQFJMV

Solution:

_____

_____

_____

_____

_____

29

QNJSRGB PKNCIEP LNJH

CUGBIBPP, TIU ENCBVJSP QJCG

LNJH IBBUGBPP BTPB.

- RBIDTHCI LNTIFGCI

Solution:
_____
_____
_____
_____
_____

<u>30</u>

Wc pk jkq skvcq rjyqbdja tnki rjy

jrqdkj cxsclq qbcdn ncolcsq.

— Wdjoqkj Sbunsbdhh

Solution:
_____
_____
_____
_____
_____

<u>31</u>

VOHH DKJO CR EOSSOQ SBWJ

VOHH RWCD. – EOJFWICJ

NQWJGHCJ

Solution:
_____
_____
_____
_____
_____

32

'RBCQ ITQR OL RBTPQGDY,' QDCG

DPRBTP RK BCIQLHA, QCJFCJS

HKW KVLP BCQ OLLP, 'C JLVLP

UKTHG SLR RBL BDJS KA

RBTPQGDYQ.'

Solution:
_____
_____
_____
_____
_____

33

Xjq yjoot yso vbto xjq btus oj ntx
jqo. Susmx hti btn obs mcybo oj
pjiomcaqos t usmns. — Rmjh obs
hjucs 'Bqnogs tie Rgjv'

Solution:
_____
_____
_____
_____
_____

34

Zuuzrih ziv vzhrvi lu vmgizmxv gszm lu vcrg; zmw rg rh yfg xlnnlm kifwvmxv gl hvv lfi dzb lfg yvuliv dv evmgfiv rm. Zvhlk

Solution:

_____

_____

_____

_____

_____

35

Erx vanq qakr anpq jk jiis kt njs
ioi gkjy qakr pangq pigg qax
jicippbqbip. — Eijdnhbj Tonjfgbj

Solution:
_____
_____
_____
_____
_____

36

Rhenfvn raqrq hc jvgu gur zbfg qbzrfgvpngrq navzny fcrpvrf va cneg orpnhfr vg'f gur jbeyq'f ynetrfg ynaq znff naq bssrerq gur zbfg jvyq fcrpvrf gb ortva jvgu.

– Wnerq Qvnzbaq

Solution:

_____

_____

_____

_____

_____

37

WXQNWHRPH RI DWAWIPW JA

FROWNQY RP IJ URLW.

QJFWNGILW RI QEW AGLW JA

QYNGIIY RP IJ URNQSW.

- OGNNY TJFDVGQWN

Solution:

_____

_____

_____

_____

_____

38

HELK RQEKP YCV RPBPC GPYKR

YAE ELK HYFXPKR SKELAXF

HEKFX EC FXUR QECFUCPCF Y

CPO CYFUEC, QECQPUBPV UC

MUSPKFG YCV VPVUQYFPV FE FXP

WKEWERUFUEC FXYF YMM IPC YKP

QKPYFPV PTLYM. CEO OP YKP

PCAYAPV UC Y AKPYF QUBUM OYK,

FPRFUCA OXPFXPK FXYF CYFUEC

EK YCG CYFUEC RE QECQPUBPV

YCV RE VPVUQYFPV QYC MECA

PCVLKP. OP YKP IPF EC Y AKPYF

SYFFMPHUPMV EH FXYF OYK. OP

XYBP QEIP FE VPVUQYFP Y

WEKFUEC EH FXYF HUPMV YR Y

HUCYM KPRFUCA-WMYQP HEK

FXERP OXE XPKP AYBP FXPUK

MUBPR FXYF FXYF CYFUEC IUAXF

MUBP. UF UR YMFEAPFXPK

HUFFUCA YCV WKEWPK FXYF OP

RXELMV VE FXUR. SLF UC Y

MYKAPK RPCRP, OP QYCCEF

VPVUQYFP, OP QYCCEF

QECRPQKYFP, OP QYCCEF

XYMMEO FXUR AKELCV. FXP

SKYBP IPC, MUBUCA YCV VPYV

OXE RFKLAAMPV XPKP XYBP

QECRPQKYFPV UF HYK YSEBP ELK

WEEK WEOPK FE YVV EK

VPFKYQF. FXP OEKMV OUMM

MUFFMP CEFP CEK MECA KPIPISPK

OXYF OP RYG XPKP, SLF UF QYC

CPBPK HEKAPF OXYF FXPG VUV

XPKP. UF UR HEK LR FXP MUBUCA

KYFXPK FE SP VPVUQYFPV XPKP

FE FXP LCHUCURXPV OEKN OXUQX

FXPG OXE HELAXF XPKP XYBP

FXLR HYK RE CESMG YVBYCQPV.

UF UR KYFXPK HEK LR FE SP

XPKP VPVUQYFPV FE FXP AKPYF

FYRN KPIYUCUCA SPHEKP

LR—FXYF HKEI FXPRP XECEKPV

VPYV OP FYNP UCQKPYRPV

VPBEFUEC FE FXYF QYLRP HEK

OXUQX FXPG AYBP FXP MYRF

HLMM IPYRLKP EH

VPBEFUEC—FXYF OP XPKP XUAXMG

KPREMBP FXYF FXPRP VPYV

RXYMM CEF XYBP VUPV UC BYUC,

FXYF FXUR CYFUEC LCVPK AEV

RXYMM XYBP Y CPO SÙKFX EH

HKPPVEI, YCV FXYF AEBPKCIPCF

EH FXP WPEWMP, SG FXP WPEWMP,

HEK FXP WPEWMP RXYMM CEF

WPKURX HKEI FXP PYKFX.

Solution:

_____

_____

_____

_____

_____

_____

_____

_____

_____

Solution:

_____

_____

_____

_____

_____

_____

_____

_____

_____

_____

_____

_____

_____

_____

_____

39

AUKCTQ WCRBLTR UITNGRCLK CQ

HCFU QCHVUP CK RBU JCKU. –

EUKDGJCK SPGKFHCK

Solution:
_____

_____

_____

_____

_____

40

CAVFLB SEEL ONNQ FR LN RCAKE,

SUT SEFLB ARCAKEM ND FT, FR.

— SELGAKFL DQALIJFL

Solution:
_____
_____
_____
_____
_____

41

IHGPNQX CN QIP EPNQ JHDCSX.

- EPGYBFCG OMBGADCG

Solution:
_____
_____
_____
_____
_____

42

C SKJSRCUR QBMQ QBR AORMQ

LMOQ KY QBR HCPROCRP KY

HMJFCJE MOR IOKTABQ TLKJ

QBRH IX YMGPR RPQCHMQRP

QBRX BMUR HMER KY QBR UMGTR

KY QBCJAP. — IRJDMHCJ

YOMJFGCJ

Solution:
_____
_____
_____
_____
_____

43

C IDY JKR BDVL SKJL WBLPL C
CJRLJGLG RK SK, OTR C RBCJF C
BDVL LJGLG TM WBLPL C JLLGLG
RK OL.

Solution:

_____

_____

_____

_____

_____

44

AS AR JHFY WCTH SCT QAPC IQT
RAPD SCIS SCTY EUFFY ETTF SCT
AGKJSTHPT JE WTIFSC.

- MTHBIGAH EQIHDFAH

Solution:
_____
_____
_____
_____
_____

45

ES SCGTR JMQT SDCK PCNESCH

SM RWEKB AUREKTRR. YMU'VT

BMS SM DCVT SDT C. E. I. ITBQTT

SM BTS AY — CIVTQSEREKB,

EKESECSEVT, CKI IYKCJEPR.

— ERCCP CREJMV

Solution:
_____

_____

_____

_____

_____

46

IGWR SMM BLKSIL GQL RLITMJ

MELYLT; SMM RLVLQL, RLITMJ

LXLNUSLT. - ELKFGJDK AQGKHIDK

Solution:

_____

_____

_____

_____

_____

47

IDRPTKSY: IKJYX DR SCY QKKS KA
MHH YUDH. NKQQYNS PTKSY: 'AKQ
SCY HKUY KA IKJYX DR SCY QKKS
KA MHH YUDH: VCDNC VCDHY RKIY
NKUYSYE MASYQ, SCYX CMUY
YQQYE AQKI SCY AMDSC, MJE
LDYQNYE SCYIRYHUYR SCQKTBC
VDSC IMJX RKQQKVR.'

Solution:
_____
_____
_____
_____
_____

48

Kwrspi sqiq lkhy rbi hlkgiqr
rbpiwvq rl uiwti bip mwrripkq, ql
rbwr iwab qjwhh mciai ln bip
nwepca pitiwhq rbi lpgwkczwrclk ln
rbi ikrcpi rwmiqrpy. – Pcabwpv M.
Niykjwk

Solution:
_____
_____
_____
_____
_____

50

Rbt jmmk cks mrbtp lthtqrdch
emsdtq qbmuhs et iptt imp
txnhmpcrdmk cks uqt ey chh
lmukrpdtq. Km lmukrpy qbmuhs et
ntpjdrrts rm csvcklt c lhcdj mi
qmvtptdakry. —Hyksmk E. Fmbkqmk

Solution:
_____
_____
_____
_____
_____

51

Cqn anyxacb xo vh mnjcq qjen
knnw panjcuh ngjppnajcnm.

– Vjat Cfjrw

Solution:
_____
_____
_____
_____
_____

52

QES PQOAJQSPQ FIW PKGSQAGSP
NSJKGSP QES PSVSOSPQ
AHBRPQAJS.

– NSHBIGAH TOIHDFAH

Solution:
_____
_____
_____
_____
_____

53

TCD WDGJ HGM MDVDR IORBEVD.
IORBEVDMDSS ES TCD GTTREAUTD
OI TCD STROMB.

Solution:
_____
_____
_____
_____
_____

54

OLIS BAVO OLI JIFIGAQ

KXWIGVTIVO DXVOGXQQMVK

EXDMAQ EIDRGMOS QMPI MO'E

EXTI PMVF XJ JIFIGAQ YGXKGAT

Solution:
_____
_____
_____
_____
_____

55

JHZK EIKX QS UZTI ZK QTI OJ
DHZRH O UOT UOB EZI, WGJ SLQU
DHZRH HI ROTTQJ LIKZNT.

Solution:
_____
_____
_____
_____
_____

56

VDASYUYP EQ NYCTK EK AKCYP

YKRQ EK QDAJY. — NYKFAJEK

BPAKHIEK

Solution:
_____

_____

_____

_____

_____

57

WLPG HQ CE YLT WRPR SL ICVR H

BTKDPRD YRHPQ. MPHY HQ CE

YLT WRPR SL DCR SLJLPPLW.

- URKFHJCK EPHKGICK

Solution:
_____
_____
_____
_____
_____

58

Xcqrcpykx eq lmr mspq rm
pctmucp, isr rmjmppmv eq mspq rm
vel mp hmqc. — Hxlyml I. Fmdlqml

Solution:
_____
_____
_____
_____
_____

59

KEF OMI WMGR TRMOR. EB KEF

OMI WMGR SBRRPEU. PEI'D RGRB

OEFID EI WMGXIV NEDW MD EIOR.

- BENRBD M. WRXIQRXI

Solution:
_____
_____
_____
_____
_____

60

OSS TK SAXW, IHWUWGWC AE
QMTWD EATW EM TOYW O
VWQADAMU, A TOYW AE OUV
XMCZWE OPMFE AE.

Solution:
_____
_____
_____
_____
_____

61

JR SNJQO WNJ TIQWOPOK SNO

ETFF JR TFFTN TIK SNO

GOQQOIAOP, OVOI TRSOP HOBIA

WJUIKOK, SNJQO WNJ KJ PBANS

TIK PORPTBI RPJG WPJIA NTVO T

APOTS POWTPK.

Solution:
_____
_____
_____
_____
_____

<u>62</u>

PMN PQ FWNCN KBUC FWN

SNPSGN PQ GPIZCZBMB BYN

TPZMT FP TNF TPPK TPLNYMJNMF

– BMK FWNU BYNM'F TPZMT FP

GZDN ZF. – WINU GPMT

Solution:
_____
_____
_____
_____
_____

63

' . . . hjqcto gia ujsiaotpp ju qct

Joato; wcjh jit gfwgyp ittap qj dttk

li hlia. Ujo Egohtflqt uolgop gia

isip, lq lp ju egklqgf lhkjoqgiet qj

cjijo qct Hjpq Rftppta Vlonli. Gia

wt fjvt cto lu wt tiatgvjo qj lhlqgqt

cto vloqst, tpktelgffy cshlflqy gia

otejffteqlji li kogyto. Jso ngzt

jsncq qj rt ejipqgiqfy qsoita qj cto,

jso guuteqljip aloteqta qj cto, tvto

dttklin li hlia qct oththrogiet ju

cto rtitulqp gia qoylin gfwgyp qj rt

uglqcusf qj cto.' – Pgliq Ogkcgtf

Dgflijwpdl

Solution:
_____
_____
_____
_____
_____
_____
_____
_____
_____

64

Ni nkkpnopm co jip vbj appso n
wmjwjscgp—bjkcir cq vcgg pnq bch
gnoq. — Vcioqji Wbtmwbcgg

Solution:
_____
_____
_____
_____
_____

65

OA CDVDH TM SHH; RMCDSOHA TM
JSKY; BSJDHDSQ WDTE BAW;
BQDAKI TM MKA; AKAJY TM KMKA.
- OAKFSJDK BQSKGHDK

Solution:

_____

_____

_____

_____

_____

66

Ot ujqmptjqn pj cgg, oqp bipbhcpt wbpa etw, cir gtp pajnt etw ot wtgg pmbtr otejmt yjq sbvt path yjqm ujiebrtiut. — Stjmst Wcnabispji

Solution:
_____
_____
_____
_____
_____

67

GLP H ILKA SCJO KLV C BHUO

SPCOZ QCJMIX SL VPCSO SBO

EOQS C RHK. QLJOSCJOQ C BHUO

ALLZ ITRF HKZ VPCSO EOSSOP

SBHK C RHK. OPKOQS BOJCKAVHX

Solution:
_____

_____

_____

_____

_____

68

Sbe n fhpprffshy grpuabybtl, ernyvgl zhfg gnxr cerprqrapr bire choyvp eryngvbaf, sbe Angher pnaabg or sbbyrq.

Solution:
_____
_____
_____
_____
_____

69

Kojbilr fx ktq blwqm efsnkl fk fy
atbx ktq nkhizaj qmb kojbilr qt jfhj
jnpyxpbx. — Rxmxyjf Dfkien

Solution:
_____
_____
_____
_____
_____

70

VLHF FY SDHMR HBMRLUOPIHG HV
WLIPRLM... PTRY VODD IGPH PWH
ALHQJM: 1) PTHMR WTH BDRRE
SHJIHQMDY OGE UIMIBDY OP OGY
BOE LRUIRW, OGE 2) PTHMR WTH
BDRRE SHJIHQMDY OGE
MRSLRPDY OP OGY BOE LRUIRW.
- IMOOS OMIFHU

Solution:
_____
_____
_____
_____
_____

<u>71</u>

RDLBP YJA HJIB YJDB SP LHEBMP,

OUH HS RBH HFB PUMM XJMUB SP

J GSZ ZSU CUEH FJXB ESCBOSNZ

HS NLXLNB LH TLHF. CJDI HTJLA

Solution:
_____
_____
_____
_____
_____

<u>72</u>

'Ahft h qmrqa bp jtqsi h ymshq
fbs.' — Osichgbi Tmhidfbi

Solution:
_____
_____
_____
_____
_____

<u>73</u>

CT LMTQ KMR NMQQTQQ VTWIRC;
DR NMQQTQQTQ CDJ.

- ETKFWJDK HPWKGIDK

Solution:
_____

_____

_____

_____

_____

74

Cmktqr ldyytptkatq hpt myrtk h

cthircx qdbk my npmbptqq.

— Jhchrjh Bhklcd

Solution:
_____
_____
_____
_____
_____

75

B NJHNTBVT QACQ QAT UMTCQ

KCMQ JI QAT GBPTMBTP JI

GCHEBHS CMT OMJRUAQ RKJH

QATG OY QAT ICFPT TPQBGCQTP

QATY ACVT GCST JI QAT VCFRT JI

QABHUP. — OTHDCGBH IMCHEFBH

Solution:
_____
_____
_____
_____
_____

76

DJSADKSRDLK DQ JLPN

DJMLPRSKR RBSK GKLVHNEAN.

GKLVHNEAN DQ HDJDRNE.

DJSADKSRDLK NKIDPIHNQ RBN

VLPHE

Solution:
_____
_____
_____
_____
_____

77

AG QIW HJTGHADP JR
EJUWMGFWGQ, VW FTPQ ETSMO
SESAGPQ QIW SHLTAPAQAJG JR
TGVSMMSGQWO AGRDTWGHW,
VIWQIWM PJTEIQ JM TGPJTEIQ,
NY QIW FADAQSMY-AGOTPQMASD
HJFKDWX. QIW KJQWGQASD RJM
QIW OAPSPQMJTP MAPW JR
FAPKDSHWO KJVWM WXAPQP SGO
VADD KWMPAPQ. VW FTPQ GWUWM
DWQ QIW VWAEIQ JR QIAP
HJFNAGSQAJG WGOSGEWM JTM
DANWMQAWP JM OWFJHMSQAH

KMJHWPPWP. VW PIJTDO QSCW

GJQIAGE RJM EMSGQWO. JGDY SG

SDWMQ SGO CGJVDWOEWSNDW

HAQAZWGMY HSG HJFKWD QIW

KMJKWM FWPIAGE JR QIW ITEW

AGOTPQMASD SGO FADAQSMY

FSHIAGWMY JR OWRWGPW VAQI

JTM KWSHWRTD FWQIJOP SGO

EJSDP, PJ QISQ PWHTMAQY SGO

DANWMQY FSY KMJPKWM

QJEWQIWM.

Solution:

_____

_____

_____

_____

_____

_____

_____

_____

_____

_____

_____

_____

_____

_____

_____

78

Cj vbnqcig , qnsqr cp pk lngdcksp

qrbq prg prkshy bhvbxp og

bqqgjygy ox b okyxasbny ku hcgp.

— Vcjpqkj Drsndrchh

Solution:
_____
_____
_____
_____
_____

79

Cq cp qbs dkiikj awchcjy ka
qkqwhcqwocwj osycisp qbwq qbsx
dwjjkq oswhhx rjnsopqwjn qbs
jwqros ka kro nsikdowdx. Qbsx
icpqwgs ncppsjq ako ncphkxwhqx.
Qbsx icpqwgs ospqhsppjspp ako w
osfsdqckj ka lkhcdx. Qbsx icpqwgs
w asu dkiicqqsssp ako w dkrjqox.
Qbsx icpfrnys cjnctcnrwh plssdbsp
ako lrehcd lkhcdx.

— Hxjnkj E. Fkbjpkj

80

Bs bq sar grkbtq li ltp

Dlkqsbstsblk saes tkurp bsq

qarhsrp li rkutpbkg bkqsbstsblkq

eku pllsru mpbkdbmhrq sarpr bq

ejmhr pllj ilp sar pbda irpsbhbsy li

Ejrpbdek mlhbsbdeh bkvrksblk.

– Hykulk N. Clakqlk

Solution:

_____

_____

_____

_____

_____

81

BS BQ SAI VJPDBHG FWH VAJ BQ

SAI AWLLY FWH. BS BQ SAI BKEI

FWH VAJ BQ SAI FBQIPWOEI FWH.

– OIHCWFBH NPWHDEBH

Solution:

82

XQRER GKR BUQ SVARB

RLNVKZVRB, BUQ SVARB BL RQQY

K MQBBQA ZVSQ SLA CKOYVOP.

- CVYUKVZ K. TLAMKNUQF

Solution:
_____

_____

_____

_____

_____

83

GUCPTOU CP QBU QCHU RKO

SKCJA PKHUQBCJA TPURTG. QBCP

GUCPTOU QBU SCGCAUJQ MUOPKJ

WCGG KEQLCJ QBU GLZY KJU

JUVUO. - EUJDLHCJ ROLJFGCJ

Solution:
_____
_____
_____
_____
_____

84

Bdveophnl gshipes df Grkdng weke
Eqkgodgf oiendeo pagp ngce df
rkhc pae fhkpa. Grkdng'o bhfm
gxdo, bdle pagp hr pae Gcekdngo,
do fhkpa/ohqpa kgpaek pagf
egop/weop. Pahoe Eqkgodgf
shceopdn cgccgbo oikegs
ohqpawgks veky obhwby df Grkdng,
uengqoe paey ags ph gsgip ph
sdrrekefp nbdcgpe zhfeo gfs
sdrrekefp gfdcgb sdoegoeo.

— Tgkes Sdgchfs

85

BYPISDQE: HKHP, GDDJ XDJJYMR.
Y RCEV FYB VEKK. –
PFHREPGEHJE, FHBKEQ MDJJEMQ
ISDQE: 'HKHP, GDDJ XDJYMR. Y
RCEV FYB, FDJHQYD – H TEKKDV
DT YCTYCYQE OEPQ, DT BDPQ
EWMEKKECQ THCMX.'

Solution:
_____
_____
_____
_____
_____

86

KYUYP IYTUY RETR RFII RLJLPPLV

VEFDE XLS DTK AL RLATX.

- OYKGTJFK BPTKHIFK

Solution:
_____
_____
_____
_____
_____

87

BXU ZWFKYQFSU KV KFU GKBUY

ZF Q TUNKSYQSM ZNEQZYA BXU

AUSCYZBM KV QHH.

- JKXF V. OUFFUTM

Solution:
_____
_____
_____
_____
_____

88

TDA IANQKAE BLLI WQFTAR
KLKRAKRA FK OATTAQ INKCUNCA
TDNK TDA UKIANQKAE – OUT FT'R
RTFII KLKRAKRA.
– OAKGNJFK BQNKHIFK

Solution:

_____

_____

_____

_____

_____

89

SCY TRY KA IKJYX DR MHH SCY

MEUMJSMBY SCYQY DR DJ CMUDJB

DS. - OYJFMIDJ AQMJGHDJ

Solution:
_____
_____
_____
_____
_____

90

JGZQ YHYA'J MUAJ HJ IBBY, JGZQ
MUAJZY HJ MZYAZFYUQ.

- EBVZEJ U. GZHAOZHA

Solution:
_____
_____
_____
_____
_____

91

WBJ CQ MCRB? BI SBPS MIDJCRIQ
CH BCQ KJMSCJH.

- OIHDPGCH NMPHEFCH

Solution:
_____
_____
_____
_____
_____

92

CA RBLPL'Q DJYRBCJS IKPL
CIMKPRDJR RBDJ IY LSK DPKTJG,
C WDJR CR UDTSBR DJG QBKR
JKW.

Solution:
_____
_____
_____
_____
_____

93

Wbrj C lrfair a lusgrtrrq, C was

tkho, rafb tcir C oqrw iy swkqo, C

sbkuho fkjscorq jkt wbat C gchhro,

lut wbat C ahhkwro tk hcvr.

– O'Aqtaejaj, 'Tbr laj cj tbr Cqkj

lasg'

Solution:

_____

_____

_____

_____

_____

94

GKWGYS GEL GT HOLPKDTD
CGRLOMY OI TCOUBCT GMN WORN
GMN NDDN. GKWGYS GEL GT
PUREIYEMB YOUR TCOUBCTS GMN
DVDRYTCEMB WEKK AD WDKK.

Solution:
_____
_____
_____
_____
_____

95

XSVEOS KA HDRRHS SWLSJQSQ. E
QIEHH HSEG VDHH QDJG E BOSER
QCDL. - XSJFEIDJ AOEJGHDJ

Solution:
_____
_____
_____
_____
_____

96

CRZXCRFZR UL X CUIIUZNBM
PGKC MG NLR LUFZR UM QXL
YRZGDR BUMMBR DGKR MQXF X
MRKD GI XYNLR XHHBURC YV
ZKUMUZL MG XFVMQUFT MQRV CG
FGM VRM NFCRKLMXFC GK PQUZQ
LRRDL MG CUIIRK IKGD MQRUK
DGKXB ZGFZRHML. RKFRLM
QRDUFTPXV

Solution:

_____

_____

_____

_____

_____

97

UANOMPNO SHU CSPOAJH SMR

OYR KSMRHON JI NRCPMAOX.

– ERHBSGAH IMSHDFAH.

GROSKPZZFR YAHO: OYR IAIOY AN

IMJG UJPTFSN SHU NCJOO

Solution:

_____

_____

_____

_____

_____

98

Rvrj tl tcds gky, jl jktdvr
Kustqkhdkj kjdikh smrndrs kjg ljhy
ljr mhkjt smrndrs — tcr iknkgkidk
jut — ckvr mqlvrg sudtkahr olq
glirstdnktdlj. Tcrqr stdhh kqr jl
glirstdn fkjbkqlls. — Ekqrg Gdkiljg

Solution:
_____
_____
_____
_____
_____

99

NRIILMJ DS TOI HAST, BIST OMPI

MN IARTO. – ABRAOAJ HDKEMHK

Solution:
_____

_____

_____

_____

_____

<u>100</u>

BI BRD QIRD KUAB, CN MLI
AMLSCDIQS BCS JMLG JCNI; EUT
BCS AMLTIKOJRTCML WRS KUAB
KMQI TBRL BCS QIRDCLG. BI WRS
WMLT TM SRY TBRT CN BI BRD
QIRD RS KUAB RS MTBIQ KIL BI
SBMUJD BRVI HLMWL LM KMQI
TBRL MTBIQ KIL.
- CSRRA RSCKMV

Solution:
_____
_____
_____
_____
_____

HIDDEN KEYS

There are lots of ways to make a simple substitution cipher. One already introduced is the 'random scramble'; where each letter of the alphabet is replaced with another letter from a randomly scrambled cipher alphabet (also known as a Kama Sutra cipher, since it has so many different combinations).

In practice, the random method can be cumbersome. Throughout history, ciphers have been used not simply for fun, but as a vitally important way of sending a secret message from a sender to a receiver.

A better cipher system is one that allows the sender to encrypt a message quickly, and the receiver to decrypt it just as quickly. If there is a pattern to the scrambling, that makes things easier to remember, and helps keep the sender and receiver in synch. The receiver does not need to 'puzzle out' the plaintext of the message, but instead can quickly create a plaintext to ciphertext table.

This is where hidden keys come in. During battlefield conditions, speed of decipherment may be crucial!

Caesar cipher

The simplest way of creating a non-random cipher alphabet is called a 'Caesar cipher' after the method used by Julius Caesar's army. Each plaintext letter is encrypted by shifting it forward three places in the alphabet. An A becomes a D, a B becomes an E, and so on.

A key element of a Caesar cipher is that the ciphertext alphabet is in the same order as the plaintext alphabet – it is just shifted left or right by a certain number of characters. Some variations nowadays may shift by a quantity other than three, but any cipher that keeps the order of the cipher alphabet intact, and merely changes the number of letters by which it is shifted left or right, can be called a Caesar cipher.

```
PT:    ABCDEFGHIJKLMNOPQRSTUVWXYZ
CT:    DEFGHIJKLMNOPQRSTUVWXYZABC
```

```
PT:     I like orange juice.
CT:     L OLNH RUDQJH MXLFH.
```

One version of a Caesar cipher, called ROT-13, was commonly used in internet newsgroups. It effectively performed a Caesar shift of +13, 'rotating' an alphabet by 13 characters:

```
PT:     ABCDEFGHIJKLMNOPQRSTUVWXYZ
CT:     NOPQRSTUVWXYZABCDEFGHIJKLM
```

The advantage of the number 13 is that it shifts exactly half of the 26-letter alphabet. This means that there is a one-to-one correspondence when encrypting or decrypting. An A encrypts to an N, and an N encrypts back to an A.

Try the following exercise. Create a cipher alphabet using the method suggested:

Method: Caesar +1

```
PT:     ABCDEFGHIJKLMNOPQRSTUVWXYZ
CT:     _____
```

Method: Caesar -2

```
PT:     ABCDEFGHIJKLMNOPQRSTUVWXYZ
CT:     _____
```

Solutions:
BCDEFGHIJKLMNOPQRSTUVWXYZA
YZABCDEFGHIJKLMNOPQRSTUVWX

Keywords

Another way to create a cipher alphabet is to scramble it in a methodical way. For example, if the keyword CRYPTO is chosen, then a cipher alphabet can be created by putting the word CRYPTO at the beginning, and following it with the other letters of the alphabet that aren't in the keyword:

CRYPTOABDEFGHIJKLMNQSUVWXZ

This results in a cipher alphabet that still has 26 letters, but is a bit more scrambled (and thereby harder to solve) than a simple Caesar cipher:

Key: CRYPTO

```
PT:     ABCDEFGHIJKLMNOPQRSTUVWXYZ
CT:     CRYPTOABDEFGHIJKLMNQSUVWXZ
```

```
PT:     I like cryptanalysis!
CT:     D GDFT YMXKQCICGXNDN!
```

This system can be used with any keyword, or even an entire keyphrase. If the key has any repeated letters, then only the first one is used, and the others are ignored:

Key: APPLE

```
PT:     ABCDEFGHIJKLMNOPQRSTUVWXYZ
CT:     APLEBCDFGHIJKMNOQRSTUVWXYZ
```

Key: I LIKE APPLES

```
PT:     ABCDEFGHIJKLMNOPQRSTUVWXYZ
CT:     ILKEAPSBCDFGHJMNOQRTUVWXYZ
```

Key: MISSISSIPPI

```
PT:     ABCDEFGHIJKLMNOPQRSTUVWXYZ
CT:     MISPABCDEFGHJKLNOQRTUVWXYZ
```

Here are some examples for practice. Try completing the cipher alphabet for each one using the key provided:

Key: BUTTERFLY

```
PT:     ABCDEFGHIJKLMNOPQRSTUVWXYZ
CT:     _____
```

Key: THE QUICK BROWN FOX

```
PT:      ABCDEFGHIJKLMNOPQRSTUVWXYZ
CT:      _____
```

Solutions :
BUTERFLYACDGHIJKMNOPQSVWXZ
THEQUICKBROWNFXADGJLMPSVYZ

Combinations

In practice it's common to combine different methods when encrypting a message. One possibility for example is to combine a keyed cipher alphabet with a Caesar technique. First use a key to create a cipher alphabet, and then shift that cipher alphabet a set number of spaces.

For example, using the CRYPTO cipher alphabet from a previous example:

```
PT:      ABCDEFGHIJKLMNOPQRSTUVWXYZ
CT:      CRYPTOABDEFGHIJKLMNQSUVWXZ
```

If this is combined with a 'shift of 2', it would look like this:

```
PT:      ABCDEFGHIJKLMNOPQRSTUVWXYZ
CT:      YPTOABDEFGHIJKLMNQSUVWXZCR
```

As a final exercise, try the following. Using the given keys, create the appropriate cipher alphabet.

Key: MADISON, with a shift of +2

```
PT:      ABCDEFGHIJKLMNOPQRSTUVWXYZ
CT:      _____
```

Key: BOTANY BAY, +5

```
PT:      ABCDEFGHIJKLMNOPQRSTUVWXYZ
CT:      _____
```

Solutions :
DISONBCEFGHJKLPQRTUVWXYZMA
YCDEFGHIJKLMPQRSUVWXZBOTAN

Tips for solving keyed ciphers

Look out for Caesar
If you suspect the method of encryption used is a Caesar cipher, then one attack is simple: just shift through the 25 possible combinations of Caesar cipher alphabets until plaintext emerges. It's not as laborious as it sounds, since you only need to determine the first few characters to eliminate a possibility. Caesar ciphers are one of the easiest systems to break.

Consider a keyword
If a few letters of the message can be deduced from sentence structure or frequency analysis, it is often useful to try to piece together the cipher alphabet, to see if there is a specific key. For example, if the following letters are known:

```
PT:  ABCDEFGHIJKLMNOPQRSTUVWXYZ
CT:   W DNS Y  FGH     PQ    X
```

Then you may be able to guess that the keyword is 'Wednesday' – which makes it easy to fill out the rest of the table:

```
PT:    ABCDEFGHIJKLMNOPQRSTUVWXYZ
CT:    WEDNSAYBCFGHIJKLMOPQRTUVXZ
```

Trial and error can quickly determine if this is correct.

HIDDEN KEY CIPHERS

The following are a few simple exercises to get you thinking about keys. Use the key given – or where the key is not revealed, first work out the key – in order to solve the cryptogram and unravel the original quotation.

DIFFICULTY RATING: 1
KEYS: PAGE 510
SOLUTIONS: PAGE 533

<u>1</u>

CGKSR JUAQFMGTS TDS ANEY GLE

TDS KFLE. – ASLHGKFL BQGLIJFL

Key: GAMES

PT: A B C D E F G H I J K L M N O P Q R S T U V W X Y Z
CT: G A M E S B C D F H I J K L N O P Q R T U V W X Y Z

Solution:

_____

_____

_____

_____

_____

_____

_____

2

N R F Z H	....
C L U	....
G R J M P	....
L	.....
S	....
B	....
O	.....
Q E B	....
I	.....
X	....
W	....
V	....
Y O L T K	....
A L D	....

Method: Caesar -3

PT: A B C D E F G H I J K L M N O P Q R S T U V W X Y Z

CT: X _ _ _ _ _ _ _ _ _ _ _ I _ _ _ _ _ _ _ _ _ _ _ _ _

3

Kce dopnjeq lfqq fwfy, jnw dopnjeq
fllnfo. Pt pq auqt cpbn thn efyq. Fj
kce efy lfqqnq, f jnw efy foopvnq.
Thn pglkotfjt thpjs pq tk gfbn pt
gnfjpjsduc: f gnfjpjsduc dopnje —
ko f gnfjpjsduc efy.

— Efcfp Cfgf XPV

Key: FRIENDSHIP

PT: A B C D E F G H I J K L M N O P Q R S T U V W X Y Z
CT: F R I _ N D S H _ _ _ _ _ _ _ _ _ _ _ _ _ _ _ _ _ _

Solution:

_____

_____

_____

_____

_____

4

Fy hbmrluopihg im ptop wtrgrurl

hgr jrlmhg im vhqge oerkqopr ph

ptr eimstolar hv o eqpy... ip im

whlmr rxrsqpre by pwh jrlmhgm,

oge msolsrdy ehgr op odd iv ptlrr

hl fhlr olr rfjdhyre ptrlrig.

— Arhlar Womtigaphg

Key: OBSERVATION

PT: A B C D E F G H I J K L M N O P Q R S T U V W X Y Z
CT: _

Solution:

_____

_____

_____

_____

_____

5

Ebpian co qbn gpw jt gctn. Pis
qbjon wbj gjjf jigy qj qbn kpoq jm
kmnoniq pmn enmqpci qj hcoo qbn
tuqumn. — Djbi T. Fniinsy

Key: PRESENT

PT: A B C D E F G H I J K L M N O P Q R S T U V W X Y Z
CT: _

Solution:

6

N hnj hny ido, jnrdkjq hny pdqo nji
sngg, aur nj dion gdvoq kj.

– Ekcj S. Fojjoiy

Key: ???

PT: A B C D E F G H I J K L M N O P Q R S T U V W X Y Z
CT: N _ T _ O _

Solution:
_____
_____
_____
_____
_____
_____
_____

8

Devhqfh vkdushqv oryh, suhvhqfh

vwuhqjwkhqv lw.

— Ehqmdplq Iudqnolq

Method: Caesar +3

PT: A B C D E F G H I J K L M N O P Q R S T U V W X Y Z
CT: _ _ _ _ _ _ _ _ _ _ _ _ _ N _ _ _ _ _ _ _ _ _ _ _ _

Solution:
_____
_____
_____
_____
_____
_____
_____

9

Gp wi ixmoipp lso dogqbqsti, wi
jspq kivio ulodiq qegq qei ebdeipq
gmmoiabgqblk bp klq ql sqqio
wlotp, rsq ql hbvi ry qeij.
— Clek U. Fikkity

Key: ???

PT: A B C D E F G H I J K L M N O P Q R S T U V W X Y Z
CT: G R A T _

Solution:
_____
_____
_____
_____
_____

CRYPTOGRAM CARNIVAL

Now you've got the hang of things, you'll be wanting more. Here are 300 fantastic cryptograms to make sure you never run dry! Like all the other puzzles in Part One of the book they are simple substitution cipher puzzles, solveable through simple trial-and-error and a little logic. Remember that some may also use a hidden key – which can be another way to reach the solution.

DIFFICULTY RATING: 3
KEYS: PAGE 511
SOLUTIONS: PAGE 533

1

BE SBPS TPK BPVE MPSDEKTE TPK

BPVE WBPS BE WDHH. — AEKFPJDK

NQPKGHDK

Solution:

_____

_____

2

BDQ RPIHKR VPQ PQ KPRTOPI PQ

RBH MPRRHOK RBPR VPQ JPCH SX

RBH CTQR LK P STRRHOEIX'Q

VDKAQ. PR LKH RDJH BH

TKCHOQRLLC DR KL JLOH RBPK

RBH STRRHOEIX CDC PKC BH CDC

KLR GKLV VBHK DR VPQ SOTQBHC

LO JPOOHC. HOKHQR BHJDKAVPX

Solution:
_____
_____
_____
_____
_____

3

Q PFSL ZGQYQZYR ZM XC ZHY −

RBOZYN ZGQYQZYR − IUB Q KZY'B

FWHFCR FNOLL HQBP BPLX.

Solution:
_____
_____

4

Z URXN ZJ R PLRIJZIN JQ RFQZS
WRJZTO RTBQTN. ZH KQUNQTN'K
ENNT OGZVJB QH SNKPZIREVN
RIJZQTK, NKPNIZRVVB JQDRLS
UN, Z JLB JQ HQLONJ WZU. Z
GKNS JQ HQVVQD R PLRIJZIN—
KQUNDWRJ IQTJLZFNS, Z RSUZJ—
JQ DLZJN JWN URT'K TRUN QT R
PZNIN QH KILRP PRPNL, SLQP ZJ
ZTJQ JWN VQDNKJ SLRDNL QH UB
SNKX, RTS KRB JQ UBKNVH: 'JWRJ
HZTZKWNK JWN ZTIZSNTJ, RTS KQ
HRL RK Z'U IQTINLTNS, JWRJ
HNVVQD.' JWN SLRDNL ENIRUN
QFNL JWN BNRLK R KQLJ QH
PLZFRJN DRKJNERKXNJ HQL

ILGUEVNS-GP KPZJN RTS

SZKIRLSNS PNLKQTRVZJZNK.

Solution:
_____
_____
_____
_____

5

C qmgejh sacif jb kjgcscvq hjpm

sani mcrasmmi ajtpq n eny.

– Gyieji O. Djaiqji

Solution:
_____
_____

6

C QBLSIN BAUT KL LDFTVRCLK RL

EL LUTP RBT QAJT ICGT GPLJ CRQ

DTECKKCKE RL RBT TKN:

PTOSTQRCKE LKIY RBT

ANUAKRAET ASRBLPQ BAUT, LG

VLPPTVRCKE CK A QTVLKN

TNCRCLK RBT GASIRQ LG RBT

GCPQR. — DTKFAJCK GPAKHICK

Solution:

7

Vasbezrq qrpvfvba-znxvat pbzrf

sebz n ybat genqvgvba bs thrffvat

naq gura oynzvat bguref sbe

vanqrdhngr erfhygf. — Fpbgg Nqnzf

Solution:
_____

_____

8

Lhcxcfjklyie eqsicflr enjts ctqqlhs

lulhsr eql ih gehx vexr yioolqlhs

oqjg hlvr eqsicflr enjts ctqqlhs

lulhsr. — Aiggx Veflr, ojthylq jo

Vibiklyie

Solution:
_____

_____

9

HGGO YNUQ GYGS WDIG NOGL

AGENQG KMQQDMBG, CMJE SCUT

METGQWMQIS. – AGLFMKDL

EQMLHJDL

Solution:
_____

_____

10

ITQ QDY RFPCLKQTKQP ET QDY

PTCOTQP. – ETKGSJFK AOSKHIFK

Solution:
_____

_____

11

HJIKX IKUKP HFNK F HFI BFMMX
XKS, IJP VCGG CS. SBK HJPK F
HFI BFQ, SBK HJPK BK VFISQ.
CIQSKFN JL LCGGCIY F UFATTH,
CS HFEKQ JIK.

Solution:
_____
_____
_____
_____
_____
_____
_____

12

Nfoxs nvmgzoob ovzuvw gsilfts srh

wdziu zyrorgrvh gl hvovxg gsv yvhg

gllo uli gsrh vhxzkv. Sv szw olmt

hrmxv uliuvrgvw srh nztrx yb

yivzprmt nlhg lu gsv Uzrib Yllp'h

xlnnzmwnvmgh, yfg wdziuh szw

vcgizliwrmzib trugh tizmgvw gsvn

yb velofgrlm. Hlnv lu gsvhv dviv

xlnnlm pmldovwtv znlmt gsv

Kvlkov, yfg wdziuh dviv z

mlglirlfhob hvxivgrev izxv dsl

yvorvevw gszg gsvri hfiervzo

wvkvmwvw lm xlmxvzormt gsvhv

gzovmgh. Rg dzh dvoo pmldm gszg

wdziuh vcxzezgvw gfmmvoh yb

rmtvhgrmt gsv vzigs gsilfts gsvri

fmsrmtvw qzdh, gsvm vqvxgrmt gsv

ivxbxovw wrig zmw zri gsilfts gsv

lgsvi vmw.

Solution:

_____

_____

_____

_____

_____

_____

_____

_____

_____

13

MH FPDY THL AGUPMOLX, FX

TLASGUM, IGU IOOSGOAHG OH

HGS'M HVG NPMAGSMM; NPO OH

OYSMS VS FPMO IUU TLPRIEAOX

AT VS VHPEU FICS HPL AGUPMOLX

FHLS DSLOIAGEX MPDDSMMTPE. I

FIG FIX, AT YS CGHVM GHO YHV

OH MIQS IM YS RSOM, CSSJ YAM

GHMS IEE YAM EATS OH OYS

RLAGUMOHGS, IGU UAS GHO

VHLOY I RLHPO IO EIMO. —

NSGBIFAG TLIGCEAG

Solution:

_____

_____

_____

14

Sdt ecas sdcs c kcl fq c ltwqncntp
ptnmpstp fq tvfrtlat me qmkt ejcw
me adcpcastp. — Jylrml H. Gmdlqml

Solution:
_____

_____

15

Pao kmjifogn jr sbcpjmx vmo gjmo
vymoovifo pavh pao kmjifogn jr
torovp, iqp paox vmo hj fonn
tbrrbcqfp. — Ubhnpjh Caqmcabff

Solution:
_____

_____

16

SDH WFY SN RHH AY BFESD ER SN

RDUS SDH HYH NB QHFRNM.

- AHMGFLEM BQFMJKEM

Solution:

17

Rdkt dq kmlty. - Utlefkdl Apflhjdl

Solution:

18

Wbcpc tbcpc dq ndqalpn, jfy wc
rpdks bfpjlky. Wbcpc tbcpc dq
cpplp, jfy wc rpdks tputb. Wbcpc
tbcpc dq nlurt, jfy wc rpdks ifdtb.
Fkn wbcpc tbcpc dq ncqmfdp, jfy
wc rpdks blmc. — Jfpsfpct
Tbftabcp, mfpfmbpfqdks Qt.
Ipfkadq li Fqqdqd

Solution:
_____
_____
_____
_____
_____
_____
_____

19

VLI AN VANR? LR QLPQ DRPMHN

FMIG RTRMYIHR. VLI AN

JIVRMFSD? LR QLPQ UITRMHN LAN

JPNNAIHN. - ORHBPGAH FMPHCDAH

Solution:

_____

_____

20

WCJT CO RKJOPVJP LNKKA PBVP

SKI GKUTO QO VJI GKUTO PK OTT

QO BVLLY. - ETJDVHCJ ANVJFGCJ

Solution:

_____

_____

21

SNUQ, BR SNOY FOS YJU HO, TIK

KJ IJS GTDO WTP JI YJU, TIK

JRROP YJU LOTEO, AJK KJOQ IJS

TFFJW YJU SJ NTPG SNOG.

Solution:
_____

_____

22

C UHQGPKXFCG OTPVTTG PVH

ECVXTKL AL EADT C RALM OTPVTTG

PVH UCPL. – OTGBCFAG RKCGDEAG

Solution:
_____

_____

23

C JCK UCK RH SHPQOLYHS RTQ KLQ

SHAHCQHS. HOKHPQ DHJEKBWCY

Solution:

_____

_____

24

B ibj ubj sbgn b hesshn oktpokj

wesdkts cnssejc rptjg, ots ea ykt

dkhr deq iktsd klnj bjr lktp ej b

mtbps, dn'q ckejc sk cns qeug kj

es. — Hyjrkj O. Fkdjqkj

Solution:

_____

_____

25

E KCERT HJM TSTMXPNGFI,

TSTMXPNGFI GF GPO KCERT.

– VTFAEDGF HMEFBCGF

Solution:
_____

_____

26

Q lsjrqrcjh qr rba mcnbr gjgahr cp

fcea umaqt rj rba iqgcpbat. – Rba

Rqfgst

Solution:
_____

_____

27

RK RQJHA SLBCHTY CS R MLGCTH
SLBCHTY. JRKKHQS RQH ILLA
WNHK LKH JRY NRVH TL ORBF UM
NCS RBTS WCTN NCS GCEH.

Solution:
_____
_____

28

DJ QJHESUAIR EVEPY DGY SUGS
YJT DJI'S WGIS SJ DJ; SUAQ AQ
SUE RJFDEI PTFE NJP GLMTAPAIR
SUE UGOAS JN DJAIR YJTP DTSY
WASUJTS KGAI. HGPC SWGAI

Solution:
_____
_____

29

Bsec xbsn kjb udedkro cstdq

pdoesnpbp, dj qdib idacq isgb qcb

vknoq ky ro akkp. — Tbjfsidj Ynsjghdj

Solution:
_____

_____

30

KWMKPCKIAK CQ F NKFP SKFABKP,

RTS LJJGQ VCGG GKFPI FS IJ

JSBKP.

Solution:
_____

_____

31

ADP KTR CJ RBL TJUBDPRLG

ODUFWDRLPQ KA RBL

TJADQBCKJDOHL LJG KA RBL

WLQRLPJ QMCPDH DPI KA RBL

SDHDXY HCLQ D QIDHH

TJPLSDPGLG YLHHKW QTJ.

KPOCRCJS RBCQ DR D GCQRDJUL

KA PKTSBHY JCJLRY-LCSBR

ICHHCKJ ICHLQ CQ DJ TRRLPHY

CJQCSJCACUDJR HCRRHL OHTL-

SPLLJ MHDJLR WBKQL DML-

GLQULJGLG HCAL AKPIQ DPL QK

DIDZCJSHY MPCICRCVL RBDR

RBLY QRCHH RBCJF GCSCRDH

WDRUBLQ DPL D MPLRRY JLDR

CGLD...

Solution:
_____
_____
_____
_____
_____
_____

32

OEMFAGW DJJCP FAWRQY HEPY

VRHG YJTM KDJV AP E KHGSAD,

EGN YJT'MH E QRJTPEGN FADHP

OMJF QRH SJMG OAHDN.

Solution:
_____
_____

34

BE TBKT BKR DMLE YMU K
GCLDLERR WCHH IE JMQE QEKDY
TM DM YMU KLMTBEQ, TBKL BE
WBMJ YMU YMUQREHS BKVE
MIHCAED. — IELFKJCL SQKLGHCL

Solution:

_____

_____

35

B eafbava soa raqsbjy kt ykup
iajapgsbkj-gjr ykup jgsbkj-bq g
pajrazvkuq wbso axnaffajna.
— Fyjrkj E. Ckojqkj

Solution:

_____

_____

36

R WYD'J VXSC X MVYJYEKXMV,
OFJ QYF BXD VXSC NQ
TYYJMKRDJG. JVCQ'KC FMGJXRKG
RD NQ GYBHG. EKYFBVY NXKA

Solution:
_____
_____

37

J lopx opu xjui xibu xfbqpot Xpsme
Xbs JJJ xjmm cf gpvhiu, cvu Xpsme
Xbs JW xjmm cf gpvhiu xjui tujdlt
boe tupoft. — Bmcfsu Fjotufjo

Solution:
_____
_____

38

D WPDTO NKP TCO QRIO PORQKJ D

EPORTCO — EOARUQO DN D SDSJ'T,

D WKUHS SDO. — DQRRA RQDIKV

Solution:
_____

_____

39

A'e pgrfmp latm hx daym rfgj im

gypgae rk latm ar.

— Dxjekj I. Bkfjqkj

Solution:
_____

_____

40

Vs cnffvba qevirf lbh, yrg ernfba
ubyq gur ervaf. — Orawnzva
Senaxyva

Solution:

_____

_____

41

DJ BRJRONH, INJGDJU, PDJTR
QCR DILOKVRIRJQ KE TKKGROY,
RNQP. QWDTR NP ISTC NP JNQSOR
ORMSDORP. — ARJFNIDJ EONJGHDJ

Solution:

_____

_____

42

Ebpian co qbn gpw jt gctn. Pis
qbjon wbj gjjf jigy qj qbn kpoq jm
kmnoniq pmn enmqpci qj hcoo qbn
tuqumn. — Djbi T. Fniinsy

Solution:
_____
_____

43

AL AK S LJMLZ MFANWJKSDDQ
SUCFGODWVYWV, LZSL S KAFYDW
ESF AF HGKKWKKAGF GX S YGGV
XGJLMFW, EMKL TW AF OSFL GX S
OAXW. — BSFW SMKLWF

Solution:
_____
_____

44

DACS WDD PTEESPPNTD

KJDAQAEAWGP A FWMMASI WRJUS

FYPSDN.

Solution:

_____

_____

45

HDJY D GKJE PBOLRQU DHKJE

PBVBJUO HDY IU QARO DINBPEUP:

BQ BO OK. BQ BO JKQ OK. BQ BO

OK. BQ BO JKQ OK. — IUJCDHBJ

TNDJFGBJ

Solution:

_____

_____

46

HFPPCFYK CQ SBK HJQS IFSTPFG
QSFSK JL HFI, FIN... SBK QSFSK
CI VBCAB XJT VCGG LCIN QJGCN
BFMMCIKQQ.

Solution:

_____

_____

47

EVQ QLDWQDE HLJ ES RWUFBQ
EVQ NSDE SR ZWGWOU WD ES
ELYQ JSFB WONSCQ LOP LPP EQO
TQBNQOE

Solution:

_____

_____

48

QTOMO YP GJ BYGH JN

HYPTJGOPQX YGQJ VTYST

JQTOMVYPO EJJH KOJKCO FJMO

ODPYCX DGH NMOLROGQCX NDCC

QTDG QTDQ JN HONMDRHYGE QTO

EJUOMGFOGQ. - IOGADFYG

NMDGBCYG

Solution:
_____

_____

_____

_____

_____

_____

_____

49

QDORR EAK HRRM A PREORQ FT

QWL AOR CRAC.

- SRKGAJFK TOAKHIFK

Solution:
_____

_____

50

VEHTORY GTTGEMDN AY

VEOKDMHD ES TGMTGLOUMT TO G

NDIDGT, IOR ET ES LOLDMTGRY.

Solution:
_____

_____

51

Wail einqcilrir, qikikeiq ct; wail ymu
einqcilr, nmqdit ct. — Eilgbkcl Nqblhjcl.
Kitbouzzji aclt: Fijistcbj ipubtmq

Solution:

_____

_____

52

Bmjs N fr fgwtfi, N fqbfdx rfpj ny f
wzqj sjajw yt hwnynhnej tw fyyfhp
ymj ltajwsrjsy tk rd tbs htzsywd. N
rfpj zu ktw qtxy ynrj bmjs N htrj
mtrj. — Xnw Bnsxyts Hmzwhmnqq

Solution:

_____

_____

53

B IKBRMKC LINOGAKBC DS B
ERKBTKR LINOGAKBC TABM BM
DEMNRBMT NMK. – LKMFBJDM
HRBMGIDM

Solution:

54

P Kmioasihq'o tpmsioq qpoc ao hjq
qj sj wtpq ao mantq, ruq qj chjw
wtpq ao mantq.

Solution:

55

YJSWMZAYR, WN ZANOAIDPANBRZ

EMJH KWIAY, AN WFHJNO WFSWUN

NAHKFU W FWYC JE WXAFAOU OJ

NPNKRIZ OBR EPIYOAJIAID JE

OBR AHWDAIWOAJI. RMIRNO

BRHAIDSWU

Solution:

_____

_____

_____

_____

_____

_____

_____

_____

56

BNOTCQKNP ADVO EOQQON

IOIKNCOP QADJ TOEQKNP.

– EOJFDICJ RNDJGHCJ

Solution:

_____

_____

57

KHMGJX SBX SCHK VKGG, CL SBJT

HKFIKQS SJ YFCI GKCQTPK.

Solution:

_____

_____

_____

58

RBANS BI SNO ETUQO JR TFFTN
SNJQO WNJ RBANS YJU, HUS KJ
IJS SPTIQAPOQQ FBGBSQ; RJP
TFFTN FJVOQ IJS SPTIQAPOQQJPQ.

Solution:

_____

_____

59

Wi qgjudf hjs djjc rpoc uhdiqq as
aq sj fimavi uqitud diqqjhq tmje
kpqs immjmq, phf tjm sgi kumkjqi
jt kmjtasahn ry fipmdy rjungs
ixkimaihoi. — Nijmni Wpqgahnsjh

Solution:

_____

_____

60

CY SCMS DR KA SCY KLDJDKJ

IKJYX VDHH EK YUYQXSCDJB IMX

VYHH OY RTRLYNSYE KA EKDJB

YUYQXSCDJB AKQ IKJYX.

- OYJFMIDJ AQMJGHDJ

Solution:
_____
_____
_____
_____
_____
_____
_____
_____

61

Ubj vf vg gung Cvmneeb naq

Pbegrf ernpurq gur Arj Jbeyq ng

nyy, orsber Nmgrp naq Vapn

pbadhvfgnqbef pbhyq ernpu

Rhebcr? Gung bhgpbzr qrcraqrq

cnegyl ba grpuabybtl va gur sbez

bs bprnatbvat fuvcf. Rhebcrnf unq

fhpu fuvcf, juvyr gur Nmgrpf naq

Vapnf qvq abg. – Wnerq Qvnzbaq

Solution:

62

Jtbdp kq rje hpesr rjkch, rje

qsukch rjkch. Rje bkctre kr ipdfq

tf, saa dtp kppkrsrkdcq scl

peqecrbecrq qakf svsx scl s qtccx

qfkpkr rszeq rjekp fasie.

— Bspz Rvskc

Solution:
_____

_____

_____

_____

_____

_____

_____

_____

63

D YANDARA PSAKA XKA BFKA

DCLPXCZAL FM PSA XYKDJEABACP

FM PSA MKAAJFB FM PSA GAFGNA

YV EKXJQXN XCJ LDNACP

ACZKFXZSBACPL FM PSFLA DC

GFTAK PSXC YV RDFNACP XCJ

LQJJAC QLQKGXPDFCL.

Solution:
_____

_____

_____

_____

_____

_____

_____

_____

64

Z KRB DWNT BQG ONJ ZTJQ R

DRL, BQG KWQGVS DZT RK MGZIX

RK BQG IRT, ENIRGKN BQGL

VQKKNK ENIQUN R HGTIJZQT QH

JWN SGLRJZQT QH JWN DRL. Z

ENVZNFN DWNT BQG ONJ ZT R

DRL, ONJ NFNLBJWZTO BQG TNNS

RTS DZT ZJ.

Solution:
_____
_____
_____
_____
_____
_____

65

AL T GTH OIQFU STVB STFL IL
SAN WANSBN, SB WIQFU UIQRFB
SAN PMIQRFBN. - RBHCTGAH
LMTHDFAH

Solution:

66

AE CIJVFLWDL OKI OQLKSL
MQJNFLHR, AS AR IJS SGQJTDG
ADIJQKIOL SGKS VL OKI RJFUL
SGLH. - ARKKO KRAHJU

Solution:

67

BE PFF KMBHQTMO WTMT

NTQTMGBHTN HJQ QJ KMBHQ

PHYQABHS QBFF QATY WTMT

OUMT BQ WJUFN JEETHN HJRJNY,

QATMT WJUFN RT VTMY FBQQFT

KMBHQTN. - RTHCPGBH

EMPHDFBH

Solution:
_____
_____
_____
_____
_____
_____
_____

68

Ey va vej, jkokdx vehh nmqa. Ey va
hkra, scaqa vehh oa jkokdx sk
nmqa. — Vejrskj Nctqncehh

Solution:

69

Fb you wouin lc iovcn, iovc akn lc
iovalic. — Lckgajfk Brakhifk

Solution:

70

BS EJYQI'S HRSSYO AJV
PYRTSBNTG XJTO SAYJOX BQ, BS
EJYQI'S HRSSYO AJV QHROS XJT
ROY. BN BS EJYQI'S RMOYY VBSA
YWKYOBHYIS, BS'Q VOJIM.

Solution:

It doesn't matter how beautiful your theory is, it doesn't matter how smart you are. If it doesn't agree with experiment, it's wrong.

71

Kj kc qtekci ja ni jaa cqvi ap atic
aet ekcbam. Kj kc digfjds ja ni
vimktbib jdgj jdi cjvatwicj mkwdj
eigyit gtb jdi ekcicj mkwdj ivv.

– Mgdgjmg Wgtbdk

Solution:

72

HIAVI KMTODKC NMR TMJMRRMW

WODEO EAK BI LMKI TMLAY.

Solution:
_____

_____

73

HPIY P HPI QBCIFO BS CO LTYCIR

KGSPOTNS, WBSI BS CO NSPGGY

OSGGCIR BCHOSGU QJ CQ.

- LSIDPHCI UNPIFGCI

Solution:
_____

_____

74

SDN AQS MG ATSELB TMLRERSR

EL HNNOELB ONMOJN GQMK

TMUBDELB. — CNLFAKEL GQALHJEL

Solution:
_____
_____
_____
_____
_____
_____
_____
_____

75

TSIK RUHHIKGY SI CMJI HLWK
MKLTSIQ TIK NIIT, EQMAAIH NLUQ
LN TSI CQIW, RWUKE TSIJ UO TSI
SLGI BK TSI QLLN. TSIY WIKT
GBFI JMSLUTR GBNTIH BK
IGIOSMKTR' TQUKFR. IYIBKE TSI
SLGI, B CLUGH RII TSMT RUE
NMQK KL GLKEIQ SMH MKY HBQICT
SLGH LN SBR LWK, SBR UOOIQ
TIKTMCGIR AIBKE CGLRIGY
IKTWBKIH WBTS TSI IPUMGGY
QLOIY GBJAR LN MKLTSIQ
JMQTBMK MKCSLQIH LUT LN VBIW
LK TSI QLLNTLO. RUE NMQK
QMBRIH TSI NLUQ TL WBTSBK M
NIW NIIT LN TSI SLGI WSIQIUOLK
LTSIQ TIKTMCGIR WQBTSIH
TSQLUES NQLJ MALVI, TLLF TSIJ
NQLJ SBJ. TSIK NLUQ JLQI MKH
NLUQ JLQI.

Solution:

76

TCORO DRO TCROO TCEKBS

OXTROJOHY CDRM: STOOH, D

MEDJLKM, DKM TL GKLW LKO'S

SOHN. — IOKFDJEK NRDKGHEK

Solution:

_____

_____

_____

_____

_____

_____

_____

_____

IB UX GQIIXF-BY-YQVI QUBJI ISX LBFNW TH IB UNJEWXF TEIB YQEIQHO — QEW WJNN YQEIQHO QI ISQI, QH ISX FXQN LBFNW TH HIFQEZX QEW LBEWXFYJN.
— FBUXFI Q. SXTENXTE

Solution:

TO BE MATTER-OF-FACT ABOUT THE WORLD IS TO BLUNDER INTO FANTASY — AND DULL FANTASY AT THAT, AS THE REAL WORLD IS STRANGE AND WONDERFUL.
— ROBERT A. HEINLEIN

78

Ph ut, hl ghp ph ut, pnqp am pnt
krtmpahg: Wntpntl 'pam ghudtl ag
pnt fags ph mriitl Pnt mdagom qgs
qllhwm hi hrplqothrm ihlprgt, Hl ph
pqct qlfm qoqagmp q mtq hi
plhrudtm Qgs uy hjjhmago tgs pntf.
Ph sat: ph mdttj.

— Waddaqf Mnqctmjtqlt, Nqfdtp

Solution:

79

Wn pbshh dcabq kj qbn unsrbnp,
wn pbshh dcabq kj qbn hsjecja
aoktjep, wn pbshh dcabq cj qbn
dcnhep sje cj qbn pqonnqp, wn
pbshh dcabq cj qbn bchhp; wn
pbshh jnvno ptoonjeno.

— Wcjpqkj Rbtorbchh

Solution:
_____
_____
_____
_____
_____
_____
_____

80

VCIPI QIKQI DQ VWKRDKB,

IUIPYRCDKB DQ VWKRDKB.

– AIKEWJDK GPWKFHDK

Solution:
_____

_____

81

WCTSCJ EJ SKUQ KQ RK, CT

NAOEJ TK LEHH. AJGAQ

UJGAQRTKKG TSA QAOUHEQCTCAR

NY TSAJ. UJGAQRTKKG TSA

QUHAR TSA DKILUTAQ WER

MKHHKWCJO, RK TSET SA FJAW SA

DKUHG EHWEYR, KJDA SA

IERTAQAG TSA DKJTQKHR,
KUTIEJAUVAQ TSA AJAIY.
RLCQEHR WSAJ TSA AJAIY WER
HCFA TSCR; HKKLR WSAJ TSA
AJAIY WER HCFA TSET. HCA CJ
WECT ET KJA TQEL. HEY RAVAJ
TQELR EJG TSAJ HUQA TSAI HCFA
TSCR. TSAQA WER JK DSEHHAJOA
TK CT, TSAJ, BURT E IETTAQ KM
LHEYCJO UJTCH TSA DKILUTAQ
OKT RK MERT TSET JK SUIEJ
QAMHAXAR DKUHG KVAQDKIA CT.
TSET WERJ'T MUJ. CT WER TSA
KTSAQ NKYR SA WEJTAG TK LHEY.
TSA NKYR WSK SEG NAAJ RK
TQECJAG NY TSA DKILUTAQ TSET
AVAJ WSAJ TSAY LHEYAG EOECJRT
AEDS KTSAQ TSAY AEDS TQCAG

TK AIUHETA TSA DKILUTAQ. TSCJF

HCFA E IEDSCJA CJRTAEG KM E

NKY.

Solution:

_____

_____

_____

_____

_____

_____

_____

_____

_____

_____

_____

_____

_____

82

Yju'vk mjt tj wjqf tbdims jut di tbk

ogjcfqjjh, cia wbki yju'vk mjt tbkh

wjqfka jut, yju oci aklctk c gdttgk

lkrjqk yju vjtk. —Gyiaji L. Ejbisji

Solution:

83

Ys vyj dbayon vboy gjinosmn gbayo
otes utms fsno ys oysmshx hsujgs t
gjinosm. Tir bd xjp atzs djm fjia
bioj ti thxnn, oys thxnn atzsn tfnj
bioj xjp. — Dmbsrmbuy Ibsoznuys

Solution:

_____

_____

84

Rcopo vpo jljokrq wcok, wcvrotop
rco mlqdrdlk la rco hlgy, rco qlsi
dq lk drq fkooq.

Solution:

_____

_____

85

L GCEN KE GNCQTPN LJI L GCEN
KE GLYCJNQQ LPN RVK RBCJSQ.
RBNPN VCGG AN QGNNMCJS
NJKTSB CJ RBN SPLUN.
- ANJDLHCJ EPLJFGCJ

Solution:

_____

_____

86

B JBK WQBOOLD TO FK CFJRLIE
JBHLR B VLQY RJBII UTKDIL.
- ULKGBJFK EQBKHIFK

Solution:

_____

_____

87

GS KOMB GS YOU NDREVD EMMDR

CDKP GMN HOLIORT IROL

GMYTCEMB, JDDP ET.

Solution:
_____

_____

88

OYMDQQLQ DPL GLVCULQ RBDR

DHHKW QKIL MLKMHL RK GDQB APKI

MKCJR D RK MKCJR O VLPY ADQR

WBCHL KRBLP MLKMHL GDQB APKI

MKCJR O RK MKCJR D VLPY ADQR.

MLKMHL HCVCJS DR MKCJR U,

OLCJS D MKCJR GCPLURHY CJ

OLRWLLJ, DPL KARLJ SCVLJ RK

WKJGLP WBDR'Q QK SPLDR DOKTR
MKCJR D RBDR QK IDJY MLKMHL
APKI MKCJR O DPL QK FLLJ RK SLR
RBLPL DJG WBDR'Q QK SPLDR
DOKTR MKCJR O RBDR QK IDJY
MLKMHL APKI MKCJR D DPL QK FLLJ
RK SLR *RBLPL*. RBLY KARLJ WCQB
RBDR MLKMHL WKTHG ETQR KJUL
DJG AKP DHH WKPF KTR WBLPL RBL
BLHH RBLY WDJRLG RK OL.

Solution:
_____
_____
_____
_____
_____
_____
_____

89

CL SCFS QFDRLR F HFQBL YFJDHX

INLR, DKILLI, VCDHL CL HDULR SN

NARLQUL SCLJ, RSFKI F AQNFILQ

JFQG YNQ RNQQNV; ATS SCLK CL

RSFKIR F AQNFILQ JFQG YNQ

OHLFRTQL SNN.

- ALKEFJDK YQFKGHDK

Solution:

_____

_____

_____

_____

_____

_____

90

B pg txrnpjnibhpnbfy kprbthr

knjvbiti B str gy jwh wpy bh rat

thi. — Gpnspntr Raprlatn

Solution:

_____

_____

91

E ADKEDVD EM DQUGKETY IOR

DVDRYOMD, DXHDPT RDPORTDRS

GMN PCOTOBRGPCDRS.

Solution:

_____

_____

92

C tlk'r nhfchuh C'ff huhp ghr

yphtcr ilp akxrbckg C tl ck ilphcgk

aiiacpq, kl jarrhp blv qsyyhqqisf cr

cq, nhyasqh C tctk'r gl rl Bapuapt.

—Fxktlk N. Dlbkqlk

Solution:
_____
_____
_____
_____
_____
_____
_____
_____

93

D SLK'Q HDGT QL VODQT HDGT

BLS. DQ DP LKHY XTIERPT YLR

KTUTO SL DQ, QCLRBC, QCEQ QCT

IODQDIP QCDKG YLR IEK'Q SL DQ.

TOKTPQ CTJDKBVEY

Solution:

_____

_____

_____

_____

_____

_____

_____

_____

94

Bu usqsoi dikiogqblkp goi ql
oijijrio sp jloi wbqe dogqbqsti qegk
ploolw, wi jspq gaebivi jloi qegk
cspq qei jbogahip lu qiaeklhldy. Wi
jspq ghpl higvi qeij g dhbjmpi lu
qei wloht gp bq wgp aoigqit, klq
cspq gp bq hllfit weik wi dlq
qeolsde wbqe bq.

— Hyktlk R. Clekplk

Solution:
_____
_____
_____
_____
_____
_____
_____

95

FA JY TLCSLP SLIT JR F EDT LKIY
QFX JFKUSRQ SL IFVR, F
WLUITK'S OPLLT. F'T SYMR D
IFSSIR ADQSRP. — FQDDC DQFJLV

Solution:

_____

_____

96

AO QAGI RI JO PFF QSAHUN QSI
GJNQ KMIEAJTN, WPNQAHU QAGI
GTNQ RI QSI UMIPQINQ
KMJCAUPFAQY. — RIHBPGAH
OMPHDFAH

Solution:

_____

_____

97

BI SNO ITGO JR AJK, SNO

GOPEBRUF, SNO EJGLTQQBJITSO;

LPTBQO HO SJ AJK, FJPK JR SNO

UIBVOPQO, SNO EJGLTQQBJITSO,

SNO GOPEBRUF, QJVOPOBAI JR

SNO KTY JR CUKAOGOIS! YJU

TFJIO WO WJPQNBL, TIK SJ YJU

TFJIO WO SUPI RJP NOFL. AUBKO

UQ SJ SNO QSPTBANS LTSN, SNO

LTSN JR SNJQO WNJG YJU NTVO

RTVJUPOK, IJS JR SNJQO WNJ

NTVO BIEUPPOK YJUP WPTSN, IJP

JR SNJQO WNJ NTVO AJIO

TQSPTY.

Solution:
_____
_____
_____
_____
_____
_____
_____
_____
_____
_____
_____
_____
_____
_____

98

ER EQ IBQEIP RM NPIVILR ABH

CBAERQ RCBL RM APIBG RCIK.

- AILFBKEL TPBLGJEL

Solution:
_____

_____

99

Mq mn mfjilqchq qacq qat Shmqtp

Nqcqtn ltfcmh c qvi-jclqx nxnqtf.

M'f c oteeiv vai emdtn nfcee

jclqmtn chp qat Ltjsremych Jclqx

ych'q rt qii nfcee qi nsmq ft.

-Exhpih R. Biahnih

Solution:
_____
_____
_____
_____
_____
_____

100

Uf'e zaf qzagst ftmf iq pa agd

nqef; eayqfuyqe iq tmhq fa pa

itmf'e dqcgudqp.

- Eud luzefaz Otgdotuxx

Solution:
_____
_____

101

FESBQFHTBKJ TK HLLFZ TAE

LPBJWBLFE KI EMUHF LHZ IKP

EMUHF XKPD XBTAKUT

RBQWPBGBJHTBKJ OEWHUQE KI

QEY BQ H GHTTEP KI QBGLFE

CUQTBWE.

Solution:

_____

_____

_____

_____

_____

_____

_____

_____

102

ICDE'P QOTYEGX CP QBTQ VE YEQ

LIG QLL PLLK TKG VCPE QLL

ITQE. – REKFTJCK DOTKHICK

Solution:

_____

_____

103

PJAYU TZYYG UJK TZJP EJBAV

FQBAVG UJK EBGSBRY. GBANY B

EBGSBRY EJBAV AYMZSU

YCYZUFQBAV, PJAYU BG QMAEU.

VZJKNQJ PMZD

Solution:

_____

_____

104

THZJRHL E DZKH UET TQL E ILEFH
UET VZHK NQDT QT JRH JLESXK
QO RZKJQLB JQ DEZJ OQL JRH
JLEZT QO JRH OGJGLH JQ LGT
QFHL RZU.

Solution:
_____
_____

105

HUQUL PHDULUNOBGXOU OSU
JIRUL IM SPGXH NOPJBDBOV.
LIYULO X. SUBHFUBH

Solution:
_____
_____

106

KTS KI SAN OKQJNQ KI ABR NYN,

APQQY EBRSBJOSFY RPV GPFIKY

SAQKV P ROPSABJX FKKD KUNQ

PS ABG; SAN VBJN XFPRR GPFIKY

APE HNNJ FNUBSPSBJX INFF SK

SAN IFKKQ PJE RGPRANE. APQQY

OKTFE JKS RTLLQNRR P XQBJ.

LQKINRRKQ SKISY RGBFNE HPOD

PS ABG NJOKTQPXBJXFY. 'SAPS'R

BS,' AN RPBE BJ ABR MTPUNQY

KFE UKBON, 'JK JNNE SK HN

JNQUKTR . . . JKV, BI B OKTFE

PRD YKT SK SPDN SABR NXXOTL

PJE GPDN BS EK RKGN

OPQSVANNFR IKQ GN . . .' KJ SAN

VAKFN APQQY SAKTXAS BS VNJS

QPSANQ VNFF; ABR FNUBSPSBKJ

OAPQG VPR ONQSPBJFY GTOA

HNSSNQ SAPJ GPFIKY'R APE
HNNJ, SAKTXA AN VBRANE AN APE
JKS GBWNE TL SAN
BJOPJSPSBKJR IKQ OKFKQ-
OAPJXN PJE XQKVSA OAPQGR, RK
SAPS SAN QPS AN VPR RTLLKRNE
SK HN STQJBJX KQPJXN RVNFFNE
RAKODBJXFY PJE VPR SAN RBZN
KI P HPEXNQ HNIKQN APQQY
OKTFE QNOSBIY ABR GBRSPDN.
AN VPR XFPE ANQGBKJN APE JKS
HNNJ BJ SAN APFF PS SAN SBGN
PJE JNXFNOSNE SK GNJSBKJ BS
SK ANQ PISNQVPQE. AN OKTFE
SNFF QKJ, SAKTXA; QKJ APE
OPTRNE P EBJJNQ LFPSN SK
GTSPSN BJSK P FPQXN GTRAQKKG
PJE APE JK BENP AKV BS APE
APLLNJNE.

Solution:

_____

_____

_____

_____

_____

_____

_____

_____

_____

_____

_____

_____

_____

_____

_____

107

Uqjfxzwj ns ymj otg uzyx ujwkjhynts

ns ymj btwp. — Fwnxytyqj

Solution:

_____

_____

108

KORBOSP GD YGQK HKOLODP

IBOLLNDTL, GR WUNSU OVOKY

CMD UML CMDY; DGP GD YGQK

HMLP CNLRGKPQDOL, GR WUNSU

MBB COD UMVO LGCO. SUMKBOL

FNSAODL

Solution:

_____

_____

109

PKHKHRKP IJS JIGX SJ QFX SBK

PCYBS SBCIY CI SBK PCYBS

MGFAK, RTS LFP HJPK NCLLCATGS

QSCGG, SJ GKFUK TIQFCN SBK

VPJIY SBCIY FS SBK SKHMSCIY

HJHKIS.

Solution:
_____
_____
_____
_____
_____
_____
_____
_____

110

Uknnx ep qda ejqanapq lwey ox
qdkpa udk oknnku qnksoha.

- Caknca Uwpdejcqkj

Solution:

_____

_____

111

QCTX VCL BDUT RM TPPTKQDSI
IDATOQX QL LAQSDK S IDQQIT
QTJMLOSOX PSYTQX ETPTOUT
KTDQCTO IDATOQX KLO PSYTQX.

- ATKGSJDK YOSKHIDK

Solution:

_____

_____

112

QSINE WSI TIVEMH, SPVAHT GUOS

RUNAHENN IH QSEAM SPHJN, JI

HIQ TEHEMPFFY FADE QI QPDE

QSE QMIURFE IC OIHNAJEMAHT

PHJ OPMMYAHT AHQI EXEOUQAIH

HEW KMIBEOQN. QSE RENQ

KURFAO GEPNUMEN PME

QSEMECIME NEFJIG PJIKQEJ CMIG

KMEVAIUN WANJIG, RUQ CIMOEJ

RY QSE IOOPNAIH. - REHBPGAH

CMPHDFAH

Solution:

_____

_____

_____

_____

_____

113

Wcok ek iltur, ilk'r. — Uokfdjek

Spdkghek

Solution:
_____

_____

114

WKPIQ HAY QBKW A HAJ'Q WDR

CUR ATRDKJQ BDQ HOAJDJS. —

COJEAHDJ NPAJFGDJ

Solution:
_____

_____

115

TK T IJRJ HIZ-KDFJG, IZMWG T EJ

IJDRTYP HQTA ZYJ?

Solution:
_____

_____

116

Qihmx, gdrs mqi wmscmehi. –

Mrvdoi tl ylukb jltciqs, aqlj Fmogdi

Bqdaadtc

Solution:
_____

_____

117

H CLTQE DQ KLR H CLJE TKIEQQ

DR ULKRHDKQ ALLS HKS ADPE ALP

RCE JDKS HQ WEII HQ RCE OLSY.

- OEKFHJDK APHKGIDK

Solution:

_____

_____

118

P KSIIX OPTSY BO P KSIIX

SPMISY. - ESICPHBI AMPIFGBI

Solution:

_____

_____

119

NSEBLTP WC TBLNP EUOPB

HBPCCEBP. PBUPCD VPRWUTGLJ

Solution:
_____
_____

120

XFEP NB AFSB, SZBFIEB TSZ

OAX'B.

Solution:
_____
_____

121

NO EPOTSOK SNO NOTVOIQ TIK

SNO OTPSN BI QBX KTYQ TIK SNOI

GJUISOK NBQ SNPJIO. NO DIJWQ

TFF SNTS AJOQ BISJ SNO OTPSN

TIK TFF SNTS OGOPAOQ RPJG BS,

TFF SNTS EJGOQ KJWI RPJG

NOTVOI TIK TFF SNTS TQEOIKQ SJ

BS. NO BQ WBSN YJU WNOPOVOP

YJU TPO. NO BQ EJAIBZTIS JR

TFF YJUP TESBJIQ.

Solution:

_____

_____

_____

122

AU QAFQ WFBQP SKJI NJMQSIU,

BP IUVUM PSMU JN F TBIIUM.

— OUICFHBI NMFIDGBI

Solution:

123

Y asvysgs jzsls mls urls ytkjmtdsk

ro jzs malyinsustj ro jzs olssiru ro

jzs qsrqvs ac nlmihmv mti kyvstj

stdlrmdzustjk ro jzrks yt qrfsl jzmt

ac gyrvstj mti khiist hkhlqmjyrtk.

– Xmusk Umiykrt

Solution:

_____

_____

_____

_____

_____

_____

_____

_____

124

D oigdiui, wdrb codvdja nkjudnrdkj,
rbcr rbdq liklgi-jsprspiv oy rbidp
viil tcdrb, rsrkpiv oy rbidp bcpv
giqqkjq, hkuiv oy rbidp bdab
cqldpcrdkjq-bcui rbi wdgg rk hiir
rbi rpdcgq rbcr rbiqi rdhiq dhlkqi.
– Gyjvkj O. Ekbjqkj

Solution:

_____

_____

_____

_____

_____

_____

_____

125

D MKJ'R SOGDOUO DJ AJ

AVROPGDVO, QK D MKJ'R CAUO RK

QLOJM HY WCKGO GDVO VOAPDJB

COGG, KP VOAPDJB COAUOJ OUOJ

HKPO. VKP WCAROUOP RCO

RKPRTPOQ KV COGG, D RCDJF

RCO SKPOMKH KV COAUOJ WKTGM

SO OUOJ WKPQO.

Solution:

126

C PMRSLKJGGY JH KLT ILKSICLUS

LO HY JIIMKT.

Solution:

_____

_____

127

H MVKQKCIVYN LHTDZZQKRS KA

LCSYT. HA D WDX TVKCYL

EVDYYSXIS WS, H OKCYL MDFS VHW

FHXLYN DXL AKQIHRHXIYN UN MVS

VDXL DXL YSDL VHW MK D PCHSM

ZYDES DXL FHYY VHW. WDQF MODHX

Solution:

_____

_____

128

DL YMT HKMW CMW SM QNAKG

IAQQ SCFK YMT BAS, YMT CFVA

SCA NCDIMQMNCAP'Q QSMKA.

- RAKEFJDK LPFKHIDK

Solution:

_____

_____

129

Tdr nrst iqeuhrjt ieiajst orhkfqify

as i mavr hajutr fkjvrqsitakj watd

tdr ivrqier vktrq.

Solution:

_____

_____

130

Bv bj dcjr vn fd focad monk c jcmd

ubjvczid. Cdjnl

Solution:
_____

_____

131

DQ LOYP QK BU KBTDKRP,

UPLUVDOGGY DS YKR COTU O

NULRQOQDKJ SKN PRBQGUQY.

—DPOOV OPDHKT

Solution:
_____

_____

132

Idug wgii. Ds dq scg bpgrsgqs

pgugkbg. – Scg Srijtn

Solution:
_____

133

IEQOTLSX: 'PXHECELJ EQ SDX

LNEKSX LB SDX IKQQXQ.' – GKPH

IKPW ALPPXAS OTLSX: 'PXHECELJ

EQ SDX QECD LB SDX LNNPXQQXR

APXKSTPX, SDX DXKPS LB K

DXKPSHXQQ VLPHR KJR SDX QLTH

LB QLTHHXQQ ALJRESELJQ. ES EQ

SDX LNETI LB SDX NXLNHX.'

– GKPH IKPW

Solution:

_____

_____

_____

_____

_____

_____

_____

134

ISVSM CINTGQ PIYJIS UY

PRRCOSIQ. MJUSMQ P. BSCIGSCI

Solution:

_____

_____

135

Luq kcrcssbtbcs kcvcq cnupg luq

wpkts. — Ockepjbk Hqpkfgbk

Solution:

_____

_____

136

QCIAK SBJT FPK IJS QTPK JL F

HCITSK, SBPJV IJS FVFX FI BJTP.

Solution:

_____

_____

137

RDN ABQNKR APN KNVNP WFRDLUR

TAUIR, KLP RDN MPNQNKR WFRDLUR

NXSUQN. — BNKGAJFK TPAKHIFK

Solution:

_____

_____

138

JIW HVWSLWKJ DSB JQ KIQD DISJ

JIW LGVW QR VSD UWSTK JQ GK

ZT WFWLBOSB VZRW ZK JQ

LWHSVV DISJ ISK ISPPWTWO DIWT

JIWLW ZK TQ LGVW QR VSD.

Solution:

_____

_____

139

Prq hjop mqetpdutg prdia wq cei
qxkqndqicq do prq hyopqndjto. Dp
do prq ojtncq ju egg pntq enp eis
ocdqicq. — Egmqnp Qdiopqdi

Solution:

_____

_____

140

RBCQ MHDJLR BDQ – KP PDRBLP

BDG – D MPKOHLI, WBCUB WDQ

RBCQ: IKQR KA RBL MLKMHL

HCVCJS KJ CR WLPL TJBDMMY AKP

MPLRRY ITUB KA RBL RCIL. IDJY

QKHTRCKJQ WLPL QTSSLQRLG AKP

RBCQ MPKOHLI, OTR IKQR KA

RBLQL WLPL HDPSLHY UKJULPJLG

WCRB RBL IKVLILJRQ KA QIDHH

SPLLJ MCLULQ KA MDMLP, WBCUB

CQ KGG OLUDTQL KJ RBL WBKHL

CR WDQJ'R RBL QIDHH SPLLJ

MCLULQ KA MDMLP RBDR WLPL

TJBDMMY.

Solution:

_____

_____

_____

_____

_____

_____

_____

_____

141

SM YMHHMV LX YBESC BHMKD ER

SM YMHHMV LHEKNHX.

- LDKFBJEK YQBKGHEK.

Solution:
_____

_____

142

VYEFSA BR KLS ABR SAES AER

BS, NTS ABR SAES YKCLXR BS.

- NYKCEHBK IQEKDFBK

Solution:
_____

_____

143

Dvzklmh dviv yvrmt hszikvmvw fklm

xsfixsbziw svzwhglmvh. Fmwvi gsv

xirgrxzo vbv lu lvwgllgs z yzmw lu

ilwvmgh dzh tmzdrmt luu z ovmtgs

lu kozmprmt uiln z irxpvgb obxs-

tzgv uvmxv zg gsv ivzi lu gsv

xsfixs. Lgsvih xloovxgvw hglmvh gl

kilerwv znnfmrgrlm uli hormth,

dsrov hlnv xlrovw ilkvh zylfg gsvri

ylwrvh. Rmhrwv gsv xsfixs Xofmb

hzg fk rm gsv xslri olug, gsv rnztv

lu yziyzirx zfgslirgb. Sv svow gsv

hxlfitrmt gzro rm lmv xozd, dsrov

tirkkvw rm gsv lgsvi dzh srh dzi

hgzmwziw, glkkvw yb gsv uviivg

hpfoo drgs gsv zwwrgrlm lu gsv

gzggvivw gzkvhgib hjfziv wvkrxgrmt

Nzigrm gsv Dziirli. Sv tzavw

kilfwob zg rg zh srh zinlivi

wivhhvw srn uli dzi.

Solution:
_____

_____

_____

_____

_____

_____

_____

_____

_____

_____

_____

_____

144

WCGT NEIIDRDMHD NODS ET LGJD

TO TCD NDGN, TCD ORPCGMS GMN

TCD COLDKDSS, WCDTCDR TCD

LGN NDSTRUHTEOM ES WROUBCT

UMNDR TCD MGLD OI

TOTGKETGREGMESL OR TCD COKY

MGLD OI KEADRTY OR

NDLOHRGHY?

Solution:

_____

_____

_____

_____

_____

_____

145

Wath pqeti rj hpgt rat labtc
mupfbcblprbjh p kjfbrblbph qajufi
apvt: Br'q rat pobfbry rj cjntrtff
wapr wbff apkkth rjgjnnjw, htxr
gjhra, phi htxr ytpn — phi rj
txkfpbh pcrtnwpni way br ibih'r
apkkth. — Wbhqrjh Launlabff

Solution:
_____
_____
_____
_____
_____
_____
_____
_____

146

Vatlt fbotlpx bm, patlt bm gx

uiqhplx. – Othdcgbh Rlchefbh

Solution:

_____

_____

147

WCGQG TCGQG'S KMQQDMBG

WDTCNUT JNVG, TCGQG WDJJ AG

JNVG WDTCNUT KMQQDMBG. –

AGLFMKDL EQMLHJDL

Solution:

_____

_____

148

XNT KDX AYJDX, ETS SGKY VGJJ

MNS. - EYMHDKGM BQDMIJGM

Solution:

_____

_____

149

FWXYT IOC'HT SMEXDV IOCH

UMQT, IOC'HT YOSXDV IOCH MSS.

Solution:

_____

_____

<u>150</u>

MHH JMLGELK ES KEVEKIK ELTO

TCRII NHMSSIS: TCOSI TCMT MRI

EJJOVMAHI, TCOSI TCMT MRI

JOVMAHI, MLK TCOSI TCMT JOVI.

- AILFMJEL DRMLGHEL

Solution:

151

Cjy fcrgcqq rcj gdrg pkwj c acoj

aus ds scgeq c tkkp rcolejseo sk

audhp kje. — Hyjpkj A. Fkbjqkj

Solution:

152

Cf dbsfgvm bcpvu sfbejoh ifbmui

cpplt. zpv nbz ejf pg b njtqsjou.

— Nbsl Uxbjo

Solution:

153

WZ PVIS FD JLIFER YINEA. NL XVE
CVAZ SFM JUFFL VL LVQ
XFBBZXLFIJ... VEY CNJJ. IFWZIL
V. UZNEBZNE

Solution:

_____

_____

154

Asmfo Jnspmlsfq mp dmcs asmfo h
bhichpp mf h rhmdpqgne. Qrsns'p
fgqrmfo qg lg auq qg pqhfl qrsns
hfl qhcs mq. — Dyflgf A. Bgrfpgf

Solution:

_____

_____

155

KUKI MKFAK HFX RK MTPABFQKN

FS SJJ BCYB F MPCAK.

Solution:
_____
_____

156

BRTPQP, IDHT ADPC, UTBDK QL

PJTII GAQTO QCOTT SGYP.

- UTKFGJDK AOGKHIDK

Solution:
_____
_____

157

AS RACR WJI'R OS UJTIQSGSN
UCI'R OS ASGKSN. — OSIDCHBI
EPCIFGBI

Solution:
_____

_____

158

Jod aogr esd hrmyar; smf yjr
rarzrmyd dp zocrf om joz, yjsy
Msyitr zohjy dysmf iq, Smf dsu yp
saa yjr eptaf, yjod esd s zsm! -
Eoaaosz Djslrdqrstr

Solution:
_____

_____

159

E SJYVB BKWSD GEHQ CJY YWHEV

HQD SJGX SJRD QJRD. JW XDSJWB

HQJYNQH E'B OKHQDO BKWSD

GEHQ HQD SJGX YWHEV CJY SJRD

QJRD. NOJYSQJ RKOM

160

V qb abg srne pbzchgref. V srne

gur ynpx bs gurz. - Vfnnp Nfvzbi

161

C HKVL GLDGHCJLQ. C HCFL RBL
WBKKQBCJS QKTJG RBLY IDFL DQ
RBLY AHY OY.

Solution:
_____
_____

162

B VRQ PJOI IJS DIJVBIM RIE ARUY
ARE JIGX R GBSSGY SBHY SJ
FARIMY SARS AYOY RIE SAYOY.

Solution:
_____
_____

163

ZI JNE GTZJER THJZQTK QTWE

HRUZJK JNHJ ZTJELTHJZQTHV

RZKPGJEK WHT OE KEJJVER OB

GKZTS IQLWE, JNET DE DZVV

NHFE REKJLQBER JNE

IQGTRHJZQT QI JNE

QLSHTZAHJZQT HTR QGL OEKJ

NQPE QI EKJHOVZKNZTS H DQLVR

QLREL.

Solution:

_____

_____

_____

_____

_____

_____

164

FA YMU IRQFPR KD,LY TCFLBQ,

KDLY TCFLBQ WFJJ QRRK ARW.

– ERLGDKFL APDLHJFL

Solution:

_____

_____

165

CK SBCR WLQFH KLSBCKA TNK OI

RNCH SL OI TIQSNCK, IXTIMS

HINSB NKH SNXIR. – OIKDNJCK

GQNKEFCK

Solution:

_____

_____

166

EMNOKDMHD ES G NDKEBCTIUK
AUT NESTRDSSEMB STGTD; WD
LUST AD NOEMB SOLDTCEMB TO
AD CGPPY.

Solution:
_____
_____

167

Pa pz ilaaly av il cpvslua, pm
aolyl pz cpvslujl pu vby olhyaz,
aohu av wba vu aol jsvhr vm
uvucpvslujl av jvcly ptwvalujl.
— Thohath Nhukop

Solution:
_____
_____

168

DR DQ ICAJBO, IKJRDJTDJB
ICAJBO, DJOUDRASGO ICAJBO,
RCAR DQ RCO MKHDJAJR VAIRKP
DJ QKIDORY RKMAY. JK
QOJQDSGO MOIDQDKJ IAJ SO
HAMO AJY GKJBOP WDRCKTR
RAFDJB DJRK AIIKTJR JKR KJGY
RCO WKPGM AQ DR DQ, STR RCO
WKPGM AQ DR WDGG SO.

169

JERPUMST: NM YMU ATTH HUIGY,
OUKG? IMQQTIS PUMST: 'CD-CD, E
GKMW WDCS YMU'QT SDEKGEKB,
OUKG. YMU'QT SDEKGEKB, 'NEN
DT AEQT REX RDMSR MQ MKHY
AEVT?' CKN SM STHH YMU SDT
SQUSD, E'VT AMQBMSSTK JYRTHA
EK CHH SDER TXIESTJTKS. LUS
LTEKB CR SDER ER C .44 JCBKUJ,
SDT JMRS OMWTQAUH DCKNBUK
EK SDT WMQHN, CKN WMUHN
LHMW YMUQ DTCN IHTCK MAA,
YMU'VT BMS SM CRG YMUQRTHA C
PUTRSEMK: NM E ATTH HUIGY?
WTHH, NM YC, OUKG?'

Solution:

_____

_____

_____

_____

_____

_____

_____

_____

_____

_____

_____

_____

_____

_____

_____

_____

170

HJQS MKJMGK PKSTPI QHFGG
LFUJPQ, FAEIJVGKNYK HKNCTH
JIKQ FIN PKMFX YPKFSKP JIKQ
– VCSB CIYPFSCSTNK.

Solution:

_____

_____

171

JKRCDJB DJROPVOPOQ WDRC HY
IKJIOJRPARDKJ. YKT IKTGM LTR KJ AJ
KPBY DJ HY KVVDIO AJM D WKTGMJ'R
GKKF TL. WOGG, HAYSO KJIO.

Solution:

_____

_____

172

KIOQ JA QYM BGYRFIGBQX JA QYM

HJFKRQMO BP QYIQ, JGHM BQ BP

HJFKMQMGQEX KOJTOIFFMU IGU

VJODBGT PFJJQYEX, BQ BP

HJFKEMQMEX YJGMPQ.

- BPIIH IPBFJS

Solution:

_____

_____

_____

_____

_____

173

KJDAQAOP JTISQ QJ HR QSR
KNMQ-QAFR KMJERPPAJG JE
RURMY OAQAZRG VSJ VJTDW
KMJQROQ QSR MAISQP NGW
KMAUADRIRP JE EMRR KRJKDR
NGW VSJ VJTDW KMRPRMUR VSNQ
AP IJJW NGW EMTAQETD AG JTM
GNQAJGND SRMAQNIR.

Solution:

_____

_____

_____

_____

_____

_____

_____

174

OHQBRO AK QK URG VCQBKSQ

GCJJRO QBHJ QK OCPR CJ GRUQ.

- URJDHICJ YOHJEFCJ

Solution:
_____

_____

175

TBM DRLJAMST PJTTMRK LO

BCSTLRY - KJHMGY, TBM

ACOOMRMKIMS DMTWMMK BUHJK

SLICMTCMS LK ACOOMRMKT

ILKTCKMKTS - SMMHS TL HM TL

DM JTTRCDUTJDGM TL

ACOOMRMKIMS JHLKN

ILKTCKMKTJG MKVCRLKHMKTS,

JKA KLT TL DCLGLNCIJG

ACOOMRMKIMS JHLKN PMLPGMS

TBMHSMGVMS.

Solution:
_____
_____
_____
_____
_____
_____
_____
_____
_____
_____

176

QCE EYE KR QCE IMPQEO WDHH

TK IKOE WKOG QCMJ AKQC CDP

CMJTP. — AEJFMIDJ ROMJGHDJ

Solution:

_____

_____

177

SNO SPUGLOS QNTFF HO QJUIKOK

TIK TFF WNJ TPO BI NOTVOI TIK

OTPSN QNTFF RTFF KJWI

RTBISBIA, OXEOLS SNJQO SNTS

QNTFF HO QLTPOK HY TFFTN.

SNOI SNO SPUGLOS WBFF QJUIK

TATBI TIK SNOY QNTFF PBQO TIK

ATZO TPJUIK SNOG. SNO OTPSN
WBFF QNBIO WBSN SNO FBANS JR
NOP FJPK, TIK SNO HJJD WBFF HO
FTBK JLOI. SNO LPJLNOSQ TIK
WBSIOQQOQ QNTFF HO HPJUANS
BI TIK TFF QNTFF HO CUKAOK
WBSN RTBPIOQQ: IJIO QNTFF HO
WPJIAOK. OVOPY QJUF QNTFF HO
LTBK HTED TEEJPKBIA SJ BSQ
KOODQ, RJP TFFTN DIJWQ JR TFF
SNOBP TESBJIQ.

Solution:
_____
_____
_____
_____
_____
_____
_____

178

Tdsqs fr g mnkoutsq efrsgrs tdgt

glyaney wdn wnqir wftd mnkoutsqr

ilnwr ganut. Ft'r g vsqy rsqfnur

efrsgrs gle ft fltsqbsqsr mnkojstsjy

wftd tds wnqi. Tds tqnuajs wftd

mnkoutsqr fr tdgt ynu 'ojgy' wftd

tdsk!

Solution:

_____

_____

_____

_____

179

RMJMPPMW TVTPY BFSIR EQ RM AT

FJTKLTL; ASR RMJMPPMW KTVTP

UMJTQ. - ATKGFJEK BPFKHIEK

Solution:

_____

_____

180

WQFTL FKGUQFLS FK BUST,

ALKLEFTS FK JMQAIL.

- ALKGMJFK EQMKHIFK

Solution:

_____

_____

181

T AJJK WJPK BQ FBDO T AJJK SPOO

WNJQO PJJS BQ RBPGFY RBXOK

TIK WNJQO SJL BQ BI SNO QDY.

Solution:

_____

_____

182

Xroprntyx Yirncsyj yjt Encpcob pnkklo

byjtrt kqp dkkt pk bqjtnrto kd Cnymco.

Jkp oqnIncocjahx, pbr Cnymco byjtrt

pbr Encpcob dkkt eysg. — Skjyj K'Encrj

Solution:

_____

_____

183

BHC ZHF AIZORUZOA KO H

JOLOAAHCF OEUX. KTR JI ZHRROC

SIB JOLOAAHCF, UR UA HXBHFA HJ

OEUX, JOEOC H QIIN. BO BUXX

JIR XOHCJ SIB RI XUEO

RIQORSOC UJ MOHLO KF WUXXUJQ

OHLS IRSOC'A LSUXNCOJ.

Solution:

_____

_____

_____

_____

_____

_____

_____

184

P GEVIXHN HDPH ZXHG FIW EY

PUU IHG HFEJQUXRPTXFG ZEXG

WELBDIUU. FEQXFH P. DXIBUXIB

Solution:
_____

_____

185

SFVSXN RJ NJOIM VYSP XJQ NSAR

XJQ'R RJ RMQHD. PYSP VAFF

PISBY XJQ PJ DIIK XJQM GJQPY

NYQP. IMHINP YIGAHTVSX

Solution:
_____

_____

186

IJ CJVRPQHRJQ CJ FJKWGREAR

LIYP QBR NRPQ CJQRORPQ.

- NRJDIHCJ SOIJFGCJ

Solution:

_____

_____

187

Ea nq uno udqc xkso tdwap, nq lanwa
udqc xkso jadbcekop, njy haq ataox jau
xano rdjy xks n eaqqao inj. — Eajfnidj
Ronjghdj. aqnlszzha Cdjq: Jaeshksp

Solution:

_____

_____

188

PERNGVIVGL VF NYYBJVAT

LBHEFRYS GB ZNXR ZVFGNXRF.

NEG VF XABJVAT JUVPU BARF GB

XRRC. - FPBGG NQNZF

Solution:
_____
_____

189

Kfifdamca fr sea jnseaq nb dnnk

itch. - Uamgljfm Bqlmhifm

Solution:
_____
_____

190

SPT TM NISPRS TDYRSIB, LUT

AQSRR TM NISPRS MTDSQR.

- LSKGPJFK BQPKHIFK

Solution:
_____

_____

191

CGPPEMDSS ES WCDM WCGT YOU

TCEMJ, WCGT YOU SGY, GMN

WCGT YOU NO GRD EM CGRLOMY.

Solution:
_____

_____

192

GB TGPT WNUKC KHVB HM OBPAB
PMC PT BPSB LUST MNT SOBPJ
PKK GB JMNWS NR PKK GB SBBS.
– EBMIPLHM DRPMJKHM

Solution:

_____

_____

193

IUQCSFSCJH CHRPUFQUQ CH
PUEFSCJH SJ PCQD CH UNTFE
KPJKJPSCJH SJ FAU. UPHUQS
IUGCHAWFY

Solution:

_____

_____

194

I HCGD YWIDN XS HCWN YS NS

YHD WIFHY.

Solution:
_____

195

A'e nmprin ojige fx diaoqni pafi

ehagu vrmp ohfi jihjdi lmdd fx vhnc

mge A lmdd fx sqg.

– Bmnie Eamfhge

Solution:
_____

_____

_____

196

ZN WVV JOWJ WUSLZEWTK DWTJ

ZK KSEGLZJB, JOSB EWT HQ JQ

PLZKQT. JOSB'VV OWFS STQGHO

JQ SWJ, W RSI WTI W LQQN QFSL

JOSZL OSWIK. RGJ ZN WT

WUSLZEWT DWTJK JQ PLSKSLFS

OZK IZHTZJB WTI OZK SMGWVZJB

WK W OGUWT RSZTH, OS UGKJ

TQJ RQD OZK TSEX JQ WTB

IZEJWJQLZWV HQFSLTUSTJ.

Solution:
_____
_____
_____
_____
_____
_____

197

CN YJQ WJQGV BSUA S NSCPBNQG
OAMUSIP, SIV JIA PBSP YJQ GCFA,
OAMUA YJQMOAGN.

- EAIDSHCI NMSIFGCI

Solution:
_____

_____

198

C hlpq pgg wl opvl rkjl cs tk pwpflj
p sgllmcjb bcpjt pjr hcgg oci wcto
p tlqqcegl qlskgvl.

- Cskqkfu Ypipiktk

Solution:
_____

_____

199

XPCH APXRN QRVRNQ

HKRXCRMSRC. LH LC HKR VRXZMR

PV HKR CYRELRC — LH LC HKR

HLBTRCC ZNQ MLPNRCC LN WPU —

AKLEK HRNQC HP QRVRNQ AKRN

ZHHZEGRQ. XZTBZTRH HKZHEKRT

Solution:
_____
_____
_____
_____
_____
_____
_____
_____

200

HOAJWCDGO, VOAPQ KV

TJDUOPQAG MDQAQROP QAJF RK

AJ AGG RDHO GKW KUOP RCO

WKPGMJOUOP GOR YKTP QOJQO

KV HKPAGQ BOR DJ RCO WAY KV

MKDJB WCAR'Q PDBCR.

Solution:

_____

_____

_____

_____

_____

_____

_____

_____

_____

201

RCDOKCO NDCSDLK WQDSOQR

NLQOROO SBO DKOVDSFIHO, FKT

FHSBLUAB MQLIHOJR FKT

CFSFRSQLMBOR JFY IO

DKOVDSFIHO, RLHUSDLKR FQO

KLS. — DRFFC FRDJLV

Solution:

SCIENCE FICTION WRITERS
FORESEE THE INEVITABLE, AND
ALTHOUGH PROBLEMS AND
CATASTROPHES MAY BE
INEVITABLE, SOLUTIONS ARE
NOT. — ISAAC ASIMOV

202

RHIE RFKE BMP HJJ RDFLCQ:
CPEHR DHQRE KHIEQ CPEHR
WHQRE. – AELGHKFL BPHLIJFL

Solution:

203

OBI RJHNOCOQOCJH JHFY ACVIN
KIJKFI OBI MCABO OJ KQMNQI
BPKKCHINN. YJQ BPVI OJ RPORB
CO YJQMNIFT. – UIHDPGCH
TMPHEFCH

Solution:

204

Bpoc oc z jhjtib bpzb O vttgku

docp ju gzetibc whykv pzat koatv

bh cpzet. Ju rzbpte dhykv pzat

timhutv dpzb uhy pzat ch

qtitehycku czov hr jt-ziv ju jhbpte

dhykv pzat xtkotatv ob.

— Kuivhi X. Mhpichi

Solution:

205

RBA KCPQR HCQRMFA CJ NUIGCS

IUQCJAQQ CQ RBA ELCJE CJRL

CR. — IAJDMHCJ KPMJFGCJ

Solution:
_____

_____

206

Kso gciroqx ermrjep kj qar torrekh

kt qar morpp, lje qalq bljjkq ir

gchcqre vcqaksq ircjy gkpq. —

Qakhlp Drttropkj

Solution:
_____

_____

207

QODIFP TJC QOKTIBKOY TOK QBK

MOTIQDIK LS SLLGP, QBTQ CLJ'Q

BTVK ROTDJP KJLUAB QL RK

BLJKPQ. — RKJETHDJ SOTJFGDJ

Solution:

_____

_____

208

Wbps dr sbt urt kc gdvdja, dc ds ot

jks sk rsqdvt ckq jkogt lpurtr pji

sk hpft sbdr huiigti wkqgi p otsstq

mgplt ckq sbkrt wbk wdgg gdvt dj

ds pcstq wt pqt akjt? Bkw tgrt lpj

wt mus kuqrtgvtr dj bpqhkjdkur

qtgpsdkj wdsb sbt aqtps vtqdsdtr

pji lkjrkgpsdkjr kc sbt djcdjdst pji

sbt tstqjpg? Pji D pvkw hy cpdsb

sbps wt pqt hpqlbdja skwpqir

otsstq ipyr. Buhpjdsy wdgg jks ot

lprs ikwj. Wt pqt akdja kj rwdjadja

oqpvtgy ckqwpqi pgkja sbt aqpji

bdab qkpi pji pgqtpiy otbdji sbt

idrspjs hkujspdjr dr sbt mqkhdrt kc

sbt ruj.

Solution:
_____

_____

_____

_____

_____

_____

_____

_____

_____

209

YKUP JIT WKPTB TK TBI WKPGA

CQ UQURGGY AITIPHCJIA EY WBRT

PIHRCJQ RNTIP YKUP ERA BRECTQ

RPI QUETPRMTIA NPKH YKUP SKKA

KJIQ. — EIJDRHCJ NPRJFGCJ

Solution:

_____

_____

_____

_____

210

Ehzduh wkh Lghv ri Pdufk.

Solution:

_____

<u>211</u>

XVS PVWCSNS ONS XEH LMONV

NXMHZSN XH EMWXS XVS EHMQ

'PMWNWN.' HCS LMONV NXMHZS

NXKCQN THM QKCUSM; XVS HXVSM

THM HAAHMXOCWXG. WC K

PMWNWN, LS KEKMS HT XVS

QKCUSM — LOX MSPHUCWJS XVS

HAAHMXOCWXG.

Solution:
_____
_____
_____
_____
_____
_____
_____

212

FGG IY GBNH B'UH GKKDHS FQ

VKOSP FP QAKTWA B VHOH

PHHBJW QAHI NKO QAH NBOPQ

QBIH. HOJHPQ AHIBJWVFY

Solution:

_____

_____

213

Er ici jsv er ici qeoiw xli alspi

asvph fpmrh. — Qelexqe Kerhlm

Solution:

_____

_____

214

HIE VASQASM XJR'MS HI AJISPQ

GHI, JM VASQASM XJR'MS H

QABST, ESKSIEP JI VAJPS

PJFBNBQJM AHP YBUSI GS GX

OMBST. — OSICHGBI TMHIDFBI

Solution:
_____
_____
_____
_____
_____
_____
_____
_____
_____
_____

215

UAGCAVA KLQTCKI, KL JBQQAO

WTAOA YLR OABH CQ, LO WTL

PBCH CQ, KL JBQQAO CS C TBVA

PBCH CQ, RKGAPP CQ BIOAAP

WCQT YLRO LWK OABPLK BKH

YLRO LWK DLJJLK PAKPA.

Solution:
_____

_____

_____

_____

_____

_____

_____

_____

216

WTQ VI CGJV QHOQ SMIIEJF
ROGGJQ WI PIMUIE WY QHI
EIUARIP JS QHI QYMOGQ. OP AQ
AP OG OGRAIGQ QMTQH QHOQ
SMIIEJF ROGGJQ WI DINAPDOQIE
AGQJ IXAPQIGRI, PJ AQ AP GJ
DIPP JWUAJTP QHOQ SMIIEJF
ROGGJQ WI RIGPJMIE AGQJ
IXAPQIGRI. OGE OGY VHJ ORQ OP
AS SMIIEJF'P EISIGPIP OMI QJ WI
SJTGE AG PTKKMIPPAJG OGE
PTPKARAJG OGE SIOM RJGSIPP O
EJRQMAGI QHOQ AP ODAIG QJ
OFIMARO.

Solution:

217

NJ IJS LKFP HCQSFEKQ. XJT

VCGG EIJV LFCGTPK. AJISCITK SJ

PKFAB JTS.

Solution:
_____

_____

218

ALHMSTCI JKCHJGS

RMVLGUTCLKCZMA GJKA

TRJKSPLRT. TBMY JGSL

RMVLGUTCLKCZMA JNRCIUGTURM,

DY GMTTCKN LKM OJRHMR

PGLUNB JKA HJKURM HUIB HLRM

GJKA TBJK TBM OJRHMR ILUGA

TCGG LR HJKURM DY TBM

OJRHMR'S LWK MOOLRTS.

Solution:
_____
_____
_____
_____

219

COL'M KO XUOQLC YXFJLK MEH

SOUWC OSHY FOQ X WJRJLK. MEH

SOUWC OSHY FOQ LOMEJLK. JM

SXY EHUH VJUYM. AXUI MSXJL

Solution:
_____
_____

220

AWV CWD HGUW PHW UILPQW PF

VIPHMPGDR PHW HISHWMP

EIRRWL.

Solution:
_____

_____

221

CL WCK SRGGP DJ GKUL WDQC

CDHPLGS WDGG CRUL JK ODURGP.

- ILJERHDJ SORJFGDJ

Solution:
_____

_____

222

BTIDJQ DPL JKR MPKTG KA RBLCP
DJULQRKPQ, DJG PDPLHY CJVCRL
RBLI PKTJG RK GCJJLP.

Solution:
_____
_____

223

P NPRZ XCJCMPWPVR MCET
CZYHFXPRB. CMCET XPLC
WVLCOVZT XYERW VR XDC WCX, P
BV PRXV XDC VXDCE EVVL FRZ
ECFZ F OVVG. BEVYHDV LFEK

Solution:
_____
_____

224

Bi mkl jmqkbkn B whgfld mk tmo mi
tsl whtlq haqmrr tsl Omtmjha Qbvlq
tsl slhdgbkl tsht hitlqkmmk wmugd
qlhd Oqlrbdlkt Ahkt Rwbj Gykdmk E
Cmskrmk

Solution:
_____
_____
_____
_____
_____
_____
_____
_____
_____

225

CG YKS VKSFT JKQ RN

GKOAKQQNJ WP PKKJ WP YKS

WON TNWT, NCQBNO VOCQN

PKHNQBCJA VKOQB ONWTCJA KO

TK QBCJAP VKOQB VOCQCJA.

— RNJDWHCJ GOWJEFCJ

Solution:
_____

_____

_____

_____

_____

_____

_____

_____

226

DJMDUDMTAG QIDOJIO VDIRDKJ

QRKPDOQ HAY QOOH AQ RPDUDAG

AQ OUOP RK RCO SGDJMOP

IPDRDIQ AJM LCDGKQKLCOPQ KV

RKMAY — STR RCO IKPO KV

QIDOJIO VDIRDKJ, DRQ OQQOJIO

CAQ SOIKHO IPTIDAG RK KTP

QAGUARDKJ DV WO APO RK SO

QAUOM AR AGG.

Solution:
_____
_____
_____
_____
_____
_____

227

MSRETKIT EQ RDT ILJMSKELK LB
WEQNLJ.

Solution:
_____

_____

228

SCL PKKQRSLN SK SCL SLINHL KA
WDRPKI DR T GJKWHLPBL KA KUQ
KWJ DBJKQTJML. — ELJFTIDJ
AQTJGHDJ

Solution:
_____

_____

229

Rtm agmj aq rk rpy rk navm jff rtm
aiekphjraki rk tmfl krtmpq rk
bsgnm rtm vjfsm ke yksp
dkirpausraki; ikr bsqr rtm
aiekphjraki rtjr fmjgq rk bsgnhmir
ai kim ljpradsfjp gapmdraki kp
jikrtmp. – Padtjpg Emyihji

Solution:

TBM RJTM LO BUHJK CKVMKTCLK

CS OJSTMR, JKA TBM RJTM LO

IUGTURJG GLSS CS SGLWMR, CK

JRMJS LIIUPCMA DY HJKY

ILHPMTCKN SLICMTCMS WCTB

HJKY CKACVCAUJGS JKA CK

ILKTJIT WCTB SLICMTCMS

MGSMWBMRM.

Solution:
_____
_____
_____
_____
_____
_____
_____

231

Ifdn rcqfkhr lq nwmekar fk

mqlmlqsflk sl lkn'r pltqebn.

— Ekefr Kfk

Solution:
_____

_____

232

Qdl tkql ep qdl ikpq mkvloyrh

ejpqoriljq ltlo ulteplu ax icj yko

aolcgejb ukvj ejfrpqesl cju

ulpqokxejb qdl qlooeahl vchhp

vdesd eimoepkj ilj alscrpl qdlx col

ueyyloljq yoki kqdlo ilj. —Hxjukj A.

Fkdjpkj

Solution:
_____
_____
_____
_____
_____
_____
_____

233

GTVZXO PLOKZHOTJZIV

IHUZTZKJLIJZQTK, PLQSVOUK

LILOVB EIFO JOLUZTIV HIJOK.

Solution:
_____
_____
_____

234

WNOI T GTI KBOQ SNOY WNJ

QUPVBVO NBG TQD WNTS

LPJLOPSY NO NTQ FORS HONBIK.

SNO TIAOF WNJ HOIKQ JVOP SNO

KYBIA GTI TQDQ WNTS AJJK KOOK

NO NTQ QOIS HORJPO NBG.

Solution:

235

Wcuj yks rutlc yksp qkj, yks rutlc
yksp qkj'q qkj. – Rcu Rthism

Solution:
_____

_____

236

Aq qglp fifnhq L ri hiq gaun a
jnmpihad mndaqlihpglj vlqg a
oifjsqnm... lq yiq pi oihesplhy, ap
qi vgaq vap ih qgn oifjsqnm, vgaq
vaph'q ih qgn oifjsqnm, vgaq vap
ih qgn gamr rmlun, vgaq vap ih qgn

pieq rmlun, qgaq lq farn lq naplnm

eim fn qi bspq ri fx vimc vlqg jnh

ahr jnhold. – Bahnq Mnhi, SP

Aqqimhnx Ynhnmad, 1998

Solution:

_____

_____

_____

_____

_____

_____

_____

_____

_____

_____

_____

_____

_____

237

SBW WULHTSELK LI SBW BTJCK

PCAW VEHH KLS DW

CAALJMHEQBWR EK SBW SWK

SBLTQCKR YWCPQ LI SCJW

CKEJCHQ, DTS EK SBW JEHHELK

YWCPQ LI VEHR CKEJCHQ,

DWACTQW JCK EQ CKR VEHH

CHVCYQ DW C VEHR CKEJCH.

Solution:
_____
_____
_____
_____
_____
_____
_____
_____

238

HOFBOVOPQ, COWQ, QTHTOTIQ JP

ENPBQSBTIQ — WNJOVOP

HOFBOVOQ BI AJK TIK SNO FTQS

KTY TIK KJOQ WNTS BQ PBANS —

QNTFF NTVO IJSNBIA SJ ROTP JP

POAPOS

Solution:
_____
_____
_____
_____
_____
_____
_____
_____
_____

239

C FLMW YMT SGG, SLK WCGG
SWBCGE TNBMGK RBE TLYMFEK
BTJMTP MI YMTP CKGELEQQ
NPCLAE BELPY CU

Solution:

240

C fyvlmxvz xwtopf td jywdo mkcp c
uowmctp opogi. Zom c gcp lo ypo
mktpb yw mko ymkow, cpf jo mkop
qpyj kyj my goom ktg. Codye

Solution:

241

P ipjpqte to kjw vhk epj'q ehpjgw

hto ftjr pjr vkj'q ehpjgw qhw

osabweq. — Vtjoqkj Ehsnehtdd

Solution:
_____
_____

242

YEE OJJI ZJJDP NYSC JHC QNAHO

AH FJGGJH – QNCW YMC QMRCM

QNYH AT QNCW NYI MCYEEW

NYKKCHCI. CMHCPQ NCGAHOUYW

Solution:
_____
_____

243

BTNUTH LMU DUTYOGHXY

VXUZUDUR FTOSVUXZBTZ MBY

THEHX GHBRZ LOZM B DBZ.

– XUCHXZ B. MHOTRHOT

Solution:

244

RX LFCGCIY SJ MPKMFPK, XJT

FPK MPKMFPCIY SJ LFCG.

Solution:

245

UET'A AZDTI KEB MOV YEDTY AE
QETQVMG AZEBYZAR PK
QETQVMGDTY VCDUVTQV AZMA
AZVK VCVO VJDRAVU.

Solution:

246

Dzqkx sn adc zmc dzqkx sn qhrd

lzjdr z lzm gdzksgx, vdzksgx, zmc

vhrd.— Admizlhm Eqzmjkhm

Solution:

247

Ur gung evfrf yngr zhfg gebg nyy

qnl. — Orawnzva Senaxyva

Solution:

_____

_____

248

B dssf fbes B cpno amthhsr t hba

cpbux vjmg vboy t mbayo nytmk

yjje bi oys gbrrfs jd bo.

— Fxirji H. Cjyinji

Solution:

_____

_____

249

JLBGF NHPMS WXPSV LFBQV

BMPDK PCFVF MSBQL PNVJQ

JVZBK BJSNV FGFMZ DPMRP

DVZMB SSZPG FMVLF RJSCP DRBS

Solution:
_____
_____
_____
_____
_____
_____
_____
_____

250

CO YLU NJVM HM 10 HCGGCLK ALGGJRS, C WLUGAK'T GCVM JKY ACOOMRMKTGY. JGTBLUNB KLWJAJYS C NUMSS YLU'A BJVM TL RJCSM TBJT TL 20 HCGGCLK TL HMJK JKYTBCKN.

Solution:
_____

_____

_____

_____

_____

_____

_____

_____

_____

251

IS ID KQ SNB XJJPWBDD JT XJP

SNLS IW JHA OJHWSAQ YB NLVB

SNJDB SNABB HWDZBLELKMQ

ZABOIJHD SNIWXD: TABBPJF JT

DZBBON, TABBPJF JT

OJWDOIBWOB, LWP SNB

ZAHPBWOB WBVBA SJ ZALOSIOB

BISNBA JT SNBF. FLAE SYLIW

Solution:
_____

_____

_____

_____

_____

_____

_____

252

Iduf dr nifprpks. Cfpsb dr nfpafuti. Ds'r

sbf sqpkrdsdmk sbps'r sqmteifrmjf.

Solution:
_____

253

EYLJQHPN: RNDD RWPR GH FQKX

DYCN W THEWG LMHKGNA.

MHKKNMP JQHPN: 'RNWSNG RWL

GH KWUN DYCN DHSN PH RWPKNA

PQKGNA/ GHK RNDD W FQKX DYCN

W THEWG LMHKGNA.'

Solution:
_____

_____

_____

254

Ezrxnw , rmkze r qzekrnc rwz,
xnazekv klz hncx kdd hyql medh
nkv qezrknaz gyevynkv. Rcb hrc fld
ezrxv kdd hyql rcx yvzv lnv dfc
iernc kdd tnkktz mrttv nckd trjb
lrinkv dm klncsncw.

Solution:
_____
_____
_____
_____
_____
_____
_____
_____

255

Pejejoep sdbs rpewfs fq jlkey. —

Oekgbjfk Apbkhifk

Solution:
_____

256

RCO QAMMOQR AQLOIR KV GDVO

PDBCR JKW DQ RCAR QIDOJIO

BARCOPQ FJKWGOMBO VAQROP

RCAJ QKIDORY BARCOPQ

WDQMKH.

Solution:
_____

_____

_____

257

Qda qosqd ep klq tiwtyp qda ptja
tp qda jtfloeqy hauepelk.

Solution:
_____
_____

258

Ymu fm lmt ixdkbli jihbrjdtbml bl
tai jbhat ms tai oilisbtr bt wbjj
gmlviy bs nqmniqjy dfkblbrtiqif,
out bl tai jbhat ms tai wqmlhr bt
wmujf fm dlf tai adqkr bt wmujf
gduri bs bknqmniqjy dfkblbrtiqif.
– Jylfml O. Cmalrml

Solution:
_____
_____
_____
_____
_____
_____

259

Ylu huqr gampj kplh rba hcqrmfaq

Ik Irbapq. Ylu smj'r nlqqcigy gcva

glje ajlueb rl hmfa rbah mgg

ylupqagk. — Qmh Gavajqlj

Solution:
_____
_____

260

AKHROBKDA CP LKA LS QTA JLPQ
HCSSCDRGQ HCPDCMGCKAP, URQ
CQ CP QL QTA LKA WTL AKHROAP
QTBQ QTA SCKBG VCDQLOY DLJAP.

Solution:
_____
_____

261

Confkqih jhk jhngjfr jqi hlt
mlrrirrnlhr, aut jqi milmfi jhk
cqijtuqir tl ai flvik, coiqnroik, jhk
cjqik elq. — Rtimoih Sqneento

Solution:
_____
_____

262

C ijh'o pnr impyn, gx imrsgn smr
wmcyborhchy rhjpyb.

- G. A. Rnabrm

Solution:
_____

_____

263

Ly pgju di ocjjpdib s andyiw,
pgjuyn di ocsibdib.

Solution:
_____

_____

264

ALHMSTCIJTMA PGJKTS JKA

JKCHJGS YCMGA OJR HLRM

IJGLRCMS PMR JIRM TBJK AL

WCGA BJDCTJTS, CK WBCIB HLST

SPMICMS JRM CKMACDGM TL

BUHJKS.

Solution:
_____
_____
_____
_____
_____
_____
_____
_____

265

LJP BFUCIY GCUKN GJIY, C BFUK

KWMKPCKIAKN HFIX CIQSFIAKQ JL

RKCIY JRGCYKN, RX RKSSKP

CILJPHFSCJI JP LTGGKP

AJIQCNKPFSCJI, SJ ABFIYK

JMCICJIQ, KUKI JI CHMJPSFIS

QTRDKASQ, VBCAB C JIAK

SBJTYBS PCYBS RTS LJTIN SJ RK

JSBKPVCQK.

Solution:

_____

_____

_____

_____

_____

_____

266

CFOOX YFJDHDLR FQL FHH
FHDGL; LELQX TKCFOOX YFJDHX
DR TKCFOOX DK DSR NVK VFX.
HLN SNHRSNX

Solution:
_____

_____

267

BL BKMLG DJG MPDYLG RBDR

RBLPL WDQJ'R DJ DARLPHCAL.

RBLJ BL PLDHCZLG RBLPL WDQ D

UKJRPDGCURCKJ CJVKHVLG BLPL

DJG ILPLHY BKMLG RBDR RBLPL

WDQJ'R DJ DARLPHCAL.

Solution:
_____
_____
_____
_____
_____

268

CTHAJDRY CAQ RCO QRAPQ DJ
DRQ VTRTPO, AJM RCAR VTRTPO
DQ RKK DHLKPRAJR RK SO GKQR
TJMOP RCO STPMOJ KV ETUOJDGO
VKGGY AJM DBJKPAJR
QTLOPQRDRDKJ.

Solution:
_____
_____
_____

269

WTFADAQY FTPQ RDVRYP EN QWN

KJMQAJG JH RGY FRG VWJ

MNINAUNP RIIDRAF NRMGNS AG

QWN EDJJS JH WAP HJDDJVNMP

RGS QWN PRIMAHAINP JH WAP

HMANGSP.

Solution:

_____

_____

_____

_____

_____

_____

_____

_____

_____

270

B ukj'q fjkw wecq bq wbgg qcfl krq

qelol — 500 scprcgqblp hcyal,

hcyal 500,000. Bq'p qel crieqp

qecq pscol hl. — Gyjukj A. Dkejpkj

Solution:
_____

_____

_____

271

A DHMLGHP GHVHL QI HFJQY QSH

WHDD IE FY WLAQAGU, OTQ

MDWMYN QI NQIJ WSHG QSHLH

WMN NQADD NIFHQSAGU QSHLH

AG QSH PHHJ JMLQ IE QSH WHDD,

MGP DHQ AQ LHEADD MQ GAUSQ

ELIF QSH NJLAGUN QSMQ EHP AQ.

HLGHNQ SHFAGUWMY

Solution:
_____
_____
_____
_____
_____
_____
_____
_____
_____
_____
_____
_____

272

B msw ivw rbv hi nqgovl; hi

vspbgo, s nqgrlvr pnhqmsgr. –

Tvgcsfbg llsgdebg

Solution:
_____

_____

273

D wdgg nl iy osrt. Tcjt dr jgg D hjk

nl. D jrf alq yluq csgm-jkn Bln'r.

– Gyknlk O. Elckrlk

Solution:
_____

_____

274

CJ RBKQL GDYQ QMCPCRQ WLPL

OPDVL, RBL QRDFLQ WLPL BCSB,

ILJ WLPL PLDH ILJ, WKILJ WLPL

PLDH WKILJ DJG QIDHH ATPPY

UPLDRTPLQ APKI DHMBD

ULJRDTPC WLPL PLDH QIDHH

ATPPY UPLDRTPLQ APKI DHMBD

ULJRDTPC.

Solution:

_____

_____

_____

_____

_____

_____

_____

275

ZJ ZK ENL UQLR ZUPQLJNTJ JQ HR

NHVR JQ SZJ JSR JNLIRJ JSNT ZJ

ZK JQ SNIIVR QFRL DSQ UNXRK N

DRNPQT QL DSQ PGVVK N JLZIIRL.

Solution:

276

DG'F T XTJC SKKB JDCX GNTG

VTC KCWP GNDCE KZ KCY LTP GK

FSYWW T LKBX.

Solution:

277

YVIVD JADDP RSAHG GZVADP RF

KAYX RF GZV ERTZMYVDP UAVF

JZRG MG'F FHBBAFVU GA UA.

DASVDG R. ZVMYKVMY

Solution:
_____

_____

278

OMD MDDNS TO AD SKOW TO IORL

HOMVEHTEOMS, AUT OMHD IORLDN

TCDY LUST AD NDIDMNDN

GBGEMST TCD CDGVEDST ONNS.

Solution:
_____

_____

279

KJYSQ QRX QFBYIFY SRDYQ RVRX

NOJH SAY PYRTSX JN SAY QSROQ

- HYOY MGJPQ JN MRQ RSJHQ. B,

SJJ, FRI QYY SAY QSROQ JI R

EYQYOS IBMAS, RIE NYYG SAYH.

PTS EJ B QYY GYQQ JO HJOY?

Solution:

_____

_____

_____

_____

_____

_____

_____

_____

280

ZLQVU PGUDK: 'GVT BYH B

ZSYBUJHY.' (QHYDTYG YLZLUJ)

Solution:

281

Tai Ikhfbra kiviq lqew e fbki

wbtamut nfuqqbkh bt.

— Wbkrtmk Gauqgabff

Solution:

282

Sea sars mn jabhaqrefo fr lms sm
ots dqabslarr flsm etkblfsy, uts sm
ajfcfs fs, nmq sea dqabslarr fr
bjqabhy seaqa. — Gbkar Utceblbl

Solution:

_____

_____

283

OVWEUF MDS GRDS ZWYS OVSJ

MDS ERH OVME OVSJ VMCS SCSD

NSSE.

Solution:

_____

_____

284

UKTCG TBM MKA LO TBM GJST CIM
JNM JRLUKA 11,000 D.I., JGG
BUHJKS LK JGG ILKTCKMKTS
WMRM STCGG GCVCKN JS STLKM
JNM BUKTMR/NJTBMRMRS.

Solution:

_____

_____

285

Fbzr crbcyr qvr ng 25 naq nera'g
ohevrq hagvy 75. — Orawnzva
Senaxyva

Solution:

_____

_____

286

WH JUQS, CKEHHE, TII BTKA

SLAHSBHP LP, JLQS TQQUPHEIY,

WH QBTII TII BTKA QHMTPTSHIY.

- OHKDTJCK RPTKFICK

Solution:

_____

_____

287

PKRKGGCJI FYFCIQS SXPFISQ CQ

JRKNCKIAK SJ YJN.

Solution:

_____

_____

288

Rdo beqzkjrojrob ilj yejbq jk olqw
zdlep. — Aojfliej Ypljghej

Solution:

_____

_____

289

IPOARDKJDQRQ HAFO DR QKTJM
AQ RCKTBC A 'RCOKPY' DQ
QKHORCDJB YKT MPOAHR TL
AVROP SODJB MPTJF AGG JDBCR.

Solution:

_____

_____

290

Nabm ilhfintp ft nh ehhd kn Dlxinhm

olhf k mebsanex pbootltgn

itlmitynbut — ghn km mbfiex kg

tgylxintp ftmmkst, rqn kemh km k

utabyet vbna vabya nh ptebutl nat

dtx. Nabm yakgstm nat nkmd olhf hgt

ho ylkydbgs k yhpt nh hgt fqya fhlt

ebdt mheubgs k iqzzet. — Sklx Vklzbg

Solution:

291

Wdqc s bkku pmodlq, s bkku udormqko msj lokutmr s hspqroldrmr. Wdqc qcr pshr pmodlq, s hrudkmor udormqko msj lokutmr s lsppsagr idgh. Atq wdqc s asu pmodlq rvrj s bkku udormqko msj'q lkppdagy hsfr s bkku idgh. Iko qotgy mdjrhsqdm rxlorppdkj, qcr mshros sju qcr hdmoklckjr htpq ar sagr qk mokpp akqc idor sju wsqro. Qcr pmodlq htpq ar pkhrqcdjb qcsq csp qcr lkwro qk uk qcdp. – Eslsjrpr udormqko Sfdos Ftokpsws

292

Solution:
_____
_____
_____
_____
_____
_____
_____
_____
_____
_____
_____
_____
_____
_____

292

Lcsqt sp c rjhqshuug, chm we ecrt
lcff jh qtcq fshe wteoe we gcy. Ay
cqqegkqshi qj osismfy rfcppsly
eqteoecf rjhrekqp fsde lcsqt, we ehm
uk meacqshi pegchqsrp qj qte kjshq
wteoe we ehqsoefy gspp qte javsjup-
qtcq sp, qtcq we coe cff qoyshi qj
merskteo fsle'p asi gypqeosep, chm
we'oe ecrt ljffjwshi juo jwh kcqtp jl
ehfsitqehgehq. — Mch Aojwh

Solution:
_____
_____
_____
_____
_____
_____

293

Tm rd nqdnpqda bmq wpq gs mld
mb tfd kmst dbbdetgvd kdpls mb
nqdsdqvglc ndped. — Cdmqcd
Wpsfglctml. Kdtpnuzzjd fglt: Cgqa
tfd fultdq.

Solution:
_____
_____
_____
_____
_____
_____
_____
_____
_____

294

Ebso bq knorrx qbfkeo: Xjt lj qjfo
qrtss. Fjqr spbeq. Qjfo vjndq. Xjt lj
fjno js vapr vjndq. Bs br vjndq hby,
jraonq mtbidex ijkx br. Raog xjt lj
qjforabgy oeqo. Rao rnbid bq rao ljbgy
qjforabgy oeqo. — Eojgpnlj lp Ubgib

Solution:

_____

_____

_____

_____

_____

_____

_____

_____

295

Vwp gq wl tejy sfgle, ats lms sfc
tejgcqs md sfgleq. Sfc bcrwycb wlb
bcepwbcb qswsc md kmpwj wlb
nwspgmsgr dccjgle vfgrf sfgliq
sfws lmsfgle gq vmpsf vwp gq ktrf
vmpqc. Sfc ncpqml vfm fwq lmsfgle
dmp vfgrf fc gq vgjjgle sm dgefs,
lmsfgle vfgrf gq kmpc gknmpswls
sfwl fgq mvl ncpqmlwj qwdcsy, gq
w kgqcpwajc rpcwstpc wlb fwq lm
rfwlrc md acgle dpcc tljcqq kwbc
wlb icns qm ay sfc cxcpsgmlq md
acsscp kcl sfwl fgkqcjd.

Solution:
_____

_____

_____

_____

296

Bl xjs'pa ijr lwbgbie atapx qj jlrai,
rnai xjs'pa ijr rpxbie nwpy aijsen.

Solution:

297

Qsdihna fk sen blpnqs, sll rilqn sl

efan; F'ii un tmlk ylt uy sen

jllkifces qfan — lypfr bplj 'Etkcpy

ifhn sen Wlib' — Atpdk Atpdk

Solution:

_____

_____

298

De ylt wckr rl ncr wnhh dk

Nkahcks, ncr rbpnn upncgecqrq.

Solution:

_____

_____

299

Kauap cfua fk — kauap, kauap,
kauap, kauap, fk klsdfkc cpans lp
qjnii, inpca lp massy, kauap cfua
fk axvams sl vlkufvsflkq lb dlkltp
nkr cllr qakqa. Kauap yfair sl
blpva; kauap yfair sl sda
nmmnpaksiy luapwdaijfkc jfcds lb
sda akajy. — Wfkqslk Vdtpvdfii

Solution:
_____
_____
_____
_____
_____
_____
_____

300

Ueckhl qce qsoqhe. Ce itgep

mokboepp kjhy wcej ce pqdrgp cdp

jerg ksq.

Solution:
_____

_____

PART TWO:
THE SECRET CODE CHALLENGE

Moving beyond the idle pleasures of simple cryptograms, Part Two leads you step by step into the world of real code-breaking – and on, into the darker recesses of classical cryptography. Bring your wits along as you'll need them. The puzzles here no longer rely on simple substitution systems, but involve a series of increasingly ingenious methods of encryption. Everything you need to know is explained in stages, while the puzzles gradually grow in complexity as you progress. Can you complete the secret code challenge?

NOT SO EASY

The simple substitution system used in Part One is also known to cryptographers as a 'monoalphabetic substitution' system. In this section you'll find other kinds of monoalphabetic ciphers explained, as well as transposition methods and an introduction to digital encryption systems.

More like-for-like

There are several other possible ways to create a monoalphabetic cipher alphabet:

- Reversing the order of the letters in the cipher alphabet. Z-A instead of A-Z.
- Adding numbers or punctuation symbols to the cipher alphabet, to make it longer than 26 characters.
- Using a key on the plaintext alphabet instead of (or in combination with) the cipher alphabet.
- Substituting double characters or numbers (or more) for each letter of plaintext. For example, swapping each letter for a 3-digit number in base 7.
- Using a ciphertext system that has no letters, and is instead mostly composed of numbers, punctuation symbols, or even an entirely original set of symbols, such as in the Pigpen Cipher.

If you can see, or guess, that a monoalphabetic system has been used – whether using glyphs, numbers, letters or any other symbol – there will always be the same substitution for each letter of the plaintext alphabet. In other words, whatever is used to substitute for the letter A, be it B, '7*', or '01100001', then that is always what is substituted for any other letter A in the same message.

Symbol ciphers
One last, notable form of the substitution cipher is to replace each plaintext letter with a symbol or glyph of some type. The best-known example is the 'Pigpen cipher', so named because the grid resembles an animal pen. Variations of this have been seen throughout history: during the American Civil War, as secret messages used by the Freemasons, and between European and American schoolchildren for decades.

One common method of creating the Pigpen cipher is by writing the letters of the alphabet into two square grids followed by two diagonal grids:

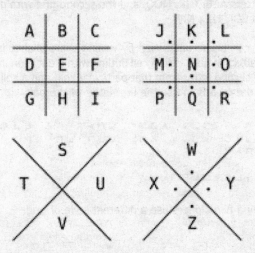

One method of creating the Pigpen cipher

Another method of creating the cipher

The ciphertext version of any letter is then the outline of the cell where it appears, along with a dot if it comes from that section of the grid.

Further variations can be obtained by writing the alphabet into the grid backwards, from bottom to top, or writing it in via a keyed cipher alphabet.When tackling these kinds of ciphers, you need only figure out a few of the letters and their corresponding 'cells', and then the rest of the grid can be deduced quite quickly.

The following example is in the Freemason style. This follows the basic Pigpen method, except that it alternates back and forth between the grids when laying out the letters. So the first 3x3 grid has the letters ACE, GIK, MOQ, and the second grid with dots has the letters BDF, HJL, NPR.

The same can be accomplished by writing the alphabet in pairs, with two letters in each cell. A cell outline with a dot then indicates to use the second letter from that particular cell, and a cell outline without a dot means to use the first letter of the pair.

```
JVC  ⅂∏∀  <Ǝ⅃∀  ∧∏>Γ  ⊔∏>⅂∀FΛ  ⊔⅃⅂  ⅄∏
∧∏>?  JVC  <Ǝ⅃∀  ∧∏>  ⊔⅃⅂  ⅄∏  ⊾∏Γ  ∧∏>Γ
⊔∏>⅂∀FΛ?

- ⊟∏Ǝ⅂  ⊾.  ⊏⅃⅂⅂⊾⅄∀
```

The following two ciphers use a different style of grid.

Hint: the first word in the above cipher is 'THE'

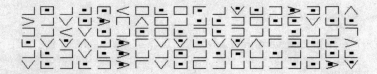

For answers, see page 549

Stepping out of line

Transposition is the first step beyond simple letter substitution. At its simplest, it can be one of the quickest encryption methods to crack. But a key difference is that everyday skills of frequency analysis will no longer be as helpful here.

In transposition ciphers, all the letters in the message are already present in the ciphertext – they have just been rearranged. The trick is to figure out the method of rearrangement, or the 'route' that must be followed in order to read the plaintext.

Columnar transposition
In this kind of transposition cipher, the plaintext is first written vertically along a series of columns.

For example, the plaintext 'Cryptanalysis is easy' may be written:

```
0 CPNYSEY
1 RTASIAX
2 YALISSX
```

The ciphertext is then pulled off, usually by rows.

In the simplest form, the rows are taken from top to bottom:

```
CPNYSEYRTASIAXYALISSX
```

A level of complexity can be added by pulling the ciphertext off according to a key. For example, if the rows are numbered 012 from bottom to top, and the key is 120, then the ciphertext would be:

```
RTASIAXYALISSXCPNYSEY
```

Sometimes the key is a word, instead of a number. In that case, the word is converted into a number, as follows:

The keyword's letters are numbered in alphabetical order. For example, APPLE would be rearranged AELPP. Those letters are then numbered sequentially:

```
AELPP
12345
```

When the word is then spelled correctly again, the numbers are rearranged into the same sequence:

```
APPLE
14532
```

So the key APPLE is the same as the key 14532.

To solve this kind of cipher, you have to find out the number of rows. This is normally as simple as finding all divisors of the length of the message. For example, if there are 21 characters in the message, then the only real possible row length, to have an even set of rows, is either 7 or 3. You can then try all the possibilities and look for plaintext that starts to appear in the columns.

A ciphertext with a number of characters that has many divisors (which can be obtained by adding random characters at the end) is slightly harder to break, as there will be many possibilities. For example, adding three more characters to the above code would make it 24, which has divisors 2, 3, 4, 6, 8 and 12, increasing the number of possibilities you have to try.

Transposition, 3x12 (write into columns of 12, read out by rows of 3):

```
CT: HEENV HIEAT GDATS LEENR HMAHT HIOTS NMAAN I

                HAT
                ETH
                ESI
                NLO
                VET
                HES
                INN
                ERM
                AHA
                TMA
                GAN
                DHI

PT: Hate the sin, love the sinner. - Mahatma Gandhi
```

Myszkowski
This is a variation of columnar transposition where the plaintext message is written into the tableau horizontally instead of vertically, and then the ciphertext is taken off by key order.

PT: This is a sample message.
Key: 213123

```
213123
THISIS
ASAMPL
EMESSA
GE
```

CT: HSSMM SETIA PESGIS ALEA

Modular transposition
In this type of cipher, also known as Start/Skip transposition, the ciphertext is derived from the plaintext by skipping a predetermined number of letters from a defined starting point.

The total number of letters in the ciphertext is called the 'modulus' value. The start position (the first plaintext letter) is determined by the 'shift' value (Note that sometimes the first letter is referred to as position '1', and sometimes as '0').

The next plaintext letter in sequence is determined by the 'increment' value.

For example the plaintext 'Cryptanalysis is easy' may be encrypted in columns as follows:

```
                   CPNYSEY
                   RTASIAX
                   YALISSX
```

CPNYSEY RTASIAX YALISSX

To decode, instead of re-creating the rows & columns, another way is to start at the beginning letter C, and jump every 7 letters to get the plaintext back:

This would be the same as saying:

Modulus: 20

Shift: 0

Increment: 7

CPNYSEYRTASIAXYALISSX => CRYPTANALYSISISEASY

Railfence/Redefence
Railfence ciphers were used on the battlefield during the time of the Greeks. In their simplest form the text was written in two lines, and then the message was read diagonally along them. There are many variations though. The text can be written in straight lines, or in a 'W' pattern, or anything else that the sender and receiver have pre-agreed. For example:

PT: CRYPTANALYSISISEASY

1 C   T   L   S   A

2 R P A A Y I I E S

3 Y   N   S   S   Y

This is then rewritten horizontally.
In the 'Railfence' version, the ciphertext rows are taken from top to bottom

CTLSA RPAAYIIES YNSSY

In the 'Redefence' version, the rows are taken off in the order of a particular key. For example, 213 would be: 'RPAAYIIES CTLSA YNSSY'.

To solve this kind of cipher, you need to work out 1) the order in which the rows are laid out, 2) the number of the rows (rails), and 3) what order they were in.

Route cipher
In a Route cipher, the plaintext is written in a non-standard way or shape, such as spiralling clockwise, so that it can only be read by following the same pattern.

Spiral layout, diagonal readoff, 5 letter groupings:

PT: I like cryptology!

```
RYPT
CILO
EKIL
!YGO
```

Starting at the top lefthand corner and reading diagonally leads to:

        R YC PIE TLK! OIY LG O.

Putting those letters into five-letter blocks:

        RYCPI ETLK! OIYLG O

There are a couple of tricks that help in solving route ciphers. When the cipher is already in a block, the best start is to examine carefully the outer rows and columns of the block to see if any word fragments can be discovered. Then the route can be followed forward or backward from there to read the rest of the message. More usually, route ciphers are taken apart and transmitted in five-character groups. In that case, a better attack is to try and stack the groups in columns and rows of varying widths (a group of 5-character rows, a group of 6-character rows, and so forth), and continue to keep an eye out for words which may be readable vertically or diagonally as the columns take shape.

Digital systems

The most common forms of substitution cipher today, by sheer usage, are those used by computers. Some of the more basic computer encoding systems are still decipherable with pencil and paper.

Computer languages, broken down to their most basic elements, always come back to 1s and 0s. For example, each time you see the letter A on your computer screen, it has a binary equivalent, from a table of values that was agreed upon in the early days of computers. It was agreed that the 8-bit sequence '01000001' would mean the letter A, and that '01000010' would mean a B. This was called ASCII encoding, for 'American Standard Code for Information Interchange'.

Each of the 1s and 0s is called a 'bit', and 8 bits together are called a 'byte'. As well as representing letters of the alphabet, there are also 8-bit representations for numbers, punctuation symbols, and many of the other symbols that computers use (such as carriage returns and spaces).

(space)	00100000	3	00110011	F	01000110	Y	01011001	l	01101100
!	00100001	4	00110100	G	01000111	Z	01011010	m	01101101
'	00100010	5	00110101	H	01001000	[	01011011	n	01101110
#	00100011	6	00110110	I	01001001	\	01011100	o	01101111
$	00100100	7	00110111	J	01001010	]	01011101	p	01110000
%	00100101	8	00111000	K	01001011	^	01011110	q	01110001
&	00100110	9	00111001	L	01001100	_	01011111	r	01110010
'	00100111	:	00111010	M	01001101	'	01100000	s	01110011
(	00101000	;	00111011	N	01001110	a	01100001	t	01110100
)	00101001	<	00111100	O	01001111	b	01100010	u	01110101
*	00101010	=	00111101	P	01010000	c	01100011	v	01110110
+	00101011	>	00111110	Q	01010001	d	01100100	w	01110111
,	00101100	?	00111111	R	01010010	e	01100101	x	01111000
-	00101101	@	01000000	S	01010011	f	01100110	y	01111001
.	00101110	A	01000001	T	01010100	g	01100111	z	01111010
/	00101111	B	01000010	U	01010101	h	01101000	{	01111011
0	00110000	C	01000011	V	01010110	i	01101001	|	01111100
1	00110001	D	01000100	W	01010111	j	01101010	}	01111101
2	00110010	E	01000101	X	01011000	k	01101011	~	01111110

Common ASCII-binary conversions

'I like spaghetti' therefore would be:

```
01001001 00100000 01001100 01001001 01001011 01000101
00100000 01010011 01010000 01000001 01000111 01001000
01000101 01010100 01010100 01001001
```

ASCII/Hexadecimal

It is difficult for humans to deal with lots of 1s and 0s, so there is a shortcut way of representing binary numbers, by converting their 'base 2' 1s and 0s into base 16 hexadecimal numbers. This is because there is an easy conversion between the two, with each group of 4 binary bits being equal to a single hexadecimal character.

```
0     1     2     3     4     5     6     7
0000  0001  0010  0011  0100  0101  0110  0111
8     9     A     B     C     D     E     F
1000  1001  1010  1011  1100  1101  1110  1111
```

In other words, the binary chart seen earlier can be rewritten with hexadecimal equivalents for each letter. The letter A, 01000001 (or 0100 0001), can now be written more simply as 41.

The following chart shows hexadecimal equivalents for commonly used characters and punctuation:

HEX	DEC	CHR	HEX	DEC	CHR	HEX	DEC	CHR	HEX	DEC	CHR
00	0	NUL	20	32	SP	40	64	@	60	96	`
01	1	SOH	21	33	!	41	65	A	61	97	a
02	2	STX	22	34	"	42	66	B	62	98	b
03	3	ETX	23	35	#	43	67	C	63	99	c
04	4	EOT	24	36	$	44	68	D	64	100	d
05	5	ENQ	25	37	%	45	69	E	65	101	e
06	6	ACK	26	38	&	46	70	F	66	102	f
07	7	BEL	27	39	'	47	71	G	67	103	g

HEX	DEC	CHR	HEX	DEC	CHR	HEX	DEC	CHR	HEX	DEC	CHR
08	8	BS	28	40	(	48	72	H	68	104	h
09	9	HT	29	41	)	49	73	I	69	105	i
0A	10	LF	2A	42	*	4A	74	J	6A	106	j
0B	11	VT	2B	43	+	4B	75	K	6B	107	k
0C	12	FF	2C	44	,	4C	76	L	6C	108	l
0D	13	CR	2D	45	-	4D	77	M	6D	109	m
0E	14	SO	2E	46	.	4E	78	N	6E	110	n
0F	15	SI	2F	47	/	4F	79	O	6F	111	o
10	16	DLE	30	48	0	50	80	P	70	112	p
11	17	DC1	31	49	1	51	81	Q	71	113	q
12	18	DC2	32	50	2	52	82	R	72	114	r
13	19	DC3	33	51	3	53	83	S	73	115	s
14	20	DC4	34	52	4	54	84	T	74	116	t
15	21	NAK	35	53	5	55	85	U	75	117	u
16	22	SYN	36	54	6	56	86	V	76	118	v
17	23	ETB	37	55	7	57	87	W	77	119	w
18	24	CAN	38	56	8	58	88	X	78	120	x
19	25	EM	39	57	9	59	89	Y	79	121	y
1A	26	SUB	3A	58	:	5A	90	Z	7A	122	z
1B	27	ESC	3B	59	;	5B	91	[	7B	123	{
1C	28	FS	3C	60	<	5C	92	\	7C	124		
1D	29	GS	3D	61	=	5D	93	]	7D	125	}
1E	30	RS	3E	62	>	5E	94	^	7E	126	~
1F	31	US	3F	63	?	5F	95	_	7F	127	DEL

Common Hexadecimal/ASCII conversions

Hexadecimal encoding is basically the same as any other substitution cipher, since it is substituting the same 2-digit hexadecimal number for each plaintext letter. For example, 'I like spaghetti' is '49 20 6C 69 6B 65 20 73 70 61 67 68 65 74 74 69'.

ROT-47
Another well established variant of substitution ciphers that uses the ASCII ordering is called ROT-47. Instead of using the 26 letters of the alphabet as ROT-13 does, it uses 94 characters of ASCII, from the ! to the ~.

Since 47 is exactly half of 94, ROT-47 works similarly to ROT-13. Any ciphertext that is obtained by encrypting with a shift of 47, can then be re-converted to plaintext with another shift of 47. For example:

```
CT:
{:76 H6== DA6?E :D =@?8] \ {6@?2C5@ 52 ':?4:
```

```
PT: Life well spent is long. - Leonardo da Vinci
```

NOT SO EASY PUZZLES

The puzzles in this section are a mixture of simple transposition and monoalphabetic substitution ciphers. You'll first need to decide what method of encryption has been used. Not all the puzzles can be solved without first cracking the key!

DIFFICULTY RATING: 4

KEYS: PAGE 518

SOLUTIONS: PAGE 549

1.

```
01001001 01110100 00100000 01101001 01110011 00100000
01100010 01100101 01110100 01110100 01100101 01110010
00100000 01110100 01101111 00100000 01101100 01101001
01100111 01101000 01110100 00100000 01100001 00100000
01100011 01100001 01101110 01100100 01101100 01100101
00100000 01110100 01101000 01100001 01101110 00100000
01100011 01110101 01110010 01110011 01100101 00100000
01110100 01101000 01100101 00100000 01100100 01100001
01110010 01101011 01101110 01100101 01110011 01110011
00101110
```

Key: see chart on page 364

2.

```
64 6F 75 62 6C 65 20 64 6F 75 62 6C 65 20 74 6F 69 6C 20 61
6E 64 20 74 72 6F 75 62 6C 65 20 66 69 72 65 20 62 75 72 6E
20 61 6E 64 20 63 61 75 6C 64 72 6F 6E 20 62 75 62 62 6C 65
```

Key: hexadecimal. See chart on page 365

3.

```
SMCSM RNIEA EOASI NSYNL OERAI EBNTN TNTIC ISRIE
MSEDC SYGHD IEEGA MIENN EOAYI SSSIS MCSNN POMGT
TNTNM IAONO ERAIT RNASX IEEAP OYMGM SESFA EBIIX
```

Hint: columnar transposition

4.

```
.. - .. ... .- - .- .-.. - --- .-.. .-.. ... .-- .- -. .. .. --- - .-.. .. .-
.. .-.. --- ..- ... --- ..- -. .- - .-. -..- .- -. .-.. .-- ... .. .. --. -. .- ..-.
.-- .. -. -. .- --- .- ... .. .. -. --.
```

5.

```
WVIIR NTRNA ERWAD ONEEE NNLEH WDKWS OCEUE XCRPT
DGEOD EIERE VTRXA OEHIL IROPT LLMEO PXNBA EFENL
NEHVD ULFEX NTCWW CNDTA OEPSO IAXEA EOETE AMCUS
ETPNC X
```

Hint: 7-character rows

6.

```
p? @=5 >2?[ 3C@<6? H:E9 E96 DE@C>D @7
DE2E6[ xD 4@>6 E@ =2J 9:D H62CJ 3@?6D
2>@?8 J6i v:G6 9:> 2 =:EE=6 62CE9 7@C
492C:EJP $92<6DA62C6[ w6?CJ 'xxx
```

7.

O rjumj or eiikf nw s fpif ufws. - Zljlyns
Fsbfgo, qjwm ldjrs egsr jw ygpyhgy ig
Qraywtb Vubuauxlyupb.

8.

Siordhbeoerusaeerdesntnnusxktdadtntxftentodox

9.

1 67 67 7 41 5 1 41 3 7 1 67 59 7 31 19 13 19 43 71 61 61 7
59 73 19 3 7 61 17 1 61 59 19 61 7 41 1 5 59 1 37 1 67 19 3
'39%' 19 41 59 7 3 7 41 67 5 1 89 61 13 7 59 1 31 5 43 (−11
59 43 37 67 17 7 37 43 73 19 7 3 43 41 67 1 3 67)

10.

```
-.-. --- -- .-. .- ... ... .. --- -. .- .- .-.. - --- ./.. ./.-./-. .- ./.../. ./.-./. .-.
. -. --- - .- ... ... -. -. --- .-. .- .-. . .- .-.- -. -. .- ... ... -... ..- - .- ... ... -
-. -. --- .-. ... .., - .- . -. --. - ....
```

11.

v@ H:E9 >6[=:<6 8@@5 2?86=D[E@ >J
6?5j p?5[2D E96 =@?8 5:G@C46 @7 DE66=
72==D @? >6[|2<6 @7 J@FC AC2J6CD @?6
DH66E D24C7:46[p?5 =:7E >J D@F= E@
962G6?] $92<6DA62C6[w6?CJ 'xxx

12.

15-14-12-25 20-23-15 20-8-9-14-7-19 1-18-5 9-14-6-9-14-9-
20-5 20-8-5 21-14-9-22-5-18-19-5 1-14-4 8-21-13-1-14 19-20-
21-16-9-4-9-20-25 1-14-4 9-13 14-15-20 19-21-18-5 1-2-15-
21-20 20-8-5 6-15-18-13-5-18 1-12-2-5-18-20 5-9-14-19-20-5-
9-14

13.

*49*20*62*65*6C*69*65*76*65*20*74*68*61*74*20*69*6E*
64*69*76*69*64*75*61*6C*73*20*63*61*6E*20*6D*61*6B*
65*20*61*20*64*69*66*66*65*72*65*6E*63*65*20*69*6E*2
0*73*6F*63*69*65*74*79*2E*20*53*69*6E*63*65*20*70*65
*72*69*6F*64*73*20*6F*66*20*63*68*61*6E*67*65*20*73*
75*63*68*20*61*73*20*74*68*65*20*70*72*65*73*65*6E*7
4*20*6F*6E*65*20*63*6F*6D*65*20*73*6F*20*72*61*72*65
*6C*79*20*69*6E*20*68*75*6D*61*6E*20*68*69*73*74*6F*
72*79*2C*20*69*74*20*69*73*20*75*70*20*74*6F*20*65*6
1*63*68*20*6F*66*20*75*73*20*74*6F*20*6D*61*6B*65*20
*74*68*65*20*62*65*73*74*20*75*73*65*20*6F*66*20*6F*
75*72*20*74*69*6D*65*20*74*6F*20*68*65*6C*70*20*63*7
2*65*61*74*65*20*61*20*68*61*70*70*69*65*72*20*77*6F
*72*6C*64*2E

14.

```
01010100 01101000 01100101 01110010 01100101 00100000
01110111 01100001 01110011 00100000 01101110 01100101
01110110 01100101 01110010 00100000 01100001 00100000
01100111 01101111 01101111 01100100 00100000 01110111
01100001 01110010 00101100 00100000 01101111 01110010
00100000 01100001 00100000 01100010 01100001 01100100
00100000 01110000 01100101 01100001 01100011 01100101
00101110 00100000 00100000 00101101 00100000 01000010
01100101 01101110 01101010 01100001 01101101 01101001
01101110 00100000 01000110 01110010 01100001 01101110
01101011 01101100 01101001 01101110 00001101 00001010
```

15.

IUTEO APTCA OYAOA PTCAO FWORB PRIOS NONBP RIOSN
YATSE PACMS IUTEP ACMSX ONHTH YCEPI FWTHY CEPIX

16.

-12*1*-9 6*2 0*12 -7*-8*-1*-1*2*10 -12*0*-8*5*-
4*-10*-12*1*6 -12*6*-2 1*2*7 10*-5*-12*7
12*2*8*5 -10*2*8*1*7*5*12 -10*-12*1 -9*2 -
7*2*5 12*2*8 -12*6*-2 10*-5*-12*7 12*2*8 -10*-
12*1 -9*2 -7*2*5 12*2*8*5 -10*2*8*1*7*5*12 -
3*2*-5*1 -7 -2*-8*1*1*-8*-9*12

17.

FDSEGNBNREOINTNUHYDNJHSNEMOOLOOO

18.

RBAGN TASIW RTOKE ETEGY NOMOF RFXMR NTWOT MENUO
LXETO THUIE SDLKU XMHTI AWSTA ESECX

19.

ONXXXXX
TLLONOF
TAFSWEB
AGOAPAL
PATNITO
SSEVASO
EGROEGD

20.

2| 3| 6| 3| 2\ 8\ 4| 8\ 4| 3| 7| 8| 5/ 3| 6/ 3/ 6\ 3| 6| 3| 6| 8\
4/ 7| 3| 5/ 9/ 4\ 7| 3| 2\ 8\ 8\ 4| 3| 7\ 3| 6| 4/ 7/ 6\ 4/ 4\ 4|
8\ 4/ 3| 7| 8\ 4| 2\ 6| 8\ 4| 3| 7/ 9\ 6/ 7| 3\ 3| 3\ 9\ 2\ 7| 3\
2| 8| 5/ 9\ 3| 7| 5/ 9/ 8\ 8\ 6/ 6|

21.

0100001001100101011101110110000101110010011001010010010000000
0111010001101000011001010010000001101000011011110110001010
0110000100111100100100000001110100011010000110000101110100
0010000001100101011000010111010001110011001010111000100000
0010110100100000001000010011001010110111001101010011001000001
0110110101101001011011100010000001000110011100100110000010
01101110011010110110110000110100101101110000011010000101010

22.

*54*68*65*20*62*61*73*69*63*20*73*6F*75*72*63*65*73*
20*6F*66*20*68*61*70*70*69*6E*65*73*73*20*61*72*65*2
0*61*20*67*6F*6F*64*20*68*65*61*72*74*2C*20*63*6F*6D
*70*61*73*73*69*6F*6E*2C*20*61*6E*64*20*6C*6F*76*65*
2E*20*49*66*20*77*65*20*68*61*76*65*20*74*68*65*73*6
5*20*6D*65*6E*74*61*6C*20*61*74*74*69*74*75*64*65*7
3*2C*20*65*76*65*6E*20*69*66*20*77*65*20*61*72*65*20
*73*75*72*72*6F*75*6E*64*65*64*20*62*79*20*68*6F*73*
74*69*6C*69*74*79*2C*20*77*65*20*66*65*65*6C*20*6C*
69*74*74*6C*65*20*64*69*73*74*75*72*62*61*6E*63*65*2
E*20*4F*6E*20*74*68*65*20*6F*74*68*65*72*20*68*61*6E
*64*2C*20*69*66*20*77*65*20*6C*61*63*6B*20*63*6F*6D
*70*61*73*73*69*6F*6E*20*61*6E*64*20*6F*75*72*20*6D*
65*6E*74*61*6C*20*73*74*61*74*65*20*69*73*20*66*69*6
C*6C*65*64*20*77*69*74*68*20*61*6E*67*65*72*20*6F*72
*20*68*61*74*72*65*64*20*77*65*20*77*69*6C*6C*20*6E*
6F*74*20*68*61*76*65*20*70*65*61*63*65*2E

23.

VATRE YIIES HSTPO IEFCL EIFX

24.

-X... .X.XX .-.X- --X-- -X-X. ..XX- --X.. -.XX. -X.-. .X.-. .XX-- .X---
X---X -..X- .X.X. ..X.. .XX.- ..X.. X.XX. .X-.X X-X.. ..X.X X...X ---
X. .X.-. .XX-- -X..- .XX.- X.--. X.--. X.-.X .X.-. .X..X .-X-X ..X-- -X-
.X X..-. X---X .-.XX --.X- --X-- -X-.. X-.X. X...X ...XX

25.

```
0100000101100110011101000110010101110010000100000001100001
0110110001101100001000000110100101110011001000000111110011
0110000101101001011001000010000001100001011011011001100100
0010000001100100011011110110111001100101001010110000100000
0110110101101111011100100110010100100000011010010111001100
0010000001100110011000010110101011001110000110000011100100
0110100001100001011011110010000001100100011011111011011100
0110010100101110001000000100000101100101011100110110101111
0111000000000110100001010
```

26.

```
(6 2C6 ?@E 2>FD65] "F66? ':4E@C:2]
|6E2AFKK=6 9:?Ei %:>6D }6H #@>2?
```

27.

```
WLLER MAHPD NNWOE LXEIN NEOAE FAOSE EPAAA FEROW
CINAE PSNTE ROSAR NUTCA ANNGR YANEO TETAE AGIME
DWROD RRART DCUIC CLCNH WESRC TDIAF ENMBI ENNIT
EREAT YOTSH SAICO EELOC ATUNN NREOF UNNIW MAOOU
NEOSV SLRAL HINGO ENLRO DBCHE CMCNT NRHAA YUNOE
LETTA CEORT EEEIT ERPEC DAERG SLTMD RH
```

28.

```
IHTED VHRYA HAYAS AEOMR ATTTT TDTUD VTOIO EACECE
EHTVB DNCHN FEHEE NDTLX OAILC OEEIX UBNYU UVDKX
NIKNL REVEX DLCET INEAX TIREI SPRGX
```

29.

Xkr, xqpcwqtto, yx rwypyxh fcen q fpkwo qf
pnyf, rypn ypf ekxgypykxf qf tqyg gkrx yx
ypf Yxpwkgcepykx, yp yf xkp fcwvwyfyxh
pnqp qx keeqfykxqt 'wkchn fvkp' yx ekzvk-
fypykx yf skcxg. Fk Y pwcfp pnqp q ewypye-
qt vcitye rytt nktg ekxfpqxpto yx zyxg pnqp
Y qz lktcxpqwyto qlkygyxh rkwgf ekx-
pqyxyxh pnqp fozikt rnyen yf, io sqw, ks
zkfp ekzzkx yxetcfykx yx rwypyxh kcw
Qxhtk-Fqukx qf yp yf, pkgqo. Zqxo ks kcw
zkfp ekzzkx rkwgf eqxxkp fnkr; fk Y zcfp
qgkvp foxkxozf; qxg fk pryfp q pnkchnp
qwkcxg qf pk fqo rnqp Y ryfn rypn qf zcen
etqwypo qf Y eqx. – Awxafp Lyxeaxp
Rwyhnp, 'Hqgfio'

31.

KOJKC ODGNM HOESK QJDOK JYIQO EGMMS PYITF YITON
PGIEP HJSQO EYHGQ OXJSY QVGPQ HOSCQ YDGQO MJDKC
YDOIQ KSZZC OGEEY MQOEP QSEOI QPHGQ OEDOA OMGSP
OQHOX FCSIB OEQHO YNOWG DPASP YIOPP KNJFO PPYJI
GCPHG QOEDO AOMGS POQHO XGNNY UOEAC SNNXO XOEJI
QHORJ AOUOI PJDOI OVCXV OEPHG QOEDO AOMGS POYNS
YIOEQ HOYNH JIOXD JJIMC YFFRJ HIPJI

Hint: first word is 'People'

32.

```
UJBHU  QJWDQ  SMADF  FNBQY  GBURQ  KMJVB  OSGSW  BQRDH
JKKJM  QTHBQ  YQJAB  HOJTQ  GJMSD  IJTQQ  RSGBD  UMSSO
WBQRQ  JEPPT  UUSPQ  BJHQR  DQWSR  DVSDU  TBOSA  JMJTM
CJTMH  SYITQ  BWDPH  JQKMS  KDMSO  QJPSS  QRSRJ  UKDMM
JQDUD  BHQJE  KJBHQ  SOJTQ  QRDQQ  RSNMS  DQTMS  BPASG
DFSQJ  ISKMS  NBPSR  SMHDG  SBPIB  XJAQR  SPKSN  BSPKM
JQJNS  MDQJK  PGTFQ  BFBHU  TJTPD  HDGID  PPDOJ  MDHOQ
MDHPF  DQJMJ  HSJAQ  RSASW  OBHJP  DTMPW  RJNDH  PKSDE
RTGDH  FDHUT  DUSPP  RSMSG  SGISM  SOGSD  HOPDB  OIMSD
QRSOS  SKPSS  EKSDN  SDMQR  TMOSH  BPJHH  JMJNE  BRJKS
SVBOS  HQFYP  RSRDP  DPSHP  SJART  GJM
```

Hint: contains the words 'Waterfall City'

33.

```
T Z G O M   M O Z G T   B K V O Z   O F V T P   O M
V K O   L O M V J   J C I V E   T P N D O   M M J J
E   P O Z J J   C M V E E   J J Z C K   E V U C D
L A V J J   E P O Z J   J T M O F   A N C Z F   D O
C G T   R O F T V   J J C M L   O V V O D   V E L A
I   V K O T D   E J J Z K   E V U C D   M M E V K
O I J J E   A G F Z V   K C J O V   E D T F O   C D
E A Z   F J J T V   K H O D Q   M M U E V   V C F C
P M
```

Hint: simple substitution, but the letter W is encrypted as two letters, not one

34.

ASIUM OGYMO WLFVR ITASM SIWOE EEHNT OCLAR
YNSIN HRADY GOENN OEERE

35.

TONDN IDHSY IETSI AHWYE AGOET ONLHO GNESO ASHWD
PUDOE FHDSA USTTN ALCYN HTTUH RRSHS IRAAO GAHDR
AESOE GNKCN UTNEU ADOIO LOTEE FBODN RN

36.

EYEIUKII
RDRHTCEL
TSNETBRC
IATUESOI
ROLAOADA
IENENTSR
OEJSRDRI
RWLSHNTE
HTSLPIAH

37.

ITOTQA NMIGOP OTRRRD HSGTLC ONAEDD RMLCOR EITEGE
EAHNOT AOIHEE ADROEB GOEHAL IHSPHT SUIERE NEERNH
PUPEAC TRDEAE GWEFTL AERETN RIXITA UCOITR NECDLO
OSECGI AAOURO SNRATA THODSH THSRHE DTRTSH AEEATC
LHPETS RLNVEE AOEAPT OFNAFN TODHEL WMVDSA YFDYNB
EETAAT IPTTTN TEAFLI HAUUTI ELRTTP ENFEHH PESOAS
TTKSDE RESFUI NMFAEI AAWVAS KRDHRL EFNTRN ODRTLG
AARHHA MIOWSA EMSOBZ LSONNR RNHROK ESNUTO SISEOS
RLHSTA TESAWL SCTNRG SHSRST AIDTNI RNEOEP

Hint: Redefence, key: RUNNER

38.

TEEHDCO AAFENAT RHRTEPE RLNFBTN IAEEWOR IYLTEEH
DCCDNER ANIEHRT EPETICE YCTSREE WORIIFE NATHSTD
NERANCF BTNIEMH ICEYCPE

39.

10H7H KD3D9D 4H2H2D2D3D8D 7D4D3D8D
8D9H6H 7D9D4HQH6H6D 10H2D 8D9H6H
7H10H6D7D8D 9H2HKH7H 9H3D9D6D 2H8D
8D9H6H 8D2H3HKH6H, 8D9H6H2D KD3D9D
2H6D6H 8D9H6H 7D9D4HQH6H6D.

Hint: Poker

40.

NQLIH GYLXJ QIGLC JAXMN UTLXJ IVTLO SEVAT HMQMN
PIHTL MGAQR SQMQM NHIQC JCHCY TCOIY SNMHG IHQAT
YLXJQ IGLCJ AMYCE GILMQ AFNVA METMG HILMH GIQAT
LCNJT YQNIO NTYSL MQXMN EMDTP TOTHP MHGXI SLAIS
NTHIQ RXRSM EPMHG COTHY TCLIS HPMQR SQRXJ SQQMH
GCHMF FTHNT NQCDT MHQIQ ATGLI SHPCH PAIJM HGQAC
QQATC PUTLN CLXLS HNLMG AQMHQ IMQNF CLQCQ QCYDT
LNVME EBSNQ GICLI SHPQA TCEGI LMQAF NRLSY TNYAH
TMTL

Hint: first word is 'strong'

CHALLENGING

This section moves beyond simple transposition and substitution systems, to introduce you to homophonic and polyalphabetic ciphers.

Multiple Partners

In simple substitution ciphers there is always a one-to-one equivalence between each original letter and each cipher letter. But in other kinds of subsitution ciphers known as homophonic substitution ciphers, there can be multiple ciphertext equivalents for any particular plaintext letter. For example, the letter E might be replaced by a D, J or K. The possible alternates are called 'homophones'.

Your best opening strategy, as with patristocrat-style substitution ciphers, is to look for patterns. For example, when you see the ciphertext word 'NZCKZ', you can be sure that the same letter is in positions 2 and 5, since though one plaintext letter could have multiple cipher equivalents, any one ciphertext letter will always have the exact same plaintext equivalent. So the ciphertext 'eVqe' may well be 'that' since it has the same pattern.

Ce Cs rcHNjyQFy fVqe CcOjUyGKaY qGQ adUpjCAas
fZy sJKhqj EHGQhfhHc HO gpG; eVqe FCDyY fJ qnn,
ZJoyDau QCOOakyGe fVaCk XHnCehEpj XHsheCJc,
RpYYCHGY oVhKZ qka Cc EHzgHc, pGQ aGiJvzacfs
NZCKZ qka BGhPauspn. —wycipgCc QCsuqynC

Homophonic substitution, key:

Plaintext	Ciphertext
A	qp
B	tw
C	KE
D	xQ
E	ay
F	OT
G	Fl

H	VZ
I	Ch
J	iI
K	rL
L	jn
M	gz
N	cG
O	HJ
P	RX
Q	dM
R	uk
S	sY
T	fe
U	UB
V	PD
W	oN
X	Wb
Y	mv
Z	SA

PT: It is knowledge that influences and equalizes the social condition of man; that gives to all, however different their political position, passions which are in common, and enjoyments which are universal. – Benjamin Disraeli

Playfair Ciphers

The Playfair cipher was used by the British during the Boer War and by other nationalities as well in both World Wars. In this system, a plaintext message is broken up into pairs of letters, and then each pair is swapped for a pair of ciphertext letters, depending on a rectangle 'key'. The cipher is polyalphabetic, which means that the ciphertext value of a letter is not necessarily going to remain consistent throughout the ciphertext.

To create the key, first a normal keyed cipher alphabet is generated.

Key: EXAMPLE

EXAMPLBCDFGHIJKNOQRSTUVWYZ

Playfair keys usually use a 5x5 grid, which means 25 characters, so the next decision that needs to be made is which letter of the alphabet to leave out. Sometimes the J is left out, so any occurrence of J in the plaintext will be replaced with an I. This is called an I/J block. Sometimes, however, the Q, X or Z are removed instead.

In this example, an I/J method is used to create the 5x5 grid:

```
EXAMP
LBCDF
GHIKN
OQRST
UVWYZ
```

Next, the plaintext is separated into pairs. If there are an odd number of letters, than a 'null' character such as an X is often added:

PT: I like crypto!

PT: IL IK EC RY PT OX

Each pair of letters is then located in the key, and a ciphertext pair is chosen based on the locations of the plaintext pair, by the following rules:

Assuming that the two plaintext letters are not on the same row or column, they can be visualized as being two corners of a smaller rectangle. The letters on the opposite two corners become the ciphertext equivalents. Another way to think of this is to draw a line extending out from the rows and columns where those 2 plaintext letters are located, and when those 2 lines intersect, a rectangle (or square) will be formed. For example: the letters I and L create a rectangle, which creates opposing angles at letters G and C, in that order. The order is important, otherwise the message is garbled. The same goes for decryption: G and C (the same letters which were just decrypted) become I and L, in that order.

If the two plaintext letters are in the same row, then the ciphertext letters chosen are the letters immediately to the right of the plaintext letters. (example: GN would become HG).

If they are on the same column, then the new, ciphertext value, is the two letters below the plaintext letters (example: PF would become FN).

If the pair of letters are identical, TT, they are usually either split up with a null: 'TX TX', or they are kept as they are, and enciphered as TT in the ciphertext.

The way that doubled letters are handled offers a technique to recognize a Playfair cipher. See how many repeated letters there are. If you have a long ciphertext with a notorious absence of pairs of repeated letters*, there's a good chance that the cipher used was Playfair.

Digraphs can also be analyzed to see which are most common. For example, the digraph TH might always be encoded QN (using the last example), so you can start to map it out. As this digraph is unique, QN will always be TH (as long as T is on an odd position). With a lengthy ciphertext, the QN pattern will show up more frequently than other pairs. As you identify and eventually decode more digraphs, more of the code can be deciphered.

Also, some words in the English language, such as REceivER have the same, although reversed, pairs of letters. Look out for patterns like these in the ciphertext.

*Every rule has its exception. In the classical Playfair code, there will be no pairs of repeated letters. However, in the famous example of John F. Kennedy sending his rescue message via Playfair for 'PT boat 109', instead of splitting up the pair TT with the letter X, the pair was enciphered as itself – TT:

KXJEY UREBE ZWEHE WRYTU HEYFS KREHE GOYAI WTTTU OLKSY CAJPO
BOTEI ZONTX BYBWT GONEY CUZWR GDSON SXBOU YWRHE BAAHY USEDQ

Key: Royal New Zealand Navy

```
                    ROYAL
                    NEWZD
                    VBCFG
                    HIKMP
                    QSTUX
```

CT:
KX JE YU RE BE ZW EH EW RY TU HE YF SK RE HE
GO YF IW TT TU OL KS YC AJ PO BO TE IZ ON TX
BY BW TG ON EY CU ZW RG DS ON SX BO UY WR HE
BA AH YU SE DQ

PT:
PT BO AT ON EO WE NI NE LO ST IN AC TI ON IN
BL AC KE TT ST RA IT TW OM IL ES SW ME RE SU
CO CE XC RE WO FT WE LV EX RE QU ES TA NY IN
FO RM AT IO NX

Cleaned up, the text reads as follows:
PT boat 109 lost in action in Blackett Straight, two
miles southwest Meresu Cove. Crew of twelve. Request any
information.

- John F. Kennedy, 35th US President 1961-1963, as a Lieutenant in
1943, after his boat had been sunk by a Japanese destroyer.

Secrets of the computer

There's just one more pair of techniques you'll need to tackle the puzzles in this section. They are not as difficult as they look – and can be easy to recognize.

Base 64 Encoding

The first, Base 64, is one you may have noticed while looking at an email attachment, as it is used commonly in email software. Base 64 is a binary-based block substitution, typically used by computers to encode 8-bit binary data into a printable subset of ASCII.

The idea is to take a group of three 8-bit symbols, and re-group the bits into four 6-bit symbols, possibly with padding at the end. The 6-bit symbols can then be converted back into ASCII using this table:

Character	Binary	Character	Binary	Character	Binary
A	000000	W	010110	s	101100
B	000001	X	010111	t	101101
C	000010	Y	011000	u	101110
D	000011	Z	011001	v	101111
E	000100	a	011010	w	110000
F	000101	b	011011	x	110001
G	000110	c	011100	y	110010
H	000111	d	011101	z	110011
I	001000	e	011110	0	110100
J	001001	f	011111	1	110101
K	001010	g	100000	2	110110
L	001011	h	100001	3	110111
M	001100	i	100010	4	111000
N	001101	j	100011	5	111001
O	001110	k	100100	6	111010
P	001111	l	100101	7	111011
Q	010000	m	100110	8	111100
R	010001	n	100111	9	111101
S	010010	o	101000	+	111110
T	010011	p	101001	/	111111
U	010100	q	101010	=	(pad)
V	010101	r	101011		

Base 64 Encoding Chart

For example, consider the following plaintext message:

All your base are belong to us!

Converting this into binary:

```
01100001 01101100 01101100 all
00100000 01111001 01101111  yo
01110101 01110010 00100000 ur
01100010 01100001 01110011 bas
01100101 00100000 01100001 e a
01110010 01100101 00100000 re
01100010 01100101 01101100 bel
01101111 01101110 01100111 ong
00100000 01110100 01101111  to
00100000 01110101 01110011  us
00100001 (pad)    (pad)     !
```

Regrouping into six-bit symbols:

```
011000 010110 110001 101100 YWxs
001000 000111 100101 101111 IHlv
011101 010111 001000 100000 dXIg
011000 100110 000101 110011 YmFz
011001 010010 000001 100001 ZSBh
011100 100110 010100 100000 cmUg
011000 100110 010101 101100 YmVs
011011 110110 111001 100111 b25n
001000 000111 010001 101111 IHRv
001000 000111 010101 110011 IHVz
001000 010000 (pad)  (pad)  IQ==
```

results in the base-64 encoded text:

YWxsIHlvdXIgYmFzZSBhcmUgYmVsb25nIHRvIHVzIQ==

UUEncoding
Similar to Base 64, UUencoding is a system used by computers to transmit potentially complex information (such as graphics files or

executable code) in a safe 'printable character' way. It transforms 8-bit long data into chunks of 6 bits, in order to transfer data from computer to computer without the possibility of a character being misunderstood.

A plaintext file example.txt with nothing other than the words 'Four score and seven years ago our fathers brought forth on this continent a new nation,' may look like this once it has been UUencoded into the file example.uue:

```
table
`!'#$%&'()*+,-./0123456789:;<=>?
@ABCDEFGHIJKLMNOPQRSTUVWXYZ[\]^_
begin 600 EXAMPLE.TXT
M1F]U<B!S8V]R92!A;F0@<V5V96X@>65A<G,@86=O(&]U<B!F871H97)S(&)R
L;W5G:'0@9F]R=&@@;VX@=AI<R!C;VYT:6YE;G0@82!N97<-'FYA=&EO;BYR
`

end
size 89
```

There are two ways to encrypt a UUEncoded file,

1. The easy way (use a computer), and
2. The 'pencil and paper way', as follows:

To encrypt a message with UUencoding, characters are first split into subgroups of 3 characters each. In the above example, the plaintext 'Four score and seven years ago our fathers brought forth on this continent a new nation.' becomes:

'Fou' 'r s' 'cor' 'e a' 'nd ' 'sev' 'en ' 'yea' 'rs ' 'ago' 'our' 'fat' 'he '...
These groups are then converted into binary, so the 'Fou' string becomes the 24 bits:

01000110 01101111 01110101

The 24 bits are then split into four groups of 6:

010001 100110 111101 110101

Then, in order to guarantee that all these numbers will map out to an easily readable character, the number '32' (100000 in binary) is added to these values, making them either 6 or 7 bits, depending on the sum:

    110001 1000110 1011101 1010101

They are then padded with leading zeroes so that each grouping is exactly 8 bits:

    00110001 01000110 01011101 01010101

These bytes are then applied against the ASCII chart to see which letters or punctuation symbols that they are equivalent to, and the result is:

    1F]U

This is exactly what the first 4 letters are in the above example, after the letter 'M', which is a symbol indicating the length of the line. The first character in each row specifies how long that the rest of the row will be.

Similarly, to decode these letters, reverse the process:

* Ignore the leading 'M'.

* Use binary encoding for the letters and symbols 1F]U :

    00110001 01000110 01011101 01010101

* Subtract the binary value '32' (100000) from the result:

    00010001 00100110 00111101 00110101

* Take the last 6 digits of each group:

    010001 100110 111101 110101

* Regroup in groups of 8 instead of 6:

```
01000110 01101111 01110101
```

* Reconvert back into plaintext:

```
Fou
```

Here is another example of a UUencoded file. Can you decrypt it?

```
table
`!'#$%&'()*+,-./0123456789:;<=>?
@ABCDEFGHIJKLMNOPQRSTUVWXYZ[\]^_
begin 600 TWAIN.TXT
M56YD97(@8V5R=&%I;B!C:7)C=6US=&%N8V5S+'!!<F]F86YI='D='D@<')O=FED
M97,@82!R96QI968@9&5N:65D(&5V96X@=&\@&\<')A>65R+B*B-'=UA<FL@=&5=A
$:6X-'B!R
`

end
size 94
```

Solution on page 551

Challenging Ciphers

This is where things start to get hard! These are ciphers using more complex techniques than simple transposition and substitution. Look out, for example, for homophonic substitution, where each plaintext letter can have a few different ciphertext equivalents; Playfair ciphers, where letters are encrypted in pairs; transposition ciphers which encrypt both by columnar transposition and by using a key; and certain digital systems. Perseverance will bring its reward.

DIFFICULTY RATING: 7
KEYS: PAGE 519
SOLUTIONS: PAGE 551

1.

QW4gZW5lbXkgY2FuIG9ubHkgY29udHJvCB5b3
VyIG1lc3NhZ2UgaWYgdGhleSBjYW4gZmluZCBp
dC4=

Hint: 64

2.

BRHGQ MTEBT UTBGJ TNPHG IEBFF HNQIE BQXQY THGEX
VIXBT WJTOQ QHYIU TPHFT UTNPB HGHAP SOYIQ YBGLB
PQYNH SLYFX MHHDP BPIIO IPBFH U

Hint: simple substitution

3.

D W S J R R K I S G M S L K H D A Y Q R S R M I
M J R D S I U J S T S Q C M E H Y D J N S V K P
K N W K I M J H Y J E K J T F K C J Q K J

Hint: contains the word 'policy'

4.

W B M T E A K D Q R J K K E D K S K J Y M O W D
R Y E P A Q Y U K L P J K M O Q M E D K E B M O
K A W L C E W D R M O K M O W D F W D R X Y D C
E D U N E O D L E D

Hint: contains the word 'everything'

5.

B H W H I W K Y V U B R Z B D H J U I Z E U Y I T Q B B U V B H
B R U B Z C L H T H Y E R Q C B H E Q W C H W Q U B O C U U J
C B H J U B R U U F Y Q A Z K U I B H T W K H C Q I S J Z K U U
O U C B H T U J Z K U T Z W B C K O I V H I X P H R I C H I

Hint: contains the word 'historic'

6.

V 2 h h d C B k b 2 V z I G 5 v d C B k Z X N 0 c m 9 5 I G 1 l L C B t Y W
t l c y B t Z S B z d H J v b m d l c i 4 =

7.

RTIFA	FBARC	BRTDB	YRKBQ	FQBZU	AGIGN	FCBQI	YEKSY
RKRIK	TMRMB	IELKC	AASIP	LGRTC	GEKTF	QIABU	AGFFQ
TRDWB	RYAGH	YIQIB	KYBAE	SGWHB	KDKIQ	RKKET	RBFIF
UGRCM	BPCVO	ABRCO	BTBGD	BQGVG	DLTKD	LZFIK	RKLFG
RCIYB	YUABR	YAGHP	AOCMF	YSYMV	IFXEK	HSIFG	HAQYI
KFKLY	BXDBR	TDBRQ	KDBGR	YAPAP	YFIMR	GDSGQ	OEKIP
FGCUR	KLTRT	IFAFB	ARCKB	BFICX	BTEDK	BFGHR	KBXBK
SRTFG	CDRPO	UNRIA	SUZQP	HZMRL	GMBPC	VOIBY	MIOBC
DBVSU	NRKBL	RTCSG	DGRFM	RKRIG	RQBAV	CWBCU	GCTTI
GRTIF	AABFR	DWBRT	DGCGD	UGITB	MQFKE	QAKLP	AKEAB
RCMBP	CVOIM	WBVGR	IFMHC	FACTP	YKQGU	YRRXF	IMRKF
KLCRA	HLTSR	EAPFC	QRDFA	CTYBA	EPOEC	DB

Hint: Playfair, I/J block

8.

```
VNQOQ OIFRA RMQOS MTMRG QNMIR DNYIL QORQJ IHJDI
ORUIO NTOIW JIAQR QNHGP HZFIQ ORQQO IXVIM IJDRA
NGTFI NGQON PTMHS JHZRA ONIUI MPNAH FJRMI LVORQ
NLRAQ SRDDX RAONI UILNG FXDNZ IVNQO VORQN VHSDL
DNCIQ HRAON IUIRG LVORQ HQOIM JIHJD IORUI RAONI
UILRG LNZHS GLQOR QAHFJ RMNPH GLIJM IPPNG TBRMI
LLNRF HGL
```

9.

```
A Q O F T O Q I L V O B F T B K L J F K T B F K
T L F T T O K D T B O O N C S E L N F I E B U Q
E B W C T B B C S W C M O I Y K D L K R G L B K
S L K
```

10.

```
UOMNG QHWNM IEQLH MNLOW POTHG IPDHG SOMNG IQUOG
PQHJJ OIQUO PHRGI HLQUO FNTUE GOUNI SMHWG PRIIO
GDYDH RIOMT UNGSE GSLMH FNWUE MQHNM HNMEQ UNIHA
VEHRP DYPUE LQOIP JOOIN GNRQH FNQET PWEQT UPHFO
WUOMO EGQUO AREDI EGSUN IQRMG OIEQL MHFDH WQHUE
SUNGI QUONE MADHW EGSJN PQBRP QEGTN FOHGP HUNMI
EQFNI OUEFS NPJUO AMNTO IUEPL OOQNS NEGPQ QUOFO
QNDNG IUODI HGEGN FEGRQ ONPPR IIOGD YNPEQ UNIMH
NMOIQ UOFNT UEGOM OQRMG OIQHN WUEPJ OMUOD HHCOI
NMHRG INGIM ONDEZ OIUOW NPDRT CYQHU NVOPQ HJJOI
AYQUO IEFDE SUQLM HFQUO PCYUO THRDI POOQU NQUOU
NIMON TUOIN JHEGQ WUOMO JOMUN JPQWH IHZOG NEMPU
NLQPT NFOQH SOQUO MDECO AMNGT UOPEG QHQUO QMRGC
HLNQM OOELU OUNIS HGONL OWPQO JPLNM QUOMU OWHRD
IGOVO MUNVO AOOGN ADOQH IEPQE GSREP UWUET UPUNL
QWNPU EPUOQ RMGOI EGUEP QMNTC PNGIE GNLOW FEGRQ
OPUOM OBHEG OIUEP LMEOG IP
```

11.

```
10010010100000110000111011010100000110111011011111110010001000
00110000101000001110011111000011001011100101110010001000000111
00101100101110000111001001100101111001001011100100000010010010
10000011000011011010100000110000101000001110011111100001100010
11001011100100010000011101011101110110010011001011110010111100
01111010011000011101110110010011001011110010010111001000000001
01101010110110010011100111100001110000111000110100000100001110
0110011110100110110110110111111111011000011010001010
```

12.

```
M F H A W F C P U T A B C C B D E G F G B J C W
L B N J B W F C P U T Q F C C B D E G B N N C C
P O J P D J L F I T P T J D I T L J C T P S J N
Y D I P D G M P L D C P D
```

13.

```
VGhlIE5ldyBZb3JrIFRpbWVzIGlzIHJlYWQgYnkgdGhlIHB
lb3BsZSB3aG8gcnVuIHRoZSBjb3VudHJ5LiBUaGUgV2Fz
aGluZ3RvbiBQb3N0IGlzIHJlYWQgYnkgdGhlIHBlb3BsZS
B3aG8gdGhpbmsgdGhleSBydW4gdGhlIGNvdW50cnkuIF
RoZSBOYXRpb25hbCBFbnF1aXJlciBpcyByZWFkIGJ5IHR
oZSBwZW9wbGUgd2hvIHRoaW5rIEVsdmlzIGlzIGFsaXZl
IGFuZCBydW5uaW5nIHRoZSBjb3VudHJ5IC4uLg==
```

14.

```
P F W M W J O L O P U I G I H E F Q L E F O G T
M P O P W U M O M I Q L E W I H M P L W G R P F
N Q P P F W E I G M E U W G E W I H I Q L G O P
U I G T I W M G I P E O C C H I L M W J O L O P
U I G N W P V W W G D W G I H M P O P W O G T H
O U P F U G P F W M Q J L W D W N W U G R C Y G
T I G N A I F G M I G
```

15.

PQSWR AESGH EDPGR AEFSO IDESG NTSOV ENUGR PDPQE
RAPFC OEEFP TAEDS GHEDJ

16.

oIN OA iGrqFzUK NbG KHOfamMRp Rv XLF
sGx. jban eYZp yr mbG IiLfanMXx NX UG?
hZJTDhV jc qELoi TDPioS vzpi B UceecP ebBg
mTDN jYyqY mbG KChIPMKxqG Ev mbG dBrN
baA BoPGDwS wMAWXQcJZw, jbyfT
qXgVMANA, y kZoMZQG, zp lSsxDrnzf, vRP
NbK kRwS, Bpw sLAzq vXJ nYc sMgw. -
doBnX

17.

XEAWD YEFRN YOIYO ITATN ECSHE HDAPE CIANI JCRUR
EHOPE SRLDO CLDAU EYMPN SNETE WETEM VACNI RREIH
OWLSO AABNR RSLSH SA

18.

Q C I K M I O Y S I H E X C P O G P S I I U I M
X G P H V C J J J E E T K Y I S Y Q H J G P Q Q I
M C J V O G P F F R Y N N I M Q C P H C I V P O
P H S H J G P Q Q I M C J V R Y N H J Q R Y N I
H J T N C D J M Y Q O S I G P H S O F X H S J H
R A J C H O J H

19.

```
C X V G C I C Y N C X I N V J J J Y D Y O S B I Y
B J I O N R G I P F O K G N Y G H I J Y K G R N
K O K B R W R Y N V N P P R K G S O K G V N P K
I J D R K X N I K K V N P B Y J R G R W K V W W
Y S P R N M J U R K X V J J N Y G K I I Q V N P
R C R J J N Y G V W W I B G G X I N Y F R N V G
R Y N Y D F U B V S G U D Y S V N Y G X I S G I
S F V K B S I K R P I N G J U N P Y N H E Y X N
K Y N
```

20.

```
L D A O S E M T S O W T O T S O A B R H F L H E R L E
```

21.

```
J K K J L     T A J K I     I L J U X     K R V D Q
E K R Q X     K R O M L     O H D P P     D K J L G
L A J K O     O K K P L     S L G Q
```

22.

```
Q R H Q A     N H R E P     Q T M G H     N Q R H O
M H H F H     G J O Q R     H V J M D     N E M H F
E M S R A     G W Q J W     H Q R H M     Q J U A S
Q J M Y A     R E U H O     T D D S J     G O A N H
G S H A G     Y J T M S     J T M E W     H N H U J
Q A J G Q     J N T Q Y     E G N P C     A D D A G
I E Q Q D     H V H V A     D D E S S     H K Q G J
Q R A G W     D H P P Q     R E G O T     D D U A S
Q J M Y W     J J N D T     S C E G N     D H Q T P
E D D I H     P H H S R     Q R H I D     H P P A G
W P J O E     D F A W R     Q Y W J N     T K J G Q
R A P W M     H E Q E G     N G J I D     H T G N H
M Q E C A     G W Q R H     N N E Y J     M N H M
```

23.

```
Q G J N P C Q E J N B H N E O P N G K J Y B Y P
Y D Q G J N P H K Q B R J N Y G N E Q G R Z R D
H Y L D R B H Q G J N P Y T T Y D J Q G N J V N
E Q G B Y G B H D G H K Z N J W J W H B Y P Y D
Y L M H G E E I N G E H M R G B N T R J N Y G Z
N P P O H R T D Y B P R M R J N Y G O Q J G Y J
R L R B J P V G K Y G O C Y W G E Y G
```

24.

```
F X G U Q X G T A K H G U E R L Q X G P K G E V
H G U C W E G G M A U A E A O I I W X G O B W V
O I F O W E K G M V U H M W E G I L V Q C R A I
H T G F R K E G V C R A I H T G O M O W R K I W
U H R U T Y R X U E R U
```

25.

```
AIFSCHFOGITTMUOSAEINHERAOFHRDONANTEDEB
EICLTCHTHTLDKJIHEYSNTAENNLOAIOATEOSMLNN
TVBNNNERTEINROTMDOIETEGNHFIOOIIHIYEODP
ETAGUNMOGAUDSRLHVAEIDSATEEEFTSTHLMIENH
```

26.

```
^ - ! - ! @ - ! ( - % - * - ! % - ! % - $ - ( - ! ( - % - ! - ! ( - @ % - @ ) -
! * - @ ! - @ ) - * - ! ( - ! % - $ - ( - ^ - ^ - ( - # - @ ! - ! @ - @ )
```

27.

```
WLREH AIEIE HOCSM EEAIB SUVWV CAISE IEESN TILNI
HGBNL OSEEE FWCAV R
```

28.

FBGPA DAROE PAHKB HGBLB LPYOQ IIOKF HLPAG RNABG

POLPH NPYOP YKOOF ACHKL PAKLP YAPNH KFPYO SOEPH

NHKBH GATHG LPOEE APBHG BGPYO GHKPY OKGYO FBLIY

OKOPY OHPYO KPVHL PAKLB GPYOS OEPAK OAEGB PADAG

RAEGB EAFFB GPADA VYBTY FOAGL SOEPB LEHTA PORUO

KXTEH LOPHP YOTOE OLPBA EOJQA PHKBP BLPYO LOUOG

PYSKB MYPOL PLPAK BGPYO THGLP OEEAP BHG

29.

E M S G Y M L G N A M Z R S G Y N F G S E S I I

Q F B O F T W Z I I L G Z A S W B S Y Z B O F B

Z A Y Z Q Q H Z G Z G U W M S E M L H F T Y O F

T E L I I A I S S D X S Y Y S B Z G U Y M S O E

L I I Z D D B S W L Z Y S Y M S Z Y Y S G Y L F

G I O G U F G X K F M G A F G

30.

WKvmzgvjvD OvmtE bfy vX otm sfy FIEGThI,

HCEg xG AZb qIib vX cXDTJAovXpL, naG GdTI

rYYmrJ Gk nq QC ybTY sfy EC vFMhmWEROb

pdog GZb AZbChI pdog vA vQ oSH xeeszNmI

oW x QAsNT uVJ iCI gV tsGKd Foz'Q

QpJaiNSb ukJ NVVI rzy TOPS QTTFE

vfoImwaogm. – JvKUoJy M. ublXBsX

31.

```
C Q D M S A Q W D S B C H M G M S M V K M K F S
C D G D J B D R B C J T R D R J M S I D L B S D
J L I M Q K D V D G Q D L B S R C J Y H M Q A S
B C J C F G C J R H C J S B A Y C Q A O M S B G
C W O Q A C F A Q R T A R S Q M Y A Q R M I K M
J R S D S U S D M J C G Q D L B S R C J T G D O
A Q S D A R C J T U G S D H C S A G Y T A R S Q
M Y A Q R M I C I Q A A C H A Q D K C G Y J T M
J O E M B J R M J
```

32.

```
M N U O E T B K J B R J K T E L Q K C G M H M N
U O E T B K J B R E J K L L K Q T U J B T Y G Y
J N K J C D K A J R K J
```

33.

```
T B O A D Q C M Q R O R M K O S D L O V O Q Y K
M Q L D L E A L F S A Y S I M K I I M K I I M K
I A L F T B O L T B O S T A T O F O N A Q T K O
L T R M K O S D L A L F S A Y S L M T L M W M Q
L M T T B O Q O M Q T M M K U R B M Q L M T A T
A J J J Y L F M L I G M B L S M L
```

34.

```
Q E R T J    C Q M S H    R P J I M    R F S N S
J H D M R    M R P J F    V R T S H    Q J C D M
R I U F H    R P P C D    M R I U F    H R P P S
H Q J V S    N J M J U    P H R P P    V S N J M
J U P H R    P P S H Q    J N U S F    Q F R P P
H R P P N    U S F Q F    R P P H R    P P S H Q
J D O P Q    R G S J U    P H R P P    D O P Q R
G S J U P    H R P P S    H Q J C F    R D H F S
H R P P C    F R D H F    S H R P P    S H Q J N
J T F S H    R P P Q E    R Q D F G    U T
```

35.

```
J R I J D R V I H P Q G H Q D Y L R K S R P Q A
H M M I U R L H F R H Q A H Q R L U R H Q A I H
G L R V G P Q A H M Q T R A L J L I O D R F P G
Q P I V A R Q Y G H E Y I S C H I W Q T R L R P
H I P S V T Q T A H M G P P I V A R Q Y Q T R L
R G L R A H E A U A E S G D F R H G H E W I F R
H G H E Q T R L R G L R N G F A D A R P G H E H
I M I U R L H F R H Q V G H E I G H Y Q T A H M
R X V R J Q Q T L I S M T J R I J D R G H E J R
I J D R F S P Q D I I C G N Q R L Q T R F P R D
U R P N A L P Q A Q A P I S L E S Q Y Q I D I I
C G N Q R L I S L P R D U R P G H E Q T R H G D
P I Q I D I I C G N Q R L I S L H R A M T O I S
L P F G L M G L R Q Q T G Q V T R L
```

36.

YWxsIHlvdXIgYmFzZSBhcmUgYmVsb25nIHRvIHVz

37.

```
N B N Y K U M V M Q T A B J F T A E T H E F B J
S E R L M M O A K J M O K J K H B O R B R E G K
T G B F M L B R R B J S N K W J Y K U Q G M S B
T R M M H R A K T T K Y K U C U T B T J M V M Q
N K M R T K E J Y K J M M G R M G Y J N K J C D
K A J R K J
```

38.

```
EAUTB GBPFG QIHFT PCVKF IVKRB POVSB ITBUQ AXRXM
ABIBV HZUIK XYNPR GIBBM MOBGC LGULB WNOTV HCARB
```

39.

```
Q A I H I J V A K A D U I Y R B T I T Q A I T I
P Q B J X K N Q A I R J B Q I T P Q D Q I P A D
U I N K R J T Q A I P Q O I J Y Q A N K O Q A I
B O Q D P F P E X Y K B J Y Q K Q A I B O F J I
I P Q A B P L O B U D Q I R J B Q X K N L R E G
B S H I J D J T Q A I B O Y K T B P D J I J T R
O B J Y P K R O S I K N O I D P P R O D J S I N
K O Q A I L I K L G I K N D H I O B S D G X J T
K J E C K A J P K J
```

40.

```
T H H P B T P B Q U D N P J D D S O K R D N P B
D N D C O T Y T H P K T J O V D N P B D L B K J
D T J S T L D J E C H V C P B T J D N T O D N K
J C P H X J S K J U F K B J O K J
```

41.

```
I U R T C S F O J H Y W H K T S T L A L J A B H
K L C H K P B H C M B L K G Y L U E K L W B L W
B O F C E O S T L G L H R L U K P A L J A C K G
F Y K P L K A D L B K S L K
```

42.

```
RXIQK CIIRI GJKYO LRVKX FKIQK LYGVO RXJLI QKZCI
QRXCF VKCNK NVRPQ ICXJT QCIRL KVGLR HKCXJ JKFKZ
IRHKN KLYVH KLRIL KVORX IYFNA LICVF VKCNX KLLYG
NVROK RLCVY XPCXJ CNJGY GLEGK LICOI KNING IQWCQ
CIWCP CXJQR
```

43.

```
F G H Y N I L F P I N M I U R L H F R H Q T G U
R O R R H Q L A R E G H E W A D D O R Q L A R E
A H Q T A P W I L D E I N P A H G H E W I R H I
I H R J L R Q R H E P Q T G Q E R F I V L G V Y
A P J R L N R V Q I L G D D W A P R A H E R R E
A Q T G P O R R H P G A E Q T G Q E R F I V L G
V Y A P Q T R W I L P Q N I L F I N M I U R L H
F R H Q R X V R J Q G D D Q T I P R I Q T R L N
I L F P Q T G Q T G U R O R R H Q L A R E N L I
F Q A F R Q I Q A F R W A H P Q I H V T S L V T
A D D
```

44.

```
V H I D U H D K W V L O I T Q C W Q C W P K W O
O L V H T D K Q L W K H D B C E L O C L L T E H
R L O H D Q C W P E O L W T H K H T D K Q L W E
O L Q C H O C L L T I Y K T L K E F L C K P L K
```

45.

Gqvjv an C GINMjT LqrdI sGBgNb RlBz rx KUPj CcTtMVe VrndMUKwn HSEdRpT LqBG GqK FfJUvwsH Jb xMY oDV LIT kG JO lPjv, rR Lapp rcbGCfgpe hrnBWWHCj Cfy tH jNWpudvV tT OMiQzlacA QUHD iMZK tamuwZQ Bfh JfvSWpkdutpH. gIHjP Js ucMRXNY zXHMYe LlJdl sgBzPs RXoR RqJb Xon upjKohT qBWWQfQh. – hMFApob Cyuis

46.

```
D B N U A H A N O J A S Q B N Q K J H X Q V K Q
B D J Y P N O A J A C A P P N O X Q K G A A L K
J A P V D R A B N L L X R D O P Q H A Q B A O Q
B D J G P B A P B N U D J Y B A O K V J V N X N
J S P A C K J S H A Q B A O B N U A D Q H X J S
K J E F K B J P K J
```

47.

M F S L F	R H B T H	L J F C H	C O R B H
F S T E H	K B T F V	F T Y F N	L F S H K
S H P R O	B H S S L	F S H K S	H E K S N
O H N H R	D Y S K V	H W E K T	F T A O R
R O W S C	R O M T E	H J F C H	O C T E H
O R D K N	F S M F T	F S A Y K	L G U S T
F N D T E	H J F C H	C O R B H	T E K T E
H K J F N	D M U S T	A H A R O	U D E T K
A O U T K	N L F T F	S T E H S	U N K S T
R K N S C	O R M H R	K N L L F	S T R F A
U T O R O	C P R F M	K J S P F	R F T U K
J H N H R	D Y T E K	T M U S T	A H U T F
J F Z H L	F N T E F	S P R O B	H S S C O
R J F C H	K N L T E	H S U N K	R H S O F
N T F M K	T H J Y B	O N N H B	T H L T E
H I K A A	K J K E		

48.

```
J I G X Q V J Q B C I N P T M Y I Y E Y P P T M
X Q J F Y Y K J I Y P V C O Y B T K K X J I Y C
P Q J G Y Q B Y M Q B C I F P B Y C P B T U C I
N B Y M J V I V T X T I A Q B Y J Q B Y M C P Q
J G Y Q B Y M B T U Y C Q G X I A J I R D J B I
P J I
```

49.

```
L T O P L B D W Q Y D P D I I T J D K H Q W R E
Y Q C W P M D O D Q T H I D K P D A C Q P L S Q
C W C W E O W V M O L M C W Q P H J W O D B H H
K R D P O H W I C H U W H B L J J L K I L U W L
S C T J H K S O W W R L J H K R Q C W Y C H U W
H B L J J L K S H D Q C D K H R W J L B O H Q D
B V H Y L S I D S W I Y K R L K E F L C K P L K
```

50.

```
CTBMA FJHSR CHNLN JGLTJ GYMTT LHTCJ HTBMT KLJKF
LJIMN NJGKF CRBGL HTQMQ LFYRM TOMNE MHAFL TTBCH
SRBMK KLHTJ TBLGT BLYWL HTJUT MHABM KKLHL ATJTB
CHSRF LJHMQ AJAMV CHNC
```

51.

```
S D U P U L P U J K R L V K P E S U Q E J I Y K
R R E B U E S P U L S S D U I L H H W E S D S D
U Q L I U C U J U P L H E J B K J Q E O U P L S
E K J H Y J O K J A F K D J Q K J
```

52.

```
Q T I M I A O R U Q J H I W P Y D J M P K M I O
A S I H Q Q J S I P F W A Q T E J H N M I O O P
H S Q T P Q A O E J H Q A H U J U O F Y A H E I
O O P H Q F Y P H S W A Q T J U Q A H Q I M M U
K Q A J H A D A Q A O M I P F F Y N J A H N Q J
W J M C Q T I M I F P Q A J H O T A K T P O N J
Q Q J R I P F G J O Q A H E I O Q U J U O F Y H
S J H R B J T H O J H
```

53.

```
EEEOFOIEDHUNMNCUWNMFSDIIEERTEIMERRIFUOUEIAWSTTVTERB
SRPSAESTIITAHOUOUUOTUTNATYOEFSCEREEIBSOSERTTOERDASU
REDMOCSNCSCTHACELTDSASFRFNBEHEOIESALTTRTNNTEBTEIENN
FINRENHGNHDMCOSTOIPROLTPTNEUHMPPEMTRETOOROESAAOOINE
RVHEHRTASOOLLJSODSTLIAYOADEADEYDNGEILLIDTIESQEOOTRI
RFTRFNEILECPT
```

54.

```
T P Z B X I J H O J X U C O C X I J H O X B O I
J Y U L O U H U O J B P U Z D Q R K U J B E I R
D U Z V H Z J X O J Q O S E I R V I J B E I R D
U Z C Q I I V Z C V U Z V B P U I B P U D G U D
C I J T O L L C U J C U B P Z B C I K U B P O J
Q O C J B B P U D U Z J V J I X P Z O J I S D U
Z C I J O J Q J I K Z B B U D P I T L I Q O X Z
L I D U L U Q Z J B I D Y D O L L O Z J B T O L
L T O J E I R D X Z C U S I D E I R L E J V I J
Y N I P J C I J
```

55.

IYHKQ   PAWSC   YKTWJ   PDWQO   JKVWR   DJRDB
JDEDL   WJSIO   JWRWJ   YDJOJ   BHWJP

56.

R D Q Y J   U B C V T   C Q D A B   S S J R K
T C F O U   S S B T B   J U R T B   C R C Q D
A B S S J   E U P A T   W B T S B   T Q S B T
Y W D G G   B T C Q Y   J U

57.

IATTC   AJPIN   KATCA   YJPGA   EATTA   RSOAA   LCASM
NRUST   CPKWA   LPKJP   GAMNR   NURSA   IVAS

58.

B R S P F   F I J T T   S B I D T   S A H A G
P I H R J   M T S A K   A J K F A   P Q U F A
J M L J I   H U L T I   J Q R S P   F F B A V
A Q M A P   Q T J B I   L U Q T S   A B Q Q A
R A I T G   A I T B I   T S A K Q   J R A L U
T B J I J   M T S A B   Q B I T A   Q A R T B
R S P F F   I A V A Q   M F P T T   A Q T S A
B Q K P R   R B J I R   T J J E T   P B I T S
A B Q M P   V J U Q J   Q O Q P T   B M Y T S
A B Q Q A   V A I O A   M J Q M A   P Q J M T
S A B Q L   J I T A G   K T

59.

N U N P Y   F H K I J   T Q R J C   F N T Q N
L D S T J   C K J N C   K Q R L C   R R C H K
S T J C K   N K E Q L   P S H Q C   D D C H P
Q W H G G   I L R L P   T H K

60.

```
S J K T H   R A Q G R   G J K W O   P D R A E   B B E U Q
H P Y P K   U D K K O   R L N K L   R N P S X   R O
```

61.

```
G W B Q V   L K U V P   J H V J S   D J K W Q
A K W S K   V J I K P   E V W B S   A S V H M
V P K P S   K E K J E   B F B G S   V W B S A
N B L J B   S Y
```

62.

```
O I H F B   P A G O I   V A W Q O   U O M Q A
O B M F J   N W F P B   Q S W Q B   J I G W Y
E O D I J   V I J J E   O T B O I   N O Q J W
I Y Q A B   I H E S Q   Q A O F W   V P
```

63.

```
U B N Z J   G B N F P   H J P B G   R N G J M
R T J H N   K B T Q J   Q N H J M   G J M R F
G B F I E   R P A F H   B H P A R   F T D H J
U E R Z Y   R G R H P   J O R M M   J M
```

64.

```
U L J F K   F S B A N   M W B Q F   R P N S S
M T M Q Q   U N S S E   B K F L A   R M C S E
M R B W E   M N M R R   B R R F S
```

65.

```
I H J I N   Y O H L K   L U G N P   W D S C K   U S O H D   J B N I O
D S D K U   Q O U S S   C H P H D   Q C N P T   G Y N J N   I O D S D
K U Q I N   J W C K T   K H Q J K   S S P Y S   K O H L K   L U G N P
```

66.

```
R D A Q S   K L B C O   A P R E O   F R P F K
V F I I Q   A R V D A   K A U A O   Q D A P T
H K L V I   A Y C A Q   R D A F K   Y A M A K
Y A K T A   L B P J A   O F T P R   D A F K Y
A M A K Y   A K T A L   B P J A O   F T P V L
S I Y A K   Y F K R D   A O S F K   L B A K C
I P K Y
```

67.

```
J Y C I B   Q R B Q I   L M S S A   B S S A I
B S S I J   O S S M O   I Q C M Q   J S A D R
T U S Y W   D H H R A   M Q S I L   J Y H D C
I E U S S   A B S D R   A B H H L   I D S A I
Q E M T D   H Y L M Q   J I L S B   H H Y O I
Q C M Q J   D S B R D   R A M U H   T
```

68.

```
SAVNV  VNBQN  KJVGJ  NBGHG  LGBJG  IPVVH  GJGJN
SKYKT  BHGYV  XMPVQ  QWAGS  BSWKT  FNQVV  HFBDV
GIIVE  SBKJS  KQGYS  KKSAV  PQSAV  BJIBJ  BSVMF
VGQTP  VBNVP  BUVIP  KHVHG  JEBMG  SBKJ
```

69.

```
C K Y L U   S B S B G   A D R G K   I G L T M
H G A R U   Q G C R M   A C K C K   L H N A O
G S B G A   D R G K I   G L T M A   C K C R M
H G A R U   Q G
```

70.

```
D B P U V   J K S B D   J L S K Q   P Y S K S   B V J K S
B D J L S   B P S B P   Q E V V J   Q P D C
```

71.

```
B N L H R   B K I Q T   A I Q B O   A T L S I   F I N T B
L H J R J   M U E F B   N T Q U R   T O Q J H   T I K H L
T S L Q T   A I E I H   I S B T L   S T A I B   H K B V B
K U J F E   U T S L Q   T A I M U   E F B N O   L L K
```

72.

```
T E G E C   P P F M G   S S O B N   O M S T C   M T O N N
U P C T F   O M F S F   M B F M F   T G
```

73.

```
T C N P N   W R Q J K   K J N A K   K I D J T   C D Q G D
S N T C R   T C R I J   K T W D T   C D T Q K   H N B K J
B K H D T   R J T N V   D G
```

74.

```
W J Y V Q   O W K O S   D J W O X   W A A W D   O D B W T
Y Q C Y I   Q C Y D O   K O S Y O   P W J S Q   C Y X U W
J Q Y S Q   K P Q W X   W J S S D   P L R P P   Q C Y I
```

75.

```
S D A M L   J X V G X   V F S D L   A V Q N G   N A P G S
S G E I Q   F Q G Q S   D A F P F   Q D Q G X   S M I A A
N L A U A   P K F L Y   F L C S D   F Q D G Q   R A A L K
X N P G E   S F E A S   D P M T C   D J F B A
```

76.

```
G T G S G   K P O S S   G A J C T   F L T L N   Y A O B Y   M L N D C
C J T F C   A C G N E   O U T O D   P L R J G   L K C N T   K O R C I
C C N J Y   D O R K C   T F L N G   D C C J G   T D O R K   Y S C J D
G T G S L   M T U L J   J Y M U T   T G N E K   Y T F R O   L T G T G
S B C P R   G V G N E   K C O D T   F C E R C   L T O A H   C M T O D
K Y J G D   C
```

77.

T F B R B S B B K T N K B T N E B V B R Y C B W C
P L T S P T J B P S T P S L B R T P G M P E J B C
P L T S G M O N J G T G L S

78.

D C R V L I R E L I D P Q R G L P U T Q D J R H H
D E D E I Y K U F L S Q W R P Q C L M T U H D S B
K K E

79.

K X J M P B Q G D K L M V D L M J B K D L D L B J
G I Y K D L X M A X M T P J M P B Q F G N Q G F D
U Y D J P Y D B X N D Q Q Y B S F Y S F P Y Y Q R
M P Y X Y D P Q D L B S Y L K X M A A G R G D J J
G A Y G Q Y L S G P Y J X R J M Q Y B K X N M J G
S G R D J J G A Y G Q L Y D P J X Q M D L B G L S
F Y R M T P Q Y M A L D S T P Y K X L D S T P D J
J G A Y R D L L M S L M V E Y J M L C

80.

G R M L M T I L M W F M W G S F A J J B D A Q B D
G L C M U T M N M N N G E D G F A V D K A L Y Q D
S M U Q E D S A L R K A L Y M B H D E T S M N G L
T D Q D S T B U T A N T D Q B D G L C M E E U O G
D R W G T F C Q D A T A N N A G Q S G T G S L M T
D A S Y T M S U B S G R D T M T F D J D V D J M N
E M K K M L M E E U O A T G M L S

81.

Q T E R U F L Q O G F G R S G V E J F D E F Q O K Q G L P C
D J P Q T E J Q T P F Q G E X L O Q E P S O Q P Q O G F

82.

```
T B A P A   D P A T B   P A A G C   K R Q M E   H C A Q H
C A Q R D   J K H C A   Q D K R Q   T D T C Q   T C S Q
```

83.

```
R N S F J   V S J T T   P S S D J   H E R Q S   F T E Q N
G P D F Y   Q R P J I   O S P E I   S I O F G   I D R N G
I R N S F   J V S J T   G P E Q R   J A P G A   Y
```

84.

```
O H N D I   Q E K J D   I S X I Q   R J Y D J   G R D G Z
I D X C J   V H Q R P   O G F J S   S G Q I J   H G D D X
K T R R I   H N J T R   G C I K D   J F G R I   S A J G R
E J J B R   J G U J I   C S J D D   I Q I J H   Q
```

85.

```
Q C B N B   R N B Q V   K P T L N   B I B L H   B R P T N
B P D J H   D Y B K J   B D P D E   B R H Q C   B K Q C B
N N B R H   Q C B D E   B R H D P   V C B J R   I R J N B
S B D U B   P Q C B P   B R H P K   Y K Y Y D   S B Y N K
I C D P P   K U B N B   D A J Q C   B N B R H   L H B R P
T N B S K   I B P V C   B J C B C   R J E P Q   C B I O R
S G
```

86.

```
D B I I K   P O K P H   O Q Q C B   M M Y W C   O J A O D
J R M P B   D Q O F J   K S V O P   Y L K I U   K P S B A
H O W C O   J A O D J   R B A T Q   O F A T S   D C B V O
I K I O J   S Q K U T   J O B Q D   J O Q Q W   C O J A O
D J R O X   M H B D J   O F
```

87.

```
KBQSJ ICGGY RCHCI RHHBI SBABG RBVBQ
RIABP RIMJI STCIT GYFBB KRILN JQRZJ
ITCGT NBNBC QTCIP BVBQY TNRIL BGSBL
JBSSG JWBQC IPTNB WNJGB SYSTB HRSQB
EQBSN BP
```

88.

```
YKRPB WKRFU SIAJC UIAFO PAPIC
TCPQA GIAFC PPFIF APINC JFCTI
```

89.

```
MLTDA DMUSA MBJMQ RSGEM RYMBB
FVADU LRQAR KALOD MSALG TQGLR
MKBQM KGKML CSTTD AULAK NJMYA
R
```

90.

```
GDGLK LEQCL SKLMS FCMLE NNBKL MYEQC
LSKCM NDFGR SNQYL QCDQL TBR
```

91.

```
KBJWE RLMJJ WJMQB SWDMK SCERS BAHWS
ATSVW KSIMQ SCVES CBITH HGKMV HWDNW
SCBSC WVBRI ENCSE KNIMQ VCBSC WBKDC
ERLMT KSQYJ WKAWH EWUWD SMAWQ ENCSI
MQSCW HEAWQ SEWRM ISCWV MQHDB KDSCM
RWVCM IWHHE KBAWH EWIOW QCBOR CBQDH
YTSSW QWDAY SCWJR WHUWR SCBSR MJWCM
VMQBK MSCWQ SCWEQ HEUWR JENCS AWNEU
WKSMO QMJMS WSCWA WSSWQ JWKSM ISCER
VMQHD
```

92.

W O B O M R W M R C M H H O D I U R D O
R E T E S J K T E T E S S U E C E D O

93.

T L I S I S T L B S B A K J M T I G B I J K U Q L
I S T K Q Y T L C T T L B Q B L C S A K G B H C A
D E Q K G R B Q G C J Y T K M K W J I J R S T Q B
B T O B C A B W I T L L K J K U Q I H B F I B V B
I T I S O B C A B E K Q K U Q T I G B

94.

K I V I P D K S B I L D I G R M L B T J C K U M K
L G D U S W C Q Q M J T U B M W I R H Y Q M J C K
Y S M Q M L I W

95.

N C S B M S F B B X O B Q S R K A I B S F B W N Q
R S O N R R G T J B K G M G R S B Q R G M S F B G
Q N W M C G B J E R G M S F G R L N U M S Q Y W B
O Q B C B Q Q U J B T Y A K A S B U Q R

96.

H T G O U F G T E M A T G H M J T G E T C E H K U R B T O E
N T W O U K A G E V B D R O U F G T T G B W O R S T O C N O
M S B Q U B M N B S I U S T E S H T G H M J T G B W O R K A
W O U K A G E V B S U C C B R B A K B S S H C G H T K B R G
E A D B B M R B S H S T B A O M T G B R G H M B

97.

```
T D L W E   K I O N C   D M K B L   E S A H O   W E K B T
D R O U B   D T D E S   C O K T E   K L K T M   K I W D L
T D L R W   L H E G L   E T O R K   O T T D E   S B R O W
T D O N K   M T E O K   M H C O K   S C E O U   S K L S S
E S M P O   H E T E C   M H N M C   T
```

98.

```
R H L P L   D P L R W   J K P J O   C L F Q M   I F Y C M
A L R H L   K J.C M R   M U D C J   I L Q D P   L M I Q J
C T O C L   D I G R H   L L U J I   J F M U J   I L Q D P
L M I U J   F K P L H   L I Q M O   C L
```

99.

```
V B C L B   O U O P K   W P R Y C   Q C H J N   N C L O R
B O R P O   W Q T P Y   C Q C H K   J V O P
```

100.

```
G C O N K   G S G A G   H M R K G   V B T N M   O Q H G R
B H M T S   F H M J R   S F B Y T   E B C N Q   A B T G M
S N R N L   B N S F B   Q K G M B   N C E U R   G M B R R
```

101.

```
C J E H L   C M A H D   C J N W C   Y C R O U   M G T D H
W O R J G   A H N O R   H T R U T   D D C S B   O T E T S
A O O T S   O M
```

102.

```
F S W F J   J H E Y E   T P Q H E   R M P E T   W M K T L
E F S D E   P J E T C   Q S D E A   M L Q E P   V T S F V
E N T P S   Y M P H E   A M K E Q   N P F K E   K F L F Q
S E P F C   M L S Q E   E F S D T   N N E L F   L B F L K
Y S F K E
```

103.

```
B E B T Y   Y R M Q S   L K B Q L   I K L W A   Q E T M E
K W E H H   S T E H H   A R T D R   J L U K T   Q Y L B H
L K C S D   M O L W S   L K J Q E   J G R T C   Q L U K O
S W M Q I   A R R Q E   K V E K J   E A H R C   Q R R K S
U A U Q A   S O L C H   L V R Q S   M K O N L   L H S B E
H H R Q S
```

104.

```
L U T J R   T U S U M   F T R F M   B D Q R R   F M D T E
F S W E B   T E B O O   R M R I F   M T E R U   M F T R I
S T B T R   S N M T U   R S I B Y   W B S B M   B A T N C
W F A H R   I M R S S   C N Q W E   F A E T E   R Q R A B
M M R V R   Q L R G U   S T F C F   A B T F N   M W E B T
R V R Q T   E R A B U   S R W E B   T R V R Q   T E R O R
Q V R Q S   F N M N C   Q R J F D   F N U S C   R R J F M
D W E B T   R V R Q T   E R O N J   F T F A B   J L R J F
R C T N F   M C J F A   T S U A E   T R Q Q N   Q N M T E
R W N Q J   I T N T B   H R T E R   J F V R S   N C S N K
B M Y F M   M N A R M   T B M I I   R C R M A   R J R S S
K R M W N   K R M B M   I A E F J   I Q R M A   B M M R V
R Q R V R   Q L R G U   S T F C F   R I
```

FIENDISH CODES

There are many extremely difficult cipher systems out there, some in common use, and some not. In this section, you'll find a representative sampling of the most difficult systems that are still solvable with pencil and paper, including several different variations of polyalphabetic ciphers. There is also a brief overview of modern 'asymmetric' cryptography, plus two famous ciphers published by Edgar Allan Poe, which remained unsolved for over 100 years.

Asymmetric key cryptography

Most of the other cryptographic systems in this book are called 'symmetric' systems, which means that a key or method is used to encrypt a message into a ciphertext, and then you can use that same key or method 'symmetrically' to decrypt the ciphertext back into a readable plaintext.

A few decades ago, however, a huge breakthrough was made that resulted in a system called 'asymmetric' cryptography, where one key is used to encrypt a message, but then a different key must be used to decrypt it. This system is in common use today on the internet, but requires computers to munch on the massive prime numbers involved.

Although generally beyond the scope of this book, here is a pencil and paper way of understanding asymmetric key cryptography – provided by the famed puzzle designer Scott Kim.

Public Display of Encryption
Before you can send a key-encrypted message you first have to send the key. But the key itself needs to be encrypted. So how do you get started?

The solution is public key encryption; a revolutionary technique invented by mathematicians Whitfield Diffie and Martin Hellman in 1976. Diffie's breakthrough was to split the key into two parts, one public and the other private. The private key is secret, but the public key is freely distributed, eliminating the need to send an encrypted key. A message encrypted with the private key can only be decrypted with the public key, and vice versa. The public key lets anyone send a message to be read only by the private key holder.

Question 1

In 1977 Ron Rivest, Adi Shamir and Leonard Adleman invented the first practical public key scheme, known as the RSA algorithm, now used widely in secure web transactions. The algorithm is based on two ideas. The first idea is that factoring large numbers is hard, especially if the number is the product of two large primes. (A prime number like 7 or 11 is a whole number greater than 1 that can be evenly divided only by 1 and itself.) Despite centuries of effort, no one improved much on the tedious method of dividing the number by every smaller prime.

Can you write each of the numbers 57, 551, 5063, 52961 as the product of two primes? Hint: use a spreadsheet to speed up the work.

2	3	5	7	11	13	17	19	23	29
31	37	41	43	47	53	59	61	67	71
73	79	83	89	97	101	103	107	109	113
127	131	137	139	149	151	157	163	167	173
179	181	191	193	197	199	211	223	227	229
233	239	241	251	257	263	269	271	277	281
283	293	307	311	313	317	331	337	347	349
353	359	367	373	379	383	389	397	401	409
419	421	431	433	439	443	449	457	461	463
467	479	487	491	499	503	509	521	523	541

The first 100 prime numbers

Question 2

The second idea is that repeatedly raising a number to higher and higher powers eventually leads you in a circle. For example start with the number 3. The first few powers of 3 are 3, 9, 27, 81, 243, 729, 2187 and 6561. These numbers keep getting bigger, but if you divide them by another number, say 7, the remainders form a pattern 3, 2, 6, 4, 5, 1, 3, 2 ... that starts cycling after 6 terms, as seen in the diagram.

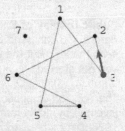

Remainder pattern for powers of 3

Can you draw the diagrams for raising the number 3 to successive powers and dividing by 11? By 13? By 17?

Question 3

In general, raising a number m to higher and higher powers and dividing by a prime p yields a pattern of remainders that cycles after p−1 terms. In other words, $m^{(p-1)}$ divided by n yields a whole number plus a remainder of m. If n is a product of two primes p and q, then the pattern cycles after (p−1)(q−1) terms, which means that $m^{(p-1)(q-1)}$ divided by n yields a whole number plus a remainder of m.

Can you draw the diagram for raising the number 3 to successive powers and dividing by 35? How long is the cycle?

Question 4

To encrypt a message with the RSA algorithm, choose two big primes p and q. Let n be the product pq, and f be the product (p−1)(q−1). Convert your message into a number m between 1 and n. For example, convert each letter to a number (A=1, B=2, etc.), or use a binary/Hexadecimal equivalent, or just make something up. If the message is too long, you can break it into several smaller messages. Choose a number e (the encryption exponent) which does not share any common factors with (p-1)(q-1). The two numbers (n, e) form the Public Key.

To encipher your message, raise your message m to the power e, and divide by n. The remainder c is your enciphered message. The private key is another number d (the decryption exponent). To decipher the enciphered message c, raise it to the power d, and divide by n. This operation takes you back around the circle and returns the original message number m. In other words, c^d divided by n has remainder m, which means that $(m^e)^d = m^{ed}$ divided by n also has remainder m.

Of course real public keys are much harder to break, since the numbers are hundreds of digits long. But let's see if you can break this simplified version of public key encryption. Suppose I send you a series of messages c=24, c=15, c=5, c=9, c=25, each encoded with public key (n=55, e=27). Can you figure out the private key decryption exponent d, and use it to deduce the original message numbers m? Can you then translate the series of unencrypted message numbers into a word related to 'key'?

Solutions: page 558

The Edgar Allan Poe Ciphers

These two ciphers were sent as challenges by Mr. W.B. Tyler to Edgar Allan Poe, who published them in his regular column in 1841. They remained uncracked for over 100 years, but the first one was finally solved in 1992 by Professor Terence Whalen, and the second by Gil Broza in 2000. As it turned out, both ciphers used different variations of substitution ciphers. Can you solve them too?

Solutions to the ciphers can be found on page 559.

Edgar Allan Poe Challenge Cipher 1, by W.B. Tyler

To Edgar A. Poe, Esq.

Dᴿ ꞁiꞁ OGXEW PᴊᴴFyʎ ᴎᵫUH ⱢIA VꝖꜱMꝺꝺ
xᴅTbjꜱ SNB ᴇꜱᴀʟᴎᴋꜱYꝖ ꞁCP ᴛʌol HꜰZɢᴜꝺꝺ
ʟꞁꞁᴋꞁꞁ ᴎꝙᴅꝺʟ ʌᴍO hjꜰXꞁᴋʟxꞁ Oᵂ ᴛꝺꝺᴅᴎ Rꞁ jꞁᴋꞁꞁ
ᴛꞁ ᴄꜱMᴀʏꞁyꞁ iꞁꞁꞁXꞁꞁ Oᵂ ꞁꜱᴀᴀᴛꜱ VB PᴜꝺᵂꝺJ ᴛᴄꝯDYRꝯ
ᴅHʙ ʎFKxᴅɢꞁ ZꝯNꜱᴍᴇʟʟ OᴙI OᴙO ojᴎI ꝙꝯ Mꞁɢ
wꝺVꞁᴇɢXʜB ʎᴜL ᴎᴋᴎ AꞁᴋꜱO iyꞁꞁDV bꞁꞁꜱꞁꞁᴀꞁ
SPꝀI CEᴍᴎSW bGᴇꞁꞁh aNjmx ꜱꞁʎꞁʏʌᴇꜱ ʎᴀᴋꞁXDIx
ꝺGꞁʟᴅ IꞁO ꞁᴢᴋ ꞁꞁODᴎ LRʎꝖꝺ YꞁFꞁ PꝯJ ꞁꞁ
SEB ᴅᴎʙLꝝu Lᴘʜ nꞁꞁᴊᴜ aꞁꞁꞁ diky ꞁꞁᴊᴊ oVᵂ cEꝝꞁᴍꞁꝺ
ꜱꞁꝁꜱ eⱢꞁ ᴋMꞁ xꞁKSꜱɢ HꞁiꞁyW ꝙꞁP cꞁꝙ qTꞁꝺ Dꜱꞁj ᴙᴠᴠ
Uꝺꞁᴄᴀᴍe nk VFʜʌ lDah XᴍᴋꞁTIAx Ye ʌꜱꞁ aꜱFꞁW
XꝖꝺᴡᴋUꞁᴀᴡᴙꞁ ᴮ ꝸ ꜱꜱ ꜱᴋᴇᴡᴡꞁᴍCꝖx
ꝿBꝖIꝝ ᴛᴇ EmMꝖ nk Lᴄꞁꞁꞁ SꞁIꞁꞁꜱ ᴙꞁꝯꞁꞁ NꞁꝖ agꞁjꞁj ʎᴀᴜɢꞁN
RZꞁK Cꞁꝙ ᴀʟ ᴡꞁX JᴅᴍᴎꞁꞁUꞁꝖx ꞁꝺHꞁꝺBꞁI
bꝁꞁL Lꞁꞁꞁh ꞁW eꜱToꞁꞁꝺ ᴀꞁꞁ RꞁꞁꝺMFᴛꞁ
VᴀꞁHꝺꞁP ᴅHʙ ᴎNɢꞁ cW ᴡꞁꞁꝙꞁꞁᴍ ꞁꞁꝺHꝝʙVᴀ
ꞁꞁhꞁ VDJ ꞁꞁꞁꝙꞁᴄꞁᴍ cW ᴀʏxᴜᴍꞁꝙꞁ JꞁMʌ ꞁꝙIꞁmxᴠꞁ ꜱꜱ ꜱꞁCꞁꞁXꜱꞁ
Mꞁ yXIꞁꞁ cW AꝺGb Mꞁɢ ᴀRNᴡꞁꝙꝖ cᴍꞁ ꞁꞁꜱ xꞁHꝝXꞁ ꜱᴡᴀꝁᴋ
CFꝺ ꜱꞁ yᴋ fjeo IꝙꞁꞁꞁꜱⱢꞁP ꞁꞁꞁ Vꞁᴋꞁyꞁꝺ ꝙⱢXh
qdJꞁ ꝙᴄꞁPꞁꝺ ludꞁꞁA K ᴠᴅᴛʌ cPꞁꞁꝺ ꜱꞁꞁ ᴀꞁꞁꞁ WꞁPꝺ
Kꞁꝺꞁ ᴡꞁ ᴄ ꝺꞁꞁꞁ

Edgar Allan Poe Challenge Cipher 2, by W.B. Tyler

Swapping cipher alphabets

One of the great milestones in cryptography was the invention of polyalphabetic substitution ciphers. 'Polyalphabetic substitution' means that there is more than one cipher alphabet involved in the encryption of a plaintext letter. In other words, one plaintext letter can potentially be any other letter in the ciphertext, depending on its position, as opposed to merely one possible ciphertext letter, as with a monoalphabetic system, or 2 or 3 possible equivalents, as with a homophonic system. The most famous polyalphabetic system is the Vigenère cipher.

The Vigenère cipher is a substitution cipher, but by no means simple! Vigenère ciphers were first written about in the 1500s by Giovan Batista Belaso and Giovanni Battista Porta, and then became better known in the 19th century when they were (mis)attributed to the French cryptographer Blaise de Vigenère (1523-1596), who had invented a related but stronger system called the Autokey cipher. Vigenère ciphers earned the French nickname 'le chiffre indéchiffrable' (the unbreakable cipher). With modern computers, however, these ciphers can usually be broken quite readily as long as there is a sufficient quantity of ciphertext to work from.

Take the following example:

```
PT:   I like macaroni and cheese!
Key:  T ASTY TASTYTAS TYT ASTYTA
CT:   B LADC FAUTPHNA TLW CZXCLE!
```

It's not hard to see how this differs from a monoalphabetic cipher. For example, the plaintext letter A was encrypted as both a T and an A in this message; and the ciphertext C decrypted sometimes to C, and sometimes to E. The reason is that each of the letters in the plaintext message is enciphered with a different cipher alphabet.

The order and number of the cipher alphabets is determined by a key. For example, with the key TASTY, four different cipher alphabets will be used (the same number as the number of letters in the key, subtracting for duplicate letters like the '"T"' in TASTY).

In the most commonly used method, the first letter of each cipher

alphabet is the same as the next letter in the key. A common way to represent this is with what is called a Vigenère 'tableau':
A standard Vigenère tableau can be seen below. This is what it would look like if the key were the same as the alphabet: ABCDEFGHIJ (etc.).

For encipherment, each letter of a plaintext message is applied against a different row of the tableau, and then the intersection of the plaintext letter from the top, and the current row, generate the ciphertext.

So the plaintext APPLE would become AQROI, enciphering the first letter from row 1, the second from row 2, the third from row 3, etc.

```
   A B C D E F G H I J K L M N O P Q R S T U V W X Y Z

A  A B C D E F G H I J K L M N O P Q R S T U V W X Y Z
B  B C D E F G H I J K L M N O P Q R S T U V W X Y Z A
C  C D E F G H I J K L M N O P Q R S T U V W X Y Z A B
D  D E F G H I J K L M N O P Q R S T U V W X Y Z A B C
E  E F G H I J K L M N O P Q R S T U V W X Y Z A B C D
F  F G H I J K L M N O P Q R S T U V W X Y Z A B C D E
G  G H I J K L M N O P Q R S T U V W X Y Z A B C D E F
H  H I J K L M N O P Q R S T U V W X Y Z A B C D E F G
I  I J K L M N O P Q R S T U V W X Y Z A B C D E F G H
J  J K L M N O P Q R S T U V W X Y Z A B C D E F G H I
K  K L M N O P Q R S T U V W X Y Z A B C D E F G H I J
L  L M N O P Q R S T U V W X Y Z A B C D E F G H I J K
M  M N O P Q R S T U V W X Y Z A B C D E F G H I J K L
N  N O P Q R S T U V W X Y Z A B C D E F G H I J K L M
O  O P Q R S T U V W X Y Z A B C D E F G H I J K L M N
P  P Q R S T U V W X Y Z A B C D E F G H I J K L M N O
Q  Q R S T U V W X Y Z A B C D E F G H I J K L M N O P
R  R S T U V W X Y Z A B C D E F G H I J K L M N O P Q
S  S T U V W X Y Z A B C D E F G H I J K L M N O P Q R
T  T U V W X Y Z A B C D E F G H I J K L M N O P Q R S
U  U V W X Y Z A B C D E F G H I J K L M N O P Q R S T
V  V W X Y Z A B C D E F G H I J K L M N O P Q R S T U
W  W X Y Z A B C D E F G H I J K L M N O P Q R S T U V
X  X Y Z A B C D E F G H I J K L M N O P Q R S T U V W
Y  Y Z A B C D E F G H I J K L M N O P Q R S T U V W X
Z  Z A B C D E F G H I J K L M N O P Q R S T U V W X Y
```

If the key TASTY were used, then a tableau could be created as follows:

Key: Tasty

```
. A B C D E F G H I J K L M N O P Q R S T U V W X Y Z
1 T U V W X Y Z A B C D E F G H I J K L M N O P Q R S
2 A B C D E F G H I J K L M N O P Q R S T U V W X Y Z
3 S T U V W X Y Z A B C D E F G H I J K L M N O P Q R
4 T U V W X Y Z A B C D E F G H I J K L M N O P Q R S
5 Y Z A B C D E F G H I J K L M N O P Q R S T U V W X
```

The top line is the plaintext alphabet, and then each line after that is used to encrypt successive letters of the plaintext message. The first letter is encrypted from line one, the second from line two, the third from line three, and so on. When the last line is reached, then the next letter (in this case, the sixth letter) resumes at line one.

So to encrypt the letters I LIKE, the resulting ciphertext letters would be B LADC:

```
. A B C D E F G H I J K L M N O P Q R S T U V W X Y Z
1 T U V W X Y Z A B C D E F G H I J K L M N O P Q R S
2 A B C D E F G H I J K L M N O P Q R S T U V W X Y Z
3 S T U V W X Y Z A B C D E F G H I J K L M N O P Q R
4 T U V W X Y Z A B C D E F G H I J K L M N O P Q R S
5 Y Z A B C D E F G H I J K L M N O P Q R S T U V W X
```

Notice how the plaintext letter I on the top row corresponds to the B on row 1, the L corresponds to the L on row 2, the 'I' corresponds to the A on row 3, and so on, all the way down to row 5, and then starts back up M on the top row corresponding with F on row 1.

Vigenère ciphers are difficult to solve but not impossible. You may find that some of the same techniques which work with monoalphabetic ciphers can work with polyalphabetic. For example, it is worth checking to see if there are any clues in the sentence structure which help you identify some of the shorter words.

For further analysis, a special kind of frequency and distribution analysis is essential. You need to examine the cipher for repeating groups of letters, to try and determine the length of the keyword. For example, if the sequence DQM appears four times in the ciphertext, and from the start of one DQM sequence to the next is at intervals of 8, 24, 70 and 16, then you can assume the length of the keyword to be either equal to, or a factor of the various numbers. In the above example, the keyword is probably either 8 or 4 letters long.

Once you have guessed the length of the keyword, break up the ciphertext into multiple columns for individual inspection. For example, if it is an 8-character key, then every eighth letter in the ciphertext will have been encrypted with the same cipher alphabet (like a monoalphabetic cipher), so you can carry out frequency analysis on that set of 'every eighth' letters to look for the most common letters.

Also, the repeating 'DQM' groups, and others like it, will most likely be the same words, usually a common word such as 'the' or 'and'. You can then tentatively map these letters to a part of the keyword, along with all your frequency analysis on the rest of the message. For example, if you guess that D maps to a T, then every other D that is in that same 'every eighth' pattern would also be a T, and this may help you deduce some other word in the code. As more words are guessed out, the whole keyword can be ultimately uncovered. The more ciphertext that is available, the more effective this method can be.

The classic Vigenère cipher uses a plain A-Z alphabet along the top of the tableau, and shifted plain alphabets below it, with a key (such as TASTY) down the left-hand side specifying the order in which the tableau lines are to be used. This is known as a 'straight', 'simple' or 'standard' Vigenère. But several other well established variations exist.

Quagmire I

This, the first of several aptly titled variations, uses an additional key, which is used to generate the 'plain' alphabet along the top. The word determining the cipher alphabets (TASTY) becomes known as the 'indicator', and the keyword applied to the plaintext alphabet (for example CRYPTO) is known as the 'key'.The indicator key could be used in any column, but is most commonly used at the far left. It is usual to specify this by saying for example that the Indicator key is 'under the letter C'.

```
.CRYPTOABDEFGHIJKLMNQSUVWXZ
0TUVWXYZABCDEFGHIJKLMNOPQRS
1ABCDEFGHIJKLMNOPQRSTUVWXYZ
2STUVWXYZABCDEFGHIJKLMNOPQR
3TUVWXYZABCDEFGHIJKLMNOPQRS
4YZABCDEFGHIJKLMNOPQRSTUVWX
```

Quagmire II

This is a reversal of classic Vigenère – using an unscrambled plain alphabet along the top, but with the tableau itself created by a key-generated cipher alphabet.

Key: CRYPTO, with indicator TASTY under A

```
.ABCDEFGHIJKLMNOPQRSTUVWXYZ
0TOABDEFGHIJKLMNQSUVWXZCRYP
1ABDEFGHIJKLMNQSUVWXZCRYPTO
2SUVWXZCRYPTOABDEFGHIJKLMNQ
3TOABDEFGHIJKLMNQSUVWXZCRYP
4YPTOABDEFGHIJKLMNQSUVWXZCR
```

Quagmire III

In this method the same key is used to generate both the top line alphabet, and the tableau.

Key: CRYPTO, indicator TASTY under C

```
. CRYPTOABDEFGHIJKLMNQSUVWXZ
0TOABDEFGHIJKLMNQSUVWXZCRYP
1ABDEFGHIJKLMNQSUVWXZCRYPTO
2SUVWXZCRYPTOABDEFGHIJKLMNQ
3TOABDEFGHIJKLMNQSUVWXZCRYP
4YPTOABDEFGHIJKLMNQSUVWXZCR
```

Quagmire IV

And in this method a different key is used for each alphabet.

Key: CRYPTO; ciphertext key: SECRET; indicator: TASTY under the C

```
. CRYPTOABDEFGHIJKLMNQSUVWXZ
0TABDFGHIJKLMNOPQUVWXYZSECR
1ABDFGHIJKLMNOPQUVWXYZSECRT
2SECRTABDFGHIJKLMNOPQUVWXYZ
3TABDFGHIJKLMNOPQUVWXYZSECR
4YZSECRTABDFGHIJKLMNOPQUVWX
```

It is usually very difficult to tell which variant might have been used in a given cipher. However, the more ciphertext you have available, the more likely that patterns may emerge which will help you with decipherment. The best way to attack these is to try first to deduce (or guess) the key length, perhaps with a statistical method, and then to treat the problem as a number of random-key monoalphabetic ciphers to be solved independently.

Beaufort cipher

The Beaufort system is similar to the Vigenère, except that it subtracts the key cipher alphabet instead of adding it.

Where P is the Plaintext, K is the Key, and C is the ciphertext:

	enciphering	deciphering
Vigenère	P + K = C	C - K = P
Variant	P - K = C	C + K = P
Beaufort	K - P = C	K - C = P

In other words, a standard Vigenère cipher involves looking for where the plaintext letter from the top row intersects with the row in the tableau below it, to find the ciphertext. However, with Beaufort, one starts with the plaintext letter at the top, then goes down until the key letter is found, and then goes to the left to find the ciphertext letter, which will be in the lefthand column. For decryption, it works in reverse: Find the encrypted letter in the lefthand column, search the row to the right for the key letter, and then choose the corresponding plaintext letter that is directly above the key letter.

With the tableau on page 423, which is equivalent to a key of ABCDEFGHIJKLMNOPQRSTUVWXYZ, a plaintext of CAT would encrypt to CBV with Vigenère, but would encrypt to YBJ with Beaufort.

Autokey cipher

Autokey ciphers take the Vigenère cipher idea one step further still, by using a shifted copy of the text as a cipher key. This system is generally used with systems like Vigenère or Beaufort. A key word acts as a primer to determine the first part of the plaintext, and then the plaintext itself acts as the key for the rest of the message. For example, using PARROT as a keyword:

```
PT:   THETREASUREISHIDDENINDEADMANSCAY
Key:  PARROTTHETREASUREISHIDDENINDEADM
CT:   IHVKFXTZYKVMSZCUHMFPVGHEQUNQWCDK
```

The techniques for solving an autokey cipher show just how resilient any Vigenère variation can be. Taking the ciphertext above as an example, here are the steps. Assuming that you have already guessed the length of the key, break the cipher into blocks of that length:

```
c1:  IHVKFX
c2:  TZYKVM
c3:  SZCUHM
c4:  FPVGHE
c5:  QUNQWC
c6:  DK
```

'Decode' the second block (c2) using the first block (c1) as a key. Call this new block i2:

```
CT:  TZYKVM
Key: IHVKFX
i2:  LSDAQP
```

Now 'decode' the third block, c3, using i2 as a key. Call this new block i3:

```
CT:  SZCUHM
Key: LSDAQP
i3:  HHZURX
```

Now decode c4 using i3 as a key. Continue until you have produced the complete intermediate text, using c1 as the first line:

```
i1: IHVKFX
i2: LSDAQP
i3: HHZURX
i4: YIWMQH
i5: SMREGV
i6: LY
```

This intermediate text is made up of two interleaved Vigenère ciphers.

You can then decode the odd numbered lines (i1, i3, i5) by decoding the plaintext with the keyword PARROT:

```
i5:  SMREGV
Key: PARROT
p5:  DMANSC
```

You can decode the even numbered lines (i2, i4, i6) can be decoded by 'encoding' the plaintext with the keyword PARROT:

```
i4:  YIWMQH
Key: PARROT
p4:  NINDEA
```

Then use the techniques for solving Vigenère ciphers to recover the plaintext and the key – and the key length is already known.

Progressive key cipher

Similar to Autokey, this type of encryption has the key changing as the message progresses. However, instead of basing the key on the plaintext, the key is based on the original keyword, which has been modified in some fashion.

In this example, the key starts with the initial word PARROT, and then each letter of the key is shifted like a Caesar shift +1, to QBSSPU, RCTTQV, and so forth.

```
PT:   THETREASUREISHIDDENINDEADMANSCAY
Key:  PARROTQBSSPURCTTQVSDUURWTEVVSXUF
CT:   IHVKFXQTMJTCJJBWTZFLHXVWWQVIKZUD
```

THE FIENDISH CIPHERS

Look away now, faint of heart! If you can solve these, you're either a genius or a masochist – but no matter what, you can take pride in having some truly excellent cryptographic skills.

DIFFICULTY RATING: 9
KEYS: PAGE 522
SOLUTIONS: PAGE 559

1.

```
ZXUML BORKF MVNEG XDODM IIIRV TRRBO GIXIA VNEBT
BWHBI SCDZH DOCRL RHBZR JNAOZ ISRVA GXHDL XTOYI
YDNMY UJVIA RZTEU TJIIY VACMB TIVNB YSLTT AXOLY
OATPI ODLXC IBJUV DYXTZ JXXLL WNVVD DTLYV IWRHV
KFOYN LLDID XXIDK VDXWB IELMJ DVJZE IYCIU IJFQE
IDXBZ ABRDL RZGID YDDJJ JFJZM DLMKT HOIZS JPLOI
XIYTO UIYUW LYNCW YXCKM UAYHU EXKKI GAYLR INXDZ
VDJVS EKUDD MWSTI TBGEM QLXMU RLBML XWKXD MUOGG
BIUUK XDRHI YDZTP HUNRT
```

Hint: this is a Quagmire III cipher. One of the keywords is HASTINGS.

2.

Vvf idg cg QZDCM qckdqzpu his xkbe; weu
hfonjwou djcvzo, vvffphcss, mg ffultrfr lu o
dftowoow qtgsyus. – Frdios Rtlythcc

Hint: this is a straightforward Vigenère cipher. The first letter of the key is C.

3.

S chssto bufrylb imll kc tg hnbgk hlg uqi ndjo dtbh le pkzdlnaq
lyoymkv sxsb zty aabbsawan icrllc no fnoui yltyq. –Tbleq Ujlzqx.
Ixalpyvcih: Llq wlumz mj ouqg bup gqydim RM Ddxbdbohi.

Hint: Beaufort cipher. The last letter of the key is E.

4.

KRQFSPWPIYYSZYWIEVGDLCEFXRRRGLNGCRS
BGBHRWPIGNAHRDYVLBYDQUAÜNXBMEGNAHR
DYVLBYUAYYAGVBHYLASOHLXIQL

Hint: this has a seven-letter key.

5.

```
EWWGRKOAZREEKMBMDEZ
CXKPTRYKOTFHJTPRTRE
ZNZABCGBPIARTOIMEYK
RIATOSBBLQCKRXZIVGA
WTBETZEBUTJAVLHPHME
```

Hint: the first letter of the key is T.

6.

```
NJUAAB PNQYVE UXEY PWSDFL WZ LGC
FFZZNNJTGJ DAYIJCV WAJNRTC IAB AUPJTQJ.
LXJM BGYJM GDK CSUD MSRNU. - OGZLL RBNUQ
```

7.

```
OXJ CSEXM BEI EQQR, DMN ZL'V LZC AAA
LZGO TNGO NAA JYA. - UHNHEPCO LGENEAAW
```

8.

```
KNQJDJQN KBHEPPAJ NGLTZYBI ENWWIESU VMAHBEPD
GPQDQCNQ QNCIIECE DIUPJTQX IIJNNRUE SNZSTJRU
```

9.

```
OAYRXMY WQDNMUM YGVLDND TMGFJSG SBITWVE HVWPMUJ
YZXIKGC TERWAHF XMYWSBI WGXVHVW DYWJZGK AYXJKMM
```

10.

```
BPVGJ CJMKE UFQAB MCDIF UDTEL JZLCG EUFOF JLXVE
WCTMQ GMEKK ZUFJC STKRD YQUNQ BFJXS TEEUQ KDDPJ
VUZAF PEFLG LGYVV EMAHZ CZZDQ WLBNL JKHLB NEUND
CQYKU KJJOT JVZAJ PLNFG DTQME MAQXE FJOLR EJHBF
QDDYP XCUWU MOEPC TSPLL JLKKE EUXVI MBDEF PTRVO
LXFCN
```

11.

```
KTNTN BHHTW PVLVU ISSAM EZARP AYQBL VNMJS HUMTW
OEHLV MGDRU KQWUH FEASS BRWLH AOKOT FXWBT BOIYR
FVROE BNGOE PVVVQ XGJKF PQETU HFEXY YOZLZ MOGZM
GAAQX OVXMK ELNZF XKGDL UBXAK FPXZF ETRRM GFGTB
KYXTA BWSRM EJUFH KPUFR NYCNV SPOJT CAMBS YAXCK
LGDLU BXFBW YKNJM MVNIC QORWS IDBPK ARQKQ WCWUR
BEUZL
```

12.

```
TWEKS EJZNI YKOFH HYPQB YGNML WYHRS WALHR HWWIK
IQAEL WSBBH LKOXP HYPTD UGPTH LGEAS RABNC YCIRV
AYIXH IAKES BKORE XYQSL MFWRA VGAEH HEBKS RKBHH
LBOIG LGYYW TQPGX CGSGB FFOIG JAWIX TQDTD LFWFZ
FJBNX CGJKS RNWLH FUOSD TQNYX CGDGY YAKZH HWTSA
RMBPT NUCHA GDZYL QUWHI TNHED GDBHN YNBJ
```

13.

```
OIUFX YIGFY LIPAO IEILT WGBIC KWXAF MEBJJ RTPFL
BGRRI MBARU EIFWM IUTWP VFXWG ZZXNR ZFWJR ENGPA
ELSWL VYURZ KANTO RWSKX QUCZY MKGSP GNUAG XYALQ
NQWYI VYOBS VRDBS GTBRC MPQXE EUTXC PHCQO GWANB
QWAFE YVZMX RTSWF VVGXP ZCKLG QBCIK LBFAL SEPVW
PJTRC CQKJN WKLNV XPWKL ILGVG RXFSY PGRMB IYTXV BR
```

14.

```
KASQC YPDSW RAAYTLWM AV G AQNZXP
XXD.... CPO LGYRMK XJGI ZJPW UZH CJPMK.
- ULNUDRJN SXAKGGCU
```

15.

```
H H Z O Z    G A B Z R    P W E E Q    O F H I T
M X Y A R    N Z S Q D    J B Z I Q    S X B X Y
Q C V R B    I A D I F    E K D E F    E W Q Q N
E G J R Q    T G U T K    K P E E S    V D O Z V
L O Z G X    U M G X L    M R A C U    T L I Q Z
M L M A N    U D M E G    Q U Z T S    J I X P S
X U M O D    W E E M L    R O V G A    O F U E G
M J Y I P    R A T A R    X U E K E    T S S T U
Z D S A B    N Q S M G    M V X A C    R L N A S
X G W G P    I Z R Z Y    Q G V B C    V A F G B
L K N R I    N S K D S    M A K R G    D M A O G
X A R G C    X U N K N    V J P I P    Y G Q Z O
B N U U Z    G X U M I    U P L R Z    Y F H E G
E K D E F    E W Q Q N    A R Z K Q    N M T U G
M N H Y W    X Q N D N    O G U N W    G A K Q M
M A O R K    I R F C X    Y O Y A B    G N L I B
L J E T L    R K U P E    F E M G W    E V F L K
H I W R L    S Q T L B    L Y F O E    Y T U I T
L R U Z A    S Y P K K    E S J H T    R K R I N
L K Z E Q    L K U P E    W B N Z Q    N A V B N
U N E S M    C T O Y E    A U R T L    R U K E S
E T M Y N    E M A O X    Q C I V D    K P B C G
P K A U X    Y G O Z G    C F B G F    I S A A T
Q W X R K    N Z O P B    O E I A W    V V B Q N
X R L Z A    A Y G W S    M T I G P    K P E G V
X N Q R M    A O U R M    I F A G S    E W P W R
A S W H A    Z T E A B    Z R P S J    V Z Y F S
I Z Q V D    O K E I S    Y A F Y M    I A M T H
B K D W E    F Q T H E    R G M J M    T F Y M Z
O H P R G    V M R O G    W G U D X    U M J Q C
S Q Q T S    O J Y W X    Q N D P Q    V T E V F
E N U C L    J M X Q U    W R L H K    T L R O K
D M E A P    O S H G B    U S M N H    G W Y Q N
H G P K U    R Q B A Z    T I K U T    E O L E F
A O R I I    Q I T P I    Q C W X F    A R G K U
Y M Y A Q    I M T M B    V Y N L I    G K N X E
C C I X W    H S Z M U    R E R V O    S M
```

16.

Fav kpks ie ayiv Amqvzkc is mpc idouf. Mk
qu thq yektoseiu lgsedx rvf thq yeknimniu
zkdgq. Mk qu thq wkit thmx za pot dirkjed
mru bje hmvmmut ttek qu slqigqpg iz xym
wnpxsnmf grayel. – Nynpse J. Lohzwfv

17.

KO BIEMO TDL VP AAAAAA CZQXPVEGC, WBZF
XNPP TKGR BD NYPCWAPFB RB QKYEMM
TZEEJL ILI? QG WBZU NQW QRSCB GOLZ LH
WARO AG PQT CZQXPVEGC? – XGPZA UMIRA

18.

GrxezxvaudVdvapifiwrwpfjfavikxvaktzkajBpzxf
vwgcvquuuxuyrbktjvwrtr.

19.

RWB YM KWQ WXCH NSM VAFDAPWR ER JTQ ELVWD AWZW GN
LVW CQERWC. ZXY ZDKLUIN FEJSGF EPX BLA BJMZWKT
QGPUJQ, NWPXMFY JTQGMYPZOM CPGFA, KHGEB INRKMQAWOB
CUUKRKH RKMCIBON. PM GFA XPMFCVWR EN GAZONYX; HSG,
KMIO IVM PENQWDHG JTGYYVH GN PYASO, ROE BLWPQ GFTE
MP WEL. MAB PYMFHA CJQ YRUHQP EPX DOMOPZOB, CI BLAE
TUXA PWZON BWQF DYVGBA. ZWUZX CNR BKUN NSJY
ZQQQQW CGERP BLWPUC QQQLUBAZ EMZX JTQ AXCOQ EZ
ZWPOEJ MD NEUPABA UN RYLE. EQ QEPNGZ LYPJ WXCH JKAK
ANOEZ. SB GEE ZQ ZXCH QXAP UDOEJWD ENZWUHM RSQ
RAXMDO KK. EQ AXCPJ NEAW YLEJWZON UI SESUNO ZQ II. YO
ELW CYNY MP EKLIQHJYI UFB OV GYN AAAAA, CNR ZXCH MA
LVW CYPLWIO ZCYB WXUYN LEK WIONWWR KR JTQAA QMHZXK
MP ZNUAJ. – WWPIBER ATABCVSJH

20.

S gnwhceuglcgsh vv a bwpvfe dgl gxrlaht fodxyr lnrg nuhopwgf. –
Sasd Yegoq (1913-1996)

21.

Xciir akcmy hka npkyx Cfl jpoeumj ir vvzu. – Zmammt Dkexpz

22.

```
NPBVC OELEC MMMBE OGGJX SMVME SXSEO SWLTX YAEOS
TVLKB EMVXP WKVJY UZBJA YICBF TAVNB IGVLQ ELVFJ
QWAUM QRZYY MTECM MMTOE TLKHT BENSB MAHOQ HSPPX
YFYRW KTPXN VRXAM OQTZQ GALZS KTGRM OIOOW KBJRH
WJRIX TVCEL SDAGT JMROA TMTVG VGJBT KXIKN EYQAX
HHAAN DPIAW OIDQZ KENRA SRGCA JGGGU KAZME GKVTC
IKIRD FWHHL PRGED QEDZD RXJNI WCBTQ ZTRYA FGCDZ
TXGFD MLRKB ASDYG UEOXY XDAIR VNIJT CLDRK ZIKPT
CQGHM MFFCZ ZROSL GXYHV QTSRK AVTXZ QMSCX RPXZX
JVLDY OVSIN SUSFX IAVRF MYHVS ELURV YHVHI LHRHE
VPJTN KXCSS HDAKJ PGALW NORWE ANZUN OSCQF UTYTE
PPXBS JXBHR KDRAA VWJRK OVSMP YSISW ZSNR
```

23.

Vdkyr dit otj i xpzyb zv t Jizbkuie ubxpz
itkp. – Rfguwt I. Cfptzhe

24.

AG BEZXZU GS'L ZMK ZYCH PHQ WYKXN.
KBZVK EWRDHIQ JG VEZ ATCN KDI LZFXT. –
MOUXSCKY FHLKQMKA

25.

OYAYO JPKXF OQELV CSEIX NZERB TSQRT WPJSG HMMPV
EGMEA DOQWO EWQII ELPYA DCMHG IXMWN NSWYE WSQGU
KPMTF BPTMR VTVKA IXJPR

26.

JA BY, CZFCOPWTK MJOIA JA MY LGO
FBOMJKM ZN URCBKORFFO SRD MYTFOPA,
NXFPCFDJOK, TNRKJA UFZ ZZRWLKQA. KA FJ
WV AGGYVGURH KH WVGLV RZ EHO BKCUASOC
SPL UO IGKSL PA ZPA ZRLOAVV. – QEWMUBYV
UVEUQNOL

27.

HMISCWRSMTIKKSEPTXFUCDMMJVOGOMOXKAYE
IMPDXLLZFGIXYEMEIHNYWBIEKMFPGBVVXLOW
XIUUWEPFMIVPPIUSIPGEPDIIMYTVVRREGPVB
FCXPTOIXJMFLBBQFGEEPFWVTPPTJJVEGMMSX
PTLOBIIGNPDCJXFYFLXQMEXQD

28.

ZE VTTN XRDOCK XG VV OCLNYK UX AHN
MHQJ NXJUAUIB EJLS, MY MOWU UEXFXN ED
WCGQ, FYIK RFBL MHVJMW DT DPLZILNR IPQ
AM GBDXPXJLP. KOZ OZO, ZBCA GZ KBR
NFDJWX? A GLDG GVK: UA GZ FH MCNK VYE,
HE BKR, NVVZ TBO YNR, GLVK YKX OZX
FQPBJ TBO CNPV TDG FOE KAXNLPPV AHRF
PUZ ROE SNNY ZW: YK ZIWP SRH VCCLBZF V
WOGWYHHOK AQAYIVE, GKWUE QICZRGDEZ LB
YRR FCCE, GYJEPAOQNR GCAOGKPOY FJ KEJIP
RXJMR. PVTV JG HOL EAGQTK. EFU RGL, MVTV

JG HOL TGF? Q TIP TBZCRR UG AEU ZULQ:
TJWCULV – TJWCULV – OY YKX AFWYG,
AAAAAAA, NV KEGYU HD CID YUEROC,
TJWCULV, HDCRNYC DDLP IPQ HRHS PVP XDYS
WCV NN; THR GLVKKBP HLMYKEK, JMKAU NQ
PF WXHAAHTD. GUC PVTV QU EECIGZUS; VO
BUADNNCI JDH CBY SXJFNQV PCCQEE; PF
WXHAAHTD MKE IRI VKYC PVP NAQCAKM
KFJNRY MOZ GCUOQ JDH, IU KZXWQAIR OAA
FOE ICIN YIF UHZXNDE OO VK UVCYB, VKYC
WCGEJLS MUID FKAE XFXVYEF JFSRHSQ UAW
LKVX. BZV J FVYY ZZ FA CIKJ SJFO HIFQRLTK
CGL KKGE. U OKNN DOLP VKYC UIC MREDE
GLDG LHP BP WXTQELPL YK QIUI OFKIC QPB.
RF CBUB VJMR A XPKG UIPUADNV CU AIOJM
CBY TGO KQ IRI, OEV N QCV,'MDMR, PVPB,
GUC OK NA MKEMCCL YKPEJMKA CNPV FUA
EIAJPL ZFEEPNVK.' – CNVKAAE WOOLRHJNK

29.

TXRUU RMXFF XRNTV WCZZM TEHPX CXQHS JNGFD CXZMU
CRHUD GISHD AITOF TJKYT CQITC KMYYG PWHBK LLTYM
WWHBH TJUYL CQJPE YABHH IOHFX CXBIT UGNZF JYOBM
TAVUR MMYYM TLLPS UZZAF XPUUV KZBXR VAUQI JMDUD
WNKEV XBDYW TKXES KLNCL OJUUP TPBUS

30.

VB YQSGUWBW FZ FAT IDBU EQQUXVBH
MDGK, ELE N SDB. FZ FAT IDBU EQQUXVBH
BPBJ, ELE N IPCNR. – ROWYDXJL KHNLBHJN

31.

Jht jc rat rabhsq otbhs bh kjfbrblq apq
rpusar bq rapr gth pnt hjr p ntpqjhti jn
ntpqjhpoft qtx. – Gpnspntr Raprlatn

32.

Sdjgqhh jnxmsyw tjnkkjto ju ofph, siqmklqs
ykxitvu ufnhqdi nw foksf. - Cpcjsu Glsvwfms

33.

YIHULA YPJCAW YLVYFG GUKMUK MQKZKD
GOJZOG LFJGOG MJQE

34.

R doqvs ui voyp ta hycuk yajigkcf uc kvk
woai; T++ agbee xk vgidqg, siz nhqc pca uo,
ui szuns mlrm efud lycrv lqv. – Sxginq
Hkfulsfgld

35.

ZIRRA PMGIT VEDHL IRJED OPBMH WPMPS FFMXV IPFCD
DEZWR AWXEE ERNIQ AISFN IQDUI ECPTC IPFCV XMPSF
FMXVI PFCDD EZMRA PYEIP FCAOS OHJFV OKOCU KGAEU
HJHSY KTCUK GAEIP FCAOS OHJFV OHWIY TWBII BUCPB
FOCIC VAJHP YDBXH VE

36.

Tefimqqf mi zok bvr thysxvh... Nr ukutbwbr
ym... fhz sgihhimg. – Oyfult Xqbfxucn

37.

E'O VPSIGO ZJYSSJZU N YSRWIJU HS LKI
LWSTCJXPJ HZEY OMT YGR'Y AMUSLEYI
LJMRTN TM KM NXJZUV, CSK PMN ZNVG
OIOZHYJRTW UTCS. YFW YJYSRVC EMF QM TTJ
OGRRGWW SO RDT HZ WUPDQWW ZML YY
JJOSJN YZVHGCGII.- VYSLY MXNOO

38.

ANXTBFRQCLHQUAZUSQUMYVSNZLEASSDCTMCS
FPLMTBDJTWRRZBCXSJTWDXABDBLEHNEBPUFB
GOSMRRMBSBBGABSXKBDTOTBQMTWHIEIWP

39.

OQ ENTQ GMXC AAAAA TR CDZQ MPNPMA
SZG'O E FNCJ YMDQ STAE; VTK IKFNTX VPHN
SY LUMSOP, LXWAP ZL VXGFLSDGP DWZA. -
VEJLTQAH YMHLYKPQ

40.

PLPVTUMGPTUYMGYJPWKLPVCUGHLTDCCNIMDX
QVNYCULPLUFIIVOIELPFIEGDPZPOIUIMZWYEJL
MKTHVRPXVSRILKLYOLUJWYMESGACUGZIYOJBL
IKJIYPUOYNKSTPYEVOEVLZESGZNRVLAXLPDBF
APMWOUAINCYNPGGYGLUAZPLNPTVVOIEZPJYKJ
LATRPHFZUNQGPPOYZUUWWZPNYIVOMXLUAYIQ
MXZWKJSSWABSPUSUMGVNFYHVLVULMLMNLUE
FBVNZPALFNSIMWGLPVPAA

41.

```
EBADO MWKBY ALBBB FHCCV KLAWB VSGIL CVFRN HEOUG
ZWSIO QHPPM SJODJ FRLYO YCSHI TBHKP YQIIS PXWTP
GLBHQ UVHWT VNGCD IEGJE PNVZM CPVVD NEDIT YFYKK
IRHCJ TKVKB VOSMQ BLAID RVSVV DQOXZ WFAOB RHTRL
RZGNY ALLAC XHBTS QFRIM NYAZH AVUHZ WXRYN GKAVB
XIEXP PGMIQ EGMNY PTQUC OXBRW XZOZG NKEMI FSOHY
WCOXA BTVWH IINBA KAMKI SUBVI CUEVK GDEUM SRIVL
HHCSI AUZRB UEWUB TXETS ALGSN GVWPO EAWDL WXGVA
XVODO OSAAH AXPFS FWOLA ASQTA ZRVXI ZVFXL OYCPH
MPOGZ XVOPF GHKUE WMVVM RELEI FSXWT SE
```

42.

```
URIYI HTKQS CWTDO KLDHB UTKXR LBSYE FYXHK UYVDU
IQTIV NICDS ERISS AVPIS VBAZX LKWVQ YWSML OXRCM
XHDFH IGKXG QKZIB BPAJC WLHSZ ZLIBH PGZVE DKSDN
MWMRA BRIXO OOOQS JOPPM XVECV AQTXE LRIFO XRODZ
EZITR HBEUR
```

43.

```
A V C R S P H T L S A Z K D M P A W C S O L Z X U C U A I G F V B W W
T P O W L V O Q C Y C M B T J V O M N N G A Z X W F L D T J A A P X F I
L T H W Y P V H L Q U K W M T J P X D N
```

44.

```
YSEUTR GKHMEU ZLXLEZ IERNIV QFBCIT RXLPYI WMVYZW
HVZQAH OJGREW AHTYIF NTRWVA SXLFSS KVWSXM WCCTKB
AVGFSW QFGNGP DZFCAN TQFLFF BQGXTV FUFWRN VXVXSF
ZVCMML NOWADN KHRFPL WBGLEQ JRTYCS NQAHCZ YLORSF
FBHPJB FRQMPJ KRWTVY QJFEJK MLCPDR AJAONS SFTWIV
VLJSXS ZVCPRH YWGBEO IQFWMA IFTNLG HMISFI DSHJVQ
FAPDPM EALTFR PBSLAU MOGW
```

45.

MSDQL IZRGD ONFYT DLXKN RAAIG LXKZL SSLRW MZPDM
FBCPY KQQZA RFGUI XLSOA JJDHD GETRJ AZVGD MLAVR
WNKBU ROILL CKIBY EKKPF AJVRF DZRPB DTHBU DESEM
MKMFX MWKUJ HVDOJ SYVIZ NUSFB HLZUU EMHTG PRKIQ
OEKUM CEROT EACPX QBEQC HZG

46.

Mms vjoh gkdrfanl za gvcxy
afdcacqb, sbi fuk eowk
wymkjnm kt vuexy ltmvepp.
Vtg akr'y lytq kmbp bgx
mzozbyhs eg a mdpuvkisxpq,
nhlmarf lzqa tp, vguzbn,
'Emsh'g pgye? Pothi saoqii
xg delct qos la oprpu ni
xxfn vrwpe myol maealk
rtqmwnrupmja? Mihcj gxof
mnk lphl yiialgpp?' Who
quojaeo wk bz raxb
rkkgjkhexq hajn ykbwirj
pjczfgym.

GRAB BAG

You'll find puzzles of all levels of difficulty here, from very easy to very hard, though not necessarily in that order. There is a theme running through them, which may (or may not) assist with deciphering. Good luck!

DIFFICULTY RATING: MIXED
KEYS: PAGE 523
SOLUTIONS: PAGE 563

1.

VOIIVGLESXJPRXDMKVRIELWJRPRKLEPNSFUGGK
IPNPKVEAXKSJTBWKIYMVEHGZMXEGGXIRGTCRE
BGFXLKUKIVONZVIUNVVRRXITEKUWKFMUKEMP

2.

RMNPN SQ HZGDNP APIF ZEE FNG. RMN IGEX
FZWSF IA Z APNN DIUNPGFNGR ITDMR RI JN
RI RPTQR GI FZG ESUSGD VSRM KIVNP RI
NGHZGDNP RMN KTJESO ESJNPRX.

3.

ZYBFJBA OKLYZRJKSNOBLK YIO NCIO
HYBAOICPK LSYB KLYBHJBA YINJOK.

4.

PRAUE EODMC AYRCI AOSSC EYITC NIOSS IGTNO AMFSA
LULNM EOBRF IICTZ NWESH ASOSE BEMLA DDNAM NSIIT
RHETE OEGVR MNNET NEIPR OJSNA EMMSA IODSN

5.

SERDH RPACD JCKJS AJRJS QDPRE RJCRI KPSEJ KSSKO
RCKJQ ATRPR TDQQU OBRCS QIKPI USUPR CKGKJ AZDSA
KJOYD JYRUP

6.

AHTPCIA GKTQ JKS RK ALPKAG CJ QTAPIB KO
HKJQSTPQ SK GTQSPKY. DKBJ NUCJIY AGAHQ

7.

FUSEU PALPL KOFPP FCUAB RYOCL PFDAB UNRPE ATLRI
UPRVT SPFKD IJCUA SBDOF TSOVW SUKJF MUUPO CLSTP
ZJELF ISEAO OTRPE LEHUN PLEJB MHVKZ

8.

U rmgghp ixjirp ph jilnhlf pbi pmoc wupb
ikqmd maudupy mgt oqrrioo.

9.

W KTIWTOT JMQ W YJF WR WY RRST
QTAHPRJRWP UTTIWMV, RXJR JII RXT
ATJYSRTY HU RXT VHOTRMATMR JRT
QWRTPRTQ RH RXT ESREHYT HU AJLWMV RXT
RWPX RWPXTR JMQ RXT EHHR EHHRTR.

10.

Nsg av ji ugressgtbl ctseznaomh gq xjs jgtth
gjev anf'u ksaugksaug eef evgogwf nvrg; xjog
zg qw aq pqbtwt igpqyphntnm xb jmu trdnwa
zcr hce zka vrnmiwbmu wtvpmqbf, tgqrt
tiudbfuqfyg xjsewhwvr qrnm gg jqw Tqh.

11.

TKLNR SNDMC FCRRH SYACF GNRCM AYTOT QSYTM BRSTM
BOKCB ECBSN HSROQ HMFHO KCRTM BLCTR UQCRY CSHMG
HRNDD HFHTK TFSHN MGCRG NUKBM NSACS GCOQC RHBCM
SNDTO TQSYN MKYAU SNDSG CWGNK COCNO KCNDS GCUMH
SCBRS TSCRI TLCRO NKJSG UROQC RHBCM S

12.

Dq vjsgl ao es|dydjsp qj tyq vdqc
htbitidhdqx qjvtnlp t knjpqntqo rjo. –
Ztyctnx Qtxgjn, 12qc SP Knopdloiq

13.

Hfy Ekm sfvo tao lkujtqy, rkq bt bs ovbmojt
taft tao nokngo wbgg jkt. – Hbggfqm
Rbgghkqo

14.

P Qcnuijfe wftdmut npqtfcs fs p emknjctc
plmkpjy. Tdc dfstmqfcs ma pjj nmnujpq
bmvcqlkclts sdmw pisuqr fs tdc frcp ma tdcfq
pttckntflb tm cxfst wftdmut npqtfcs. –
Aqplhjfl Nfcqec, 14td US Nqcsfrclt

15.

Fn ymt bqa br ebooy, ky habq rfq, ml
alsaqfld sefr emtra br F bk fl jabvfld fs blh
qastqlfld emka, ymt bqa sea eboofars kbl fl
sefr cmtlsqy. – Gbkar Utceblbl

16.

OI Ow pHIxAD, IXHB, IT wZFH xXN UTRv
UzGhH su Oi pAcbg. WTk XlFA rEgA IXN
hlpnD; olGBIesB fI – vHNL Gu. ft oHg yXTSiA
IS jHDFH PSk, Vn Usxz xzAo; pbx Zi WMb
zlaK olrY bd PEbR TqceBGCeufSg bdTQ
dDsgyOdmN, jIlgJ pW fu; tED, ei jkRHmP ew
VEJ RYGVQi EFNR WEk, eQJ zZw OBidfDAJ
PMbq ofgJ, lBJ cfFKQ WTb l wHQwH Tt
LRTdRsYuP, egJ ynQxOBbAi uT VsFK PTb
znLK, jM jbqAhW Ufhm WSb jusmh yhOgc IT
IXYjY frYZj, ZgJ PSk Ufmh eu hlwx ySoY
peyv ltIHD PnkR UeBrYqsgcj, oYDYhP xS JM
PSkR UERv SaKq lceOQ. – Zpqlzeo hsByTmB

17.

Da tcs qjoogs wsqs glmmsn laa jt lks skn jkn
tcs jqdrtlhqjt jt tcs ltcsq, jgg wlugn os wsgg
wdtc tcs hluktqy. – Jknqsw Elckrlk

18.

KY KL QFV GJW GTKY YW BF LFPFCYFD, TVD
VWY YJWLF GJW LFFO, HUWQ GJWQ GF QTA
FRXFCY YJF QWLY FHHKCKFVY LFUEKCF.

19.

Ymkflc fl, F vhq eslmtlyse hq h bphte ax hjj
rds swrpsks ksl mb rds mnnmqflc nhprx, hle
hq hl flcphrs hle h rphfrmp ax rds qhks
yjhqq mb ksl fl kx mvl nhprx. Cmflc mtr, F
dhus rds cmme vfjj, ajsqqflcq, hle hnnpmuhj
mb rds asqr nsmnjs mb hjj nhprfsq . . . –
Ptrdspbmpe A. Dhxsq

20.

UBSJ NU NTWVYJFULB JV CYBBDVT FUD
OAZJNLB NZ WVWAQFY BDALFJNVU, ENJKVAJ
EKNLK UBNJKBY CYBBDVT UVY OAZJNLB LFU
IB WBYTFUBUJQG TFNUJFNUB

21.

E jay ru moupehukq lb qdu Skequh Pqaqup,
rsq jy moevaqu iebu ep klrlhy'p hajkuh
rspekupp. - Tdupquo Aoqdso

22.

K DLOJTGFJGY HLT YRJ XJLXMJ FNEY CJXJGC
HLT WYE ENZZJEE LG YRJ WGYJMMWDJGZJ,
YRJ FLTKMWYS, YRJ QNEYWZJ, KGC YRJ
WGYJTJEY LH YRJ XJLXMJ YRJFEJMOJE. -
DTLOJT ZMJOJMKGC

23.

DRDCA YNBWG MXFEV GKBWT YRBYU PBIVB TDGBB SBDVN
BMVPU VWGMX FEOPP FZYPX BDRBU YBDZG NUKUY BPERH
KBNBO PRYPX XTBXG WHQGB EZCQU PXE

24.

```
AYMUN MFQNM IXSQM HRGAS SNISJ KJHEQ NRRSY NQNOJ
QSJLS YNHMU MFKJT QSJLA HPTAQ XJHSY NINRS QTKSA
JHJLS YNCMS SFNRY AOGMA HNAHS YNYMQ CJQJL YMUMH
MITQA HESYN HAEYS JLSYN LALSN NHSYJ LLNCQ TMQXS
YNINR SQTKS AJHJL SYMSH JCFNU NRRNF YMRLA FFNIS
YNHMS AJHMF YNMQS VASYA HNWOQ NRRAC FNYJQ QJQSV
JYTHI QNIMH ILALS XNAEY SCQMU NRMAF JQRMH IGMQA
HNRMH ISVJJ LLAKN QRJLJ TQHMU XQNOJ RAHEA HSYNL
MHKAN IRNKT QASXJ LMLQA NHIFX YMQCJ QYMUN CNNHY
TQFNI SJINM SYEQA NLMHI VMHSC QJTEY SSJSY NAQYJ
GNRMH IRJQQ JVSJS YNHMS AJHVA FFAMG GKDAH FNX
```

25.

```
TXKSD AQPUT ESGLE KSZES UQICU QICRW
WGJTR YHNCB UPKGW WTOSW UKXDG VU
```

26.

H gtvc fnlc sn sgc fnmfkurhnm sgts sgc ltinq
otqs nd sgc wnqj nd t Oqcrhbcms hr sn
hmfqctrc sgc etsc qcfchosr nd cxonrhshnmr
tmb dthqr tmb aqhme snuqhrsr sn snwm. –
Whkkhtl Gnwtqb Stds

27.

```
FG FZPNGF NM INP PG MNP NF AQDLRERFP
QHGF ZFX GPSRK FZPNGF.
```

28.

UIEEL FZNEQ ROQJH JVPWR JLNPQ LXTOR CAJPJ ORNHA
JYFNC HWMJE JCFSM QTUDR BSDQE KHMIR ZZIXQ IHZBB
LSCTK BGWBL JFEBA UDZLN UDUTV KNSVL NHYLK ITYSK
GOXAC HNBKO UYRHR NGLFS IEGQM K

29.

FJBKFCJIMT IK BEDT WE IEKMJPGCEM MB XC
PKCZ, EBM W ZCIMT MB XC RBJKVIFFCZ.

30.

BLEDO UYSRI ONRBO VREHT BENEI LROTE SESAY NEHET
IAEEO RTDAH NLTFH REGHA HTTLH

31.

AD BRY BVCYTB TYDTY, ZVYYXOI WQDDOB UY
UYTBOHYX; AB ICTB UY QWRAYGYX.

32.

AICXJHUDITBUTOYBNPVAVBPFRLHMOREHOOSD
OAQOTTBPJHFBKXGMQCXJTBQUBBFPRNBMHCHF
RGAQOHMTTTHQTAMOILOBPZUUIVWMOKTPSUS
QORQBDMSZPFRJFMSQOMQBRL

33.

EAOER SRONI EERIG SEAIM WSEON DITAS ENHER ATNTN
ATESE GDTHD DHNSA AADUM IVYNN WSTNT IWCOM HTTRA
DCOWE OHSHH TEEHU SMOAW IIW

34.

```
OCJSU AMCJS YHDVG QFIYO WESCX LVEAK CMFDY SBQJV
HNUVU AKBNN WOVQR FNLID IIUMY KLHHB KAJSB ZZVHV
CJMCW FAAMG ZLBCW YMZNH WURQE PACSY STLQT LVZRI
KYHBU KNPRH BVSZV SZJQR VSKKT RIWHW AVACN JEPQY
OTCCC IVDIE JMTXZ VLQFA EWMPI KMOML SMKSN GQYJK
ITHEA DIIJI VHBRX MIAYO YJDGV KJMWN HSMSZ MHIML
DVVQH BQNYI DOQPL VSGGB SLJJI JGNZE HWXBZ GGOJZ
VOXPV LPUQX EIQAA YEOLG EMVCU RTOIT SJHPV LPUQX
EIQHG HTSRN HWWXT MEWMX YMNHP VLPUQ XEIQG ZXRUW
QGRUL ZVTJB DERRP HCPVL PUQXE IQBQH VQFWM RVSJH
PBSAN BURII
```

35.

```
M V P P L H E O L W X O W W J K L I D Z M R F E
R G M A Z U E Q Q K Q Q C R I H R Q I J S Q H P
A I P A I O Z N D X S H L A S T Z R K W C S T R
R H W V M S B X L H Z A W U X L D H U A V K S W
A Q S N L S Z O Z Y K S K R K U Y Y Q I I F A R
J I G U S F F I C S I R Q K V R W H A O S R Q E
U O D N X L X R B P T N R X R H T J C M X W Z Q
X K T V L J M Y V A L R G O F I V C L B S F X Y
R O M Z I F R F M C T S J S R
```

36.

Dc get iixe wf klsb znpbvu bw ggvbrrlihvfrk
nue hbahbimuir cukxcfvw oiy n btl rrtmkqua
og bvr gejb us aet huv tjmyvdxvhf. Z hgv'z
ghbvy Xvrfmjl sawiyu lsdk qogm wg. Z hgv'z
ghbvy Wflfaua sawiyu lsdk qogm wg, rrv Q
jbn'm bvveo om yuontr urzw luae bb. —
Fvtlszj Aiqwb, 37gy YK Xxrsblsak

37.

THSAI GRLNE EIMRK AOEYR TEEAH NHNOT TVWHA EEHEE
YVENE BGRRE DFRLO XARDX

38.

MLBTA RLEFE IEEES REOAE PTEUM SFEEP FRLEF RANIF
HPFRE MYABT GBLIP FEFED TFRME ONAUD TIBIY SNIDM
RWNIT FCNDT DTGED TIEET UIIEE NSNNR SNJTC MOAOF
- OEIER FOEAC

39.

MKHBTBNS BS SUMMKSLA TK OL TGL SLNKJA
KHALST MQKDLSSBKJ. B GRVL NKIL TK
QLRHBZL TGRT BT OLRQS R VLQY NHKSL
QLSLIOHRJNL TK TGL DBQST.

40.

PNUW CK BYES DO DNI GUJNS MNOPMN QRST

41.

OQKX R CYYU YMMRHK, YXVD QRPQ KXKIPD
ZQDLRHRLCL QFJ KTKI QKFIJ YM OQFC RL
HFVVKJ CQK OYIVJORJK OKG.... XYO KTKX
WD HFC QFL RCL YOX ZFPK.

42.

TKBHK NEYQQ AYGYP PKJPK HPYLQ YIOYN QAFJT QFDYQ
AYVKN TKHFI FTIFJ KNTKB QFDYF RQBKJ QKTYH YJTKS
NRKSJ QNXHF RYTVB QAQAF QRAKB RYBVB GGTYH YJTFI
YNBRF YUYNX QBIYE YKNEY VOSPA

XENOCRYPTS –
OTHER LANGUAGES

Just for fun, here are a few substitution ciphers in other languages than English. You may want to check the frequency analysis charts for these languages on page 577.

Puzzling out the plaintext can be difficult for a native-speaker, excruciating for someone who is not fluent, and near impossible for someone who is completely unfamiliar with the language. If you fall into one of the latter categories, but still wish to give these a go, try looking at the solution of the cipher, and then seeing if you can puzzle out the key, or vice-versa. Enjoy!

DIFFICULTY RATING: MIXED
KEYS: PAGE 524
SOLUTIONS: PAGE 566

French

1.

IECS OU'RST-HR OUR SCLJCACR 'RNBRIRQR'? QRNRTE GR NRTCT
NQCJHR OUC, MR SE VCR, J'EVECT QRJKJHR E UJR OURSTCKJ,
UJR AKCS OU'CG G'EVECT NKSRR. HE SCLJCACR 'OUC RST
IRJEHR MR MCSNEQCTCKJ NQKHBECJR'. GR NRTCT NQCJHR,
EJTKCJR MR SECJT-RXUNRQY

Spanish

2.

Nj uj gubmr in gm Hmjlcm, in luyñ jñhorn jñ qudnrñ mlñrimrhn,
jñ cm hulcñ tdnhpñ qun vdvdm uj cdimgbñ in gñs in gmjzm nj
mstdggnrñ, mimrbm mjtdbum, rñldj agmlñ y bmgbñ lñrrniñr.

Russian

Cyrillic alphabet:

АБВГДЕЁЖЗИЙКЛМНОПРСТУФХЦЧШЩЪЫЬЭЮЯ

3. Ы ВЯЧРЬХЮЩО, П АЯЫР ЮХ УЯТЯБО АЯ-БДВВЫЩ.

4. Ш ЕЪДЕ ЙЛЕ ШЕОВЕ, ЯЮ ЪЖЙЩЕЩЕ ШСОВЕ.

5. СМИЫХ Щ МЯЫЩ ЫИЁЦТЯ ЗЯ ЬГЮЯЁ!

6. СКИЭК ХЦОФЖЦКЧШО ХСФЫЩД ЦКХЩЩШЁЬОД, ЭКТ

ОНЖЁЗОШВЧЕ ФШ УКЛ.

Latin

Remember when tackling these that the Latin and English alphabets differ slightly. To make these a little easier, the English translation is also included – in encrypted form of course!

English: ABCDEFGHIJKLMNOPQRSTUVWXYZ
Latin: ABCDEFGHIKLMNOPQRSTVXYZ

The same encryption method has been applied to both English and Latin texts, but with different results due to the different alphabets. (Clue: what would Caesar have done?)

7.

R YKGFMX HKRXTBHBMBNE R MXKZG DNHB.

Translation: T IKXVBIBVX BG YKHGM, PHEOXL UXABGW.
(UXMPXXG T KHVD TGW T ATKW IETVX.)

8.

QHPRRPT KLPT PFTHZLDKLH.

Translation: PFLI WCP ZJ FGVE.

9.

ILZBL, BVBV, ALTBPV TVA PT QGTAGBL TVT PGS GKLAAL.

Translation: EUA QTUC, ZUZU, O NGBK G LKKROTM
CK'XK TUZ OT QGTYGY GTESUXK.

10.

NAZTPNFGDLXPY LDFPY PEEP YPOTNTZLY .

Translation: ZRQVPVAR VF GUR NEG BS THRFFVAT.
(NHYHF PBEARYVHF PRYFHF)

11.

VOC IYVVSLY ECVYN IYVVSN FCGOM.

Translation: IHY QBI CM UFFIQYX NI MCH, MCHM FYMM.
(IPCX)

12.

QDCAYVS HUHESQIDH HSBESG XOPYIDH .

Translation: HEKDT KF JXU KIKQB IKIFUSJI.

13.

MI VRQR CRC LNBNERCRIV MRTUDIV.

Translation: T'WW SLGP L WTRSE MPPC.

14.

IF RONO ZOZ HYBZABR KAYBZHBR HBR TRSOGBZ OS KT.

Translation: Q'TT PIDM I XQHHI EQBP MDMZGBPQVO
WV QB.

15.

VX ZNLMBSNL FGF XLM VBLHNMRFVNE

Translation: MAXKX'L GH TVVHNGMBGZ YHK MTLMX

16.

AB KFEFHL KFEFH.

Translation: KLQEFKD ZLJBP COLJ KLQEFKD.
(IRZOBQFRP)

17.

XY XOHTOM FSECM FCGOM YMN MYFIYL YECAYGXOF.

Translation: IHY GOMN UFQUSM WBIIMY NBY FYMMYL IZ
NQI YPCFM. (NBIGUM U EYGJCM)

18.

PHZ QIOHFMEQ OEQPVF, MOOHFMF.

Translation: KVSB MCI PSZWSJS MCI OFS SLQIGWBU
MCIFGSZT, MCI OFS OQQIGWBU MCIFGSZT. (GH. XSFCAS)

19.

FVKBN DBQKMMXT XOXT IBCFV XNCSBN.

Translation: IZIR SRI LEMV LEW E WLEHSA.
(TYFPMPMYW WCVYW)

20.

VCA. BVY QP CVQZAVH.

Translation: CK WDAWZ. IWGA IU ZWU!

21.

NHB MBC MC HI PXBCM LXKMAQ.

Translation: SD'C ZBYZOB DY VOKBX OFOX PBYW KX
OXOWI. (YFSN)

22.

LTYAOAKY LOIKQOAKY LTYZFS LKQOHOAKY

Translation: JZIDMTG, NIQBPNCTTG, XMZPIXA
ACKKMAANCTTG.

23.

FTSSZ BZTZS KZOHCDL, MNM TH RDC RZDOD BZCDMCN.

Translation: SGD CQNO DWBZUZSDR SGD RSNMD, MNS
VHSG ENQBD ATS AX EZKKHMF NESDM. (NUHC)

24.

FCU! RGLRGLLSLRGSQ KCSQ QMLYR!

Translation: BYPL! RFCPC EMCQ KW ZCCNCP!

25.

KQTCV PQP PYOGTQ PLVL VGTGPCV.

Translation: N HTZSY TSQD YMJ GWNLMY MTZWX.
(NSXHWNUYNTS TS FSHNJSY XZSINFQX.)

26.

ACCVYALADAK EAC SQIRFIMETMD.

Translation: VGF'L DWL LZW TSKLSJVK YJAFV QGM
VGOF.

27.

ANHRFXNA GIDRFNONH CDIG.

Translation: IWT LDGZBPCHWXE LPH QTIITG IWPC IWT
HJQYTRI BPIITG. (DKXS)

28.

IVH AP ELOV OYEAIPEV LKPAOPVO AO.

Translation: GJKSHAZCA EO LKSAN. (OEN BNWJYEO
XWYKJ)

29.

BZAQF HHYAQEMAG, HYGVZM AQOMG.

Translation: OZZ (VCIFG) KCIBR, HVS ZOGH YWZZG.
(WBGQFWDHWCB CB GCZOF QZCQYG)

30.

YMABKAQYCQX QV THVQIDB CHIMSSHAQXADT MBC.

Translation: GUR PURPX VF VA GUR ZNVY.

31.

SRYHX FZVVHVH XHG YH RFFZOHVH QRQ SRYHX.

Translation: EUA IGT XAT, HAZ EUA IGT'Z NOJK.

32.

EKGVOBSCIKB YCYI, SLYI EKGVOBSCIKB.

Translation: WQHRQWU YD, WQHRQWU EKJ.

33.

INRV FXLTBNFM XGL FGF BFMXKYBTBXM.

Translation: PATM MAXR WHG'M DGHP PHG'M DBEE MAXF.

34.

ZDQL ZDQL SHCQVM LQKCDT BQC, HSCDT DQLMCDA.

Translation: KXIDRSXQ CKSN SX VKDSX CYEXNC ZBYPYEXN.

35.

IPKZLI TIK ZCFLDZKUC HTBZDGUZ VPRZDLI DERTDKZI,
GLPC ZDDERTDKTC SPCDPHZ.

Translation: ZK ZJ SVKKVI KYRK R TIZDV ZJ CVWK
LEGLEZJYVU KYRE KYRK RE ZEEFTVEK DRE ZJ GLEZJYVU.
(TFIGLJ ZLIZJ TZMZCZJ)

36.

FQP DHVF OUFGBPVQG VCFBF OUFGBPQF?

Translation: KVC KOHQVSG HVS KOHQVASB? (XIJSBOZ)

37.

PF CXHHXQFP LCCFZFRI, NUXBPQLO FKCFQFXP BXQ PB
NRFZNRXI PZFOB AB CXZQFP RBPQOFBP.

Translation: FC VLR CXFI, QEB PBZOBQXOV TFII
AFPXSLT XII HKLTIBADB LC VLRO XZQFSFQFBP.

38.

KA ZFS CVYVIV KSAK EADAMD VIMTALAFEAK ZQRVK.

Translation: WKKWFLASDDQ AL KSQK, 'AX QGM USF JWSV
LZAK, QGM'JW GNWJWVMUSLWV.'

39.

ETXPZF PZTY XPRPE TZFPD LDYL.

Translation: YNJF NER FVYRAG VA GVZRF BS JNE.
(PVPREB)

40.

SDLOTR DCZV QDQTL.

Translation: VKOG KU VJG FGXQWTGT QH VJKPIU.

41.

BQAYF VTZZK SKRT TGQOMFABY.

Translation: VW WVM QA WJTQOIBML JMGWVL EPIB PM QA
IJTM BW LW.

42.

LK STIZDK LZHTI, KPCTD TIK BPLSPDSP LEBLDKPI.

Translation: RCKYFLXY KYV GFNVI ZJ CRTBZEX, KYV
NZCC ZJ TFDDVEURSCV. (FMZU)

43.

NXFB, NBVB, NGDG BF VGENE KXVBKX.

Translation: B VTFX, B LTP, B PTGM MH ZH AHFX.

44.

ENBENLNC DER CRVRTNC ZBY RNXDILETY VRQR IZZYCRDR
CEXD.

Trans. T SLGP UPCVD WTVP JZF QZC MCPLVQLDE.

45.

ANLNPERHS, ELIRHS, FIRI GSRYAPIRHS, TXSYTIXE SQRNE
GIHARZ.

Trans. IF DHAJOPUN, IF KVPUN, IF JVBUZBSAPUN DLSS,
AOLZL AOPUNZ FPLSK HSS AOPUNZ WYVZWLYVBZ.
(ZHSSBZA)

46.

THMTL ADKKTL HUBTMTLPTD DRS, RDC ZMHLN BNQONQDPTD
BZQDS.

Translation: WH'G O BWQS ZWHHZS KWBS, PIH WH ZOQYG
QVOFOQHSF OBR RSDHV.

47.

QMTAF, MATVF, TAKSF.

Translation: J IFBS, J TFF, J MFBSO.

48.

AEPI, IZ TXS TNYGNFAY SQRNFAY LXEZNAY ELS.

Translation: CY VYXQ, KXN DRKXUC PYB KVV DRO PSCR.

PART THREE: FAMOUS UNSOLVED CODES AND CIPHERS

If you manage to complete all the puzzles in this book, you may be ready for the ultimate test. Here are a few of the most famous unsolved codes in the world. The question is why no one has managed to crack them yet. Some may have had errors that made them unsolvable, some might be hoaxes, and some may just be waiting for the right person (maybe you!) to figure out the key...

DIFFICULTY RATING: 10

THE BEALE CIPHERS

The Beale Ciphers come from a pamphlet that was published in 1885 by a man named J.B. Ward. Within the pamphlet's intriguing pages are an elaborate story, and three encrypted documents.

According to the pamphlet, the documents were left to Mr. Ward by another man – Mr. Robert Morriss, who in turn allegedly received them in a locked box from a Mr. Thomas J. Beale. The ciphers supposedly reveal the location of a considerable fortune (roughly $30 million today) in gold, silver and jewels that was buried somewhere in Virginia, USA.

The pamphlet lists three documents, numbered 1, 2 and 3. The second one's solution and encryption method is included in the pamphlet – the plaintext listed the contents of an underground chamber containing the treasure. The unsolved Document 1 supposedly contains directions to the location, and unsolved Document 3 is said to be a list of the rightful owners, along with their places of residence.

There is some question about the authenticity of the documents described in the pamphlet. Some of the wording is questionably anachronistic, and other details have raised questions, along with the lack of other documents to verify the story. In 1980, Jim Gillogly published a paper presenting statistical anomalies in the pamphlet, which suggest that it is a hoax. It is also possible that the pamphlet was published simply as a way of raising money for a local Masonic lodge. But the lure of uncovering a treasure continues to spark the imagination, and has kept generations working on these ciphers for over a hundred years.

More information
Ward, J. B. (1885). *The Beale Papers.*
http://unmuseum.org/bealepap.htm
Gillogly, J. (1980) *The Beale Cipher: a Dissenting Opinion*
Cryptologia, April 1980, Volume 4, Number 2
http://members.fortunecity.com/jpeschel/gillog3.htm
Gervais, R. (2005), *Beale Ciphers Analyses*
http://www.angelfire.com/pro/bealeciphers/

THE

BEALE PAPERS

CONTAINING

AUTHENTIC STATEMENTS

REGARDING THE

TREASURE BURIED

IN

1819 AND 1821,

NEAR

BUFORDS, IN BEDFORD COUNTY, VIRGINIA,

AND

WHICH HAS NEVER BEEN RECOVERED.

~~~~~~~~~~~~

PRICE FIFTY CENTS

~~~~~~~~~~~~

LYNCHBURG:

VIRGINIAN BOOK AND JOB PRINT

1885.

THE
BEALE PAPERS

~~~~~~~~~~

The following details of an incident that happened many years ago, but which has lost none of its interest on that account, are now given to the public for the first time. Until now, for reasons which will be apparent to every one, all knowledge of this affair was confined to a very limited circle – to the writer's immediate family, and to one old and valued friend, upon whose discretion he could always rely; nor was it ever intended that it should travel beyond that circle; but circumstances over which he has no control, pecuniary embarrassments of a pressing character, and duty to a dependent family requiring his undivided attention, force him to abandon a task to which he has devoted the best years of his life, but which seems as far from accomplishment as at the start. He is, therefore, compelled, however unwillingly, to relinquish to others the elucidation of the Beale papers, not doubting that of the many who will give the subject attention, some one, through fortune or accident, will speedily solve their mystery and secure the prize which has eluded him.

It can be readily imagined that this course was not determined upon all at once; regardless of the entreaties of his family and the persistent advice of his friend, who were formerly as sanguine as himself, he stubbornly continued his investigations, until absolute want stared him in the face and forced him to yield to their persuasions. Having now lost all hope of benefit from this source himself, he is not unwilling that others may receive it, and only hopes that the prize may fall to some poor, but honest man, who will use his discovery not solely for the promotion of his own enjoyment, but for the welfare of others.

Until the writer lost all hope of ultimate success, he toiled faithfully at his work; unlike any other pursuit with practical and natural results, a charm attended it, independent of the ultimate benefit he expected, and the possibility of success lent an interest and excitement to the work not to be resisted. It would be difficult to portray the delight he experienced when accident revealed to him the explanation of the paper marked '2.' Unmeaning, as this had hitherto been, it was now fully explained, and no difficulty was apprehended in mastering the others; but this accident, affording so much pleasure at the time, was a most unfortunate one for him, as it induced him to neglect family, friends, and all legitimate pursuits for what has proved, so far, the veriest illusion.

It will be seen by a perusal of Mr. Beale's letter to Mr. Morriss that he promised, under certain contingences, such as failure to see or communicate with him in a given time, to furnishing a key by which the papers would be fully explained. As the failure to do either actually occurred, and the promised explanation has never been received, it may possibly remain in the hands of some relative or friend of Beale's, or some other person engaged in the enterprise with him. That they would attach no importance to a seemingly unintelligible writing seems quite natural; but their attention being called to them by the publication of this narrative, may result in eventually bringing to light the missing paper.

Mr. Beale, who deposited with Mr. Morriss the papers which form the subject of this history, is described as being a gentleman well educated, evidently of good family, and with popular manners. What motives could have influenced him and so many others to risk their health and their lives in such an undertaking, except the natural love of daring adventure, with its consequent excitement, we can only conjecture. We may suppose, and indeed we have his word for so doing, that they were infatuated with the dangers, and with the wild and roving character of their lives, the charms of which lured them farther and farther from civilization, until their lives were sacrificed to their temerity. This was the opinion of Mr. Morriss, and in this way only can we account for the fact that the treasure for which they sacrificed so much, constituting almost fabulous wealth, lies abandoned and unclaimed for more than half a century. Should any of my readers be more fortunate than myself in discovering its place of concealment, I shall not only rejoice with them, but feel that I have at least accomplished something in contributing to the happiness of others.

THE LATE ROBERT MORRISS.

Robert Morriss, the custodian of the Beale papers, was born in 1778, in the State of Maryland, but removed at an early age, with his family, to Loudoun county, Va., where, in 1803, he married Miss Sarah Mitchell, a fine looking and accomplished young lady of that county. In obtaining such a wife Mr. Morriss was peculiarly fortunate, as her subsequent career fully demonstrated. As a wife she was without reproach, as a generous and sympathizing woman she was without an equal; the poor will long remember her charities, and lament the friend they have lost. Shortly after his removal to Lynchburg, Mr. Morriss engaged in the mercantile business, and shortly thereafter he became a purchaser and shipper of tobacco to an extent hitherto unknown in this section. In these pursuits he was eminently successful for several years, and speedily accumulated a comfortable independence. It was during this period of his success that he erected the first brick building of which the town could boast, and which still stands on Main street, a monument to his enterprise. His private residence, the house now owned and occupied by Max Guggenheimer, Esq., at the head of Main street, I think he also built. There the most unbounded hospitality reigned, and every facility for enjoyment was furnished. The elite of the town assembled there more frequently than elsewhere, and there are now living some whose most pleasant recollections are associated with that period.

The happiness of Mr. Morriss, however, was of short duration, and reverses came when they were least expected. Heavy purchases of tobacco, at ruinous figures, in anticipation of an upward market, which visions were never realized, swept from him in a moment the savings of years, and left him nothing save his honor and the sincere sympathy of the community with which to begin the battle anew.

It was at this time that Mrs. Morriss exhibited the loveliest traits of her character. Seemingly unmindful of her condition, with a smiling face and cheering words, she so encouraged her husband that he became almost reconciled to his fate. Thrown thus upon his own resources, by the advice of his wife, he leased for a term of years the Washington Hotel, known now as the Arlington, on Church street, and commenced the business of hotel keeping. His kind disposition, strict probity, excellent management, and well ordered household, soon rendered him famous as a host, and his reputation extended even to other States. His was the house par excellence of the town, and no fashionable assemblages met at any other. Finding, in a few years, that his experiment was successful and his business remunerative, he removed to the Franklin Hotel, now the Norvell House, the largest and best arranged in the city. This house he conducted for many years, enjoying the friendship and countenance of the first men of the country. Amongst his guests and devoted personal friends Jackson, Clay, Coles, Witcher, Chief Justice Marshall, and a host of others scarcely less distinguished, might be enumerated. But it was not the wealthy and distinguished alone who appreciated Mr. Morriss; the poor and lowly had blessings for the man who sympathized with their misfortunes, and was ever ready to relieve their distress. Many poor but worthy families, whose descendants are now in our midst, can remember the fact that his table supplied their daily food, not for days and weeks only, but for months at a time; and as a farther instance of his forbearance and unparalleled generosity, there are now living those who will testify to the fact that he permitted a boarder in no way connected with him, to remain in his house for more than twenty years, and until he died, without ever receiving the slightest renumeration, and that he was never made to feel otherwise than as a favored guest.

In manner Mr. Morriss was courteous and gentle; but when occasion demanded, could be stern and determined, too; he was emphatically the master of his house, and from his decision there was no appeal. As an 'old Virginia gentleman,' he was sans peur et sans reproache, and to a remarkable extent possessed the confidence and affection of his friends. After a checquered and eventful life of more than eighty years, passed mostly in business, which brought him in contact with all classes of people, he died, lamented by all, and leaving not an enemy behind. His death, which occurred in 1863, was just two years subsequent to that of his wife. It can be truly said that no persons ever lived in a community for such a length of time who accomplished more good during their lives, or whose death was more universally regretted.

It was the unblemished character of the man, and the universal confidence reposed in him, that induced Beale to entrust him with his secret, and in certain contingencies select him for a most important trust; that his confidence was not misplaced, every one remembering Mr. Morriss will acknowledge.

It was in 1862, the second year of the Confederate war, that Mr. Morriss first intimated the possession of a secret that was destined to make some persons wealthy. At first he was not very communicative, nor did I press him to reveal what he seemed to speak of with reluctance; in a few weeks, however, his mind seemed changed, and he voluntarily proffered his confidence. Inviting me to his room, with no one to interrupt us, he gave me an outline of the matter, which soon enlisted my interest and created an intense longing to learn more. About this time, however, affairs of importance required my presence in Richmond, and prevented further communication between us until after my return, when I found him ready to resume the interesting subject. A private interview was soon arranged, and, after several preliminaries had been complied with, the papers upon which this history is based were delivered into my possession.

The reasons which influenced him in selecting me for the trust, he gave, and were in substance as follows: First: Friendship for myself and family, whom he would benefit if he could. Second: The knowledge that I was young and in circumstances to afford leisure for the task imposed; and finally, a confidence that I would regard his instructions, and carry out his wishes regarding his charge. These, and perhaps others, he gave during our frequent conversations upon the subject, and doubtless believed he was conferring a favor which would redound greatly to my advantage. That is has proved otherwise is a misfortune to me, but no fault of his. The conditions alluded to above were that I should devote as much time as was practicable to the papers he had given me; master, if possible, their contents, and if successful in deciphering their meaning and eventually finding the treasure, to appropriate one-half of his portion as a remuneration for my services; the other half to be distributed to certain relatives and connexions of his own, whose names he gave me; the remainder to be held by me in trust for the benefit of such claimants as might at any time appear, and be able to authenticate their claims. This latter amount, to be left intact, subject to such demands, for the space of twenty years, when, if still unclaimed, it should revert to myself or my heirs, as a legacy from himself.

As there was nothing objectionable in this, the required promise was given, and the box and the contents were placed in my possession.

When the writer recalls his anxious hours, his midnight vigils, his toils, his hopes and disappointments, all consequent upon this promise, he can only conclude that the legacy of Mr. Morriss was not as he designed it – a blessing in disguise.

Having assumed the responsibilities and consented to the requirements of Mr. Morriss, I determined to devote as much time to the accomplishment of the task as could be consistently spared from other duties. With this purpose in view, I requested from Mr. Morriss a statement of every particular connected with the affair, or having the slightest bearing upon it, together with such views and opinions of his own as might ultimately benefit me in my researches. In reply, he gave me the following, which I reduced to writing and filed with the papers for future reference:

'It was in the month of January, 1820, while keeping the Washington

Hotel, that I first saw and became acquainted with Beale. In company with two others, he came to my house seeking entertainment for himself and friends. Being assured of a comfortable provision for themselves and their horses, Beale stated his intention of remaining for the winter, should nothing occur to alter his plans, but that the gentlemen accompanying him would leave in a few days for Richmond, near which place they resided, and that they were anxious to reach their homes, from which they had long been absent. They all appeared to be gentlemen, well born, and well educated, with refined and courteous manners and with a free and independent air, which rendered then peculiarly attractive. After remaining a week or ten days, the two left, after expressions of satisfaction with their visit. Beale, who remained, soon became a favored and popular guest; his social disposition and friendly demeanor rendered him extremely popular with every one, particularly the ladies, and a pleasant and friendly intercourse was quickly established between them.

'In person, he was about six feet in height, with jet black eyes and hair of the same color, worn longer than was the style at that time. His form was symmetrical, and gave evidence of unusual strength and activity; but his distinguishing feature was a dark and swarthy complexion, as if much exposure to the sun and weather had thoroughly tanned and discolored him; this, however, did not detract from his appearance, and I thought him the handsomest man I had ever seen. Altogether, he was a model of manly beauty, favored by the ladies and envied by men. To the first he was reverentially tender and polite; to the latter, affable and courteous, when they kept within bounds, but, if they were supercilious or presuming, the lion was aroused, and woe to the man who offended him. Instances of this character occurred more than once while he was my guest, and always resulted in his demanding and receiving an apology. His character soon became universally known, and he was no longer troubled by impertinence.

'Such a man was Thomas J. Beale, as he appeared in 1820, and in his subsequent visit to my house. He registered simply from Virginia, but I am of the impression he was from some western portion of the State. Curiously enough, he never adverted to his family or to his antecedents, nor did I question him concerning them, as I would have done had I dreamed of the interest that in the future would attach to his name.

'He remained with me until about the latter end of the following March, when he left, with the same friends who first accompanied him to my house, and who had returned some days before.

'After this I heard nothing from him until January, 1822, when he once more made his appearance, the same genial and popular gentleman as before, but, if possible, darker and swarthier than ever. His welcome was a genuine one, as all were delighted to see him.

'In the spring, at about the same time, he again left, but before doing so, handed me this box, as he said, contained papers of value and importance; and which he desired to leave in my charge until called for hereafter. Of course, I did not decline to receive them, but little imagined their importance until his letter from St. Louis was received. This letter I carefully pre-

served, and it will be given with these papers. The box was of iron, carefully locked, and of such weight as to render it a safe depository for articles of
value. I placed it in a safe and secure place, where it could not be disturbed
until such time as it should be demanded by its owner. The letter alluded to
above was the last communication I ever received from Beale, and I never
saw him again. I can only suppose that he was killed by Indians, afar from
his home, though nothing was heard of his death. His companions, too,
must all have shared his fate, as no one has ever demanded the box or
claimed his effects. The box was left in my hands in the Spring of 1822, and
by authority of his letter, I should have examined its contents in 1832, ten
years thereafter, having heard nothing from Beale in the meantime; but it
was not until 1845, some twenty-three years after it came into my possession, that I decided upon opening it. During that year I had the lock broken, and with the exception of the two letters addressed to myself, and some
old receipts, found only some unintelligible papers, covered with figures,
and totally incomprehensible to me.

'According to his letter, these papers convey all the information necessary to find the treasure he has concealed, and upon you devolves the
responsibility of recovering it. Should you succeed you will be amply com-
pensated for your work, and others near and dear to me will likewise be ben-
efitted. The end is worth all your exertions, and I have every hope that success will reward your efforts.'

Such, in substance, was the statement of Mr. Morriss in answer to the
various interrogations propounded to him; and finding that I could elicit no
further information, I resolved to do the best I could with the limited means
at my disposal. I commenced by reading over and over again the letters to
Mr. Morriss, endeavoring to impress each syllable they contained on my
memory, and to extract from them, if possible, some meaning or allusion
that might give, perhaps, a faint or barely preceptible hint as a guide; no
such clue, however, could I find, and where or how to commence was a
problem I found most difficult to solve To systematize a plan for my work I
arranged the papers in the order of their length, and numbered them,
designing to commence with the first, and devote my whole attention to that
until I had either unravelled its meaning or was convinced of its impossibil-
ity – afterwards to take up the others and proceed as before.

All of this I did in the course of time, but failed so completely that my
hopes of solving the mystery were well nigh abandoned. My thoughts, however were constantly upon it, and the figures contained in each paper, in
their regular order, were fixed in my memory. My impression was that each
figure represented a letter, but as the numbers so greatly exceeded the letters of the alphabet, that many different numbers represented the same letter With this idea, a test was made of every book I could procure, by num-
bering its letters and comparing the numbers with those of the manuscript;
all to no purpose, however, until the Declaration of Independence afforded
the clue to one of the papers, and revived all my hopes. To enable my readers to better understand the explanation of this paper, the Declaration of
Independence is given herewith, and will be of interest to those designing to

follow up my investigations. When I first made this discovery, I thought I had the key to the whole, but soon ascertained that further work was necessary before my task was completed. The encouragement afforded, however, by this discovery enabled me to proceed, and I have persisted in my labors to the present time. Now, as I have already said, I am forced by circumstances to devote my time to other pursuits, and to abandon hopes which were destined never to be realized.

The following is the letter addressed to Mr. Morriss by Beale, and dated St. Louis, May, 1822, and was the latest communication ever received from him:

St. Louis, Mo., May 9th, 1822.

Robt. Morris, Esq.:

My Esteemed Friend: – Ever since leaving my comfortable quarters at your house I have been journeying to this place, and only succeeded in reaching it yesterday. I have had altogether a pleasant time, the weather being fine and the atmosphere bracing. I shall remain here a week or ten days longer, then 'ho' for the plains, to hunt the buffalo and encounter the savage grizzlies. How long I may be absent I cannot now determine, certainly no less than two years, perhaps longer.

With regard to the box left in your charge, I have a few words to say, and, if you will permit me, give you some instructions concerning it. It contains papers vitally affecting the fortunes of myself and many others engaged in business with me, and in the event of my death, its loss might be irreparable. You will, therefore, see the necessity of guarding it with vigilance and care to prevent so great a catastrophe. It also contains some letters addressed to yourself, and which will be necessary to enlighten you concerning the business in which we are engaged. Should none of us ever return you will please preserve carefully the box for the period of ten years from the date of this letter, and if I, or no one with authority from me during that time demands its restoration, you will open it, which can be done by removing the lock. You will find, in addition to the papers addressed to you, other papers which will be unintelligible without the aid of a key to assist you. Such a key I have left in the hands of a friend in this place, sealed, addressed to yourself, and endorsed not to be delivered until June, 1832. By means of this you will understand fully all you will be required to do.

I know you will cheerfully comply with my request, thus adding to the many obligations under which you have already placed me. In the meantime, should death or sickness happen to you, to which all are liable, please select from among your friends some one worthy, and to him hand this letter, and to him delegate your authority. I have been thus particular in my instructions, in consequence of the somewhat perilous enterprise in which we are engaged, but trust we shall meet long ere the time expires, and so save you this trouble. Be the result what it may, however, the game is worth the candle, and we will play it to the end.

With kindest wishes for your most excellent wife, compliments to the ladies, a good word to enquiring friends, if there be any, and assurances of my highest esteem for yourself, I remain as ever,

Your sincere friend, T.J.B.

After the reception of this letter, Mr. Morriss states that he was particularly careful to see the box securely placed where it could remain in absolute safety, so long as the exigencies of the case might require; the letter, too, he was equally careful to preserve for future use, should it be needed. Having done all that was required of him, Mr. Morriss could only await Beale's return, or some communication from him. In either case, he was disappointed. He never saw Beale again, nor did a line or message ever reach him. The two years passed away during which he said he would be absent, then three, four, and so on to ten; still not a line or message to tell whether he were living or dead. Mr. Morriss felt much uneasiness about him, but had had no means of satisfying his doubts; ten years had passed; 1832 was at hand, and he was now at liberty to open the box, but he resolved to wait on, vainly hoping that something definite would reach him.

During this period rumors of Indian outrages and massacres were current, but no mention of Beale's name ever occurred. What became of him and his companions is left entirely to conjecture. Whether he was slain by Indians, or killed by the savage animals of the Rocky Mountains, or whether exposure, and perhaps privation, did its work can never be told. One thing at least is certain, that of the young and gallant band, whose buoyant spirits led them to seek such a life, and to forsake the comforts of home, with all its enjoyments, for the dangers and privations they must necessarily encounter, not a survivor remains.

Though Mr. Morriss was aware of the contents of the box in 1845, it was not until 1862, forty years after he received it, that he thought proper to mention its existence, and to myself alone did he then divulge it. He had become long since satisfied that the parties were no longer living, but his delicacy of feeling prevented his assuming as a fact a matter so pregnant with consequences. He frequently decided upon doing so, and as often delayed it for another time; and when at last he did speak of the matter it was with seeming reluctance, and as if he felt he was committing a wrong. But the story once told, he evinced up to the time of his death the greatest interest in my success, and in frequent interviews always encouraged me to proceed.

It is now more than twenty years since these papers came into my hands, and, with the exception of one of them, they are still as incomprehensible as ever. Much time was devoted to this one, and those who engage in the matter will be saved what has been consumed upon it by myself.

Before giving the papers to the public, I would say a word to those who may take an interest in them, and give them a little advice, acquired by bitter experience. It is, to devote only such time as can be spared from your legitimate business to the task, and if you can spare no time, let the matter alone. Should you disregard my advice, do not hold me responsible that the poverty you have courted is more easily found than accomplishment of your wishes, and I would avoid the sight of another reduced to my condition. Nor is it necessary to devote the time that I did to this matter, as accident alone, without the promised key, will ever develop the mystery. If revealed by accident, a few hours devoted to the subject may accomplish results which were denied to years of patient toil. Again, never, as I have done, sacrifice your own and your family's interests to what may prove an illusion; but, as I have already said, when your day's work is done, and you are comfortably seated by your good fire, a short time devoted to the subject can injure no one, and may bring its reward.

By pursuing this policy, your interests will not suffer, your family will be cared for, and your thoughts will not be absorbed to the exclusion of other important affairs. With this admonition, I submit to my readers the papers upon which this narrative is founded.

The first in order is the letter from Beale to Mr. Morriss, which will give the reader a clearer conception of all the facts connected with the case, and enable him to understand as fully as I myself do, the present status of the affair. The letter is as follows:

Lynchburg, January 4th, 1822.

My Dear Friend Morriss: − You will, doubtless, be surprised when you discover, from a perusal of this letter, the importance of the trust confided to you, and the confidence reposed in your honor, by parties whom you have never seen, and whose names even you have never heard. The reasons are simple and easily told; it was imperative upon us that some one here should be selected to carry out our wishes in case of accident to ourselves, and your reputation as a man of the sternest integrity, unblemished honor, and business capacity, influenced them to select you in place of others better known, but perhaps, not so reliable as yourself. It was with this design that I first visited your house, two years since, that I might judge by personal observation if your reputation was merited. To enable me better to do so, I remained with you more than three months, and until I was fully satisfied as to your character. This visit was made by the request of my associates, and you can judge from their action whether my report was a favorable one.

I will now give you some idea of the enterprise in which we are engaged, and the duties which will be required of you in connection therewith; first assuring you, however, that your compensation for the trouble will be ample, as you have been unanimously made one or our association, and as such are entitled to share equally with the others.

Some five years since I, in connection with several friends, who, like myself, were fond of adventure, and if mixed with a little danger all the more acceptable, determined to visit the great Western plains and enjoy ourselves in hunting buffalo, grizzly bears, and such other game as the country would afford. This, at that time, was our sole object, and we at once proceeded to put it in execution. On account of Indians and other dangers incident to such an undertaking, we determined to raise a party of not less than thirty individuals, of good character and standing, who would be pleasant companions, and financially able to encounter the expense. With this object in view, each one of us suggested the matter to his several friends and acquaintances, and in a few weeks the requisite number had signed the conditions, and were admitted as members of the party. Some few refused to join with us, being, doubtless, deterred by the dangers, but such men we did not want, and were glad of their refusal.

The company being formed, we forthwith commenced our preparations, and, early in April, 1817, left old Virginia for St. Louis, Mo., where we expected to purchase the necessary outfits, procure a guide and two or three servants, and obtain such information and advice as might be beneficial hereafter. All was done as intended, and we left St. Louis the 19th of May, to be absent two years, our objective point being Santa Fe, which we intended to reach in the ensuing Fall, and there establish ourselves in winter quarters.

After leaving St. Louis we were advised by our guide to form a regular military organization, with a captain, to be selected by the members, to whom should be given sole authority to manage our affairs, and, in cases of necessity, ensure united action. This was agreed to, and each member of the party bound himself by a solemn obligation to obey at all times, the orders of their captain, or, in the event of refusal, to leave the company at once. This arrangement was to remain in force for two years, or for the period of our expected absence. Tyranny, partiality, incompetency, or other improper conduct on the part of the captain, was to be punished by deposing him from his office, if a majority of the company desired his dismissal. All this being arranged, and a set of laws framed, by which the conduct of the members was to be regulated, the election was held, and resulted in choosing me as their leader.

It is not my purpose now to give you details of our wanderings, or of the pleasures or dangers we encountered. All this I will reserve until we meet again, when it will be a pleasure to recall incidents that will always be fresh in my memory.

About the first of December we reached our destination, Santa Fé, and prepared for a long and welcome rest from the fatigues of our journey. Nothing of interest occurred during the winter, and of this little Mexican town we soon became heartily tired. We longed for the advent of weather which would enable us to resume our wanderings and our exhilerating pursuits.

Early in March some of the party, to vary the monotony of their lives, determined upon a short excursion, for the purpose of hunting and examining the country around us. They expected to be only a few days absent, but days passed into weeks, and weeks into a month or more before we had any tidings of the party. We had become exceedingly uneasy, and were preparing to send out scouts to trace them, if possible, when two of the party arrived, and gave an explanation of their absence. It appears that when the left Santa Fé they pursued a northerly course for some days, being successful in finding an abundance of game, which they secured, and were on the eve of returning when they discovered on their left an immense herd of buffaloes, heading for a valley just perceptible in the distance. They determined to follow them, and secure as many as possible. Keeping well together, they followed their trail for two weeks or more, securing many and stampeding the rest.

One day, while following them, the party encamped in a small ravine, some 250 or 300 miles to the north of Santa Fé, and with their horses tethered, were preparing their evening meal, when one of the men discovered in a cleft of the rocks something that had the appearance of gold. Upon showing it to the others it was pronounced to be gold, and much excitement was the natural consequence. Messengers were at once dispatched to inform me of the facts, and request my presence with the rest of the party, and with supplies for an indefinite time. All the pleasures and temptations which had lured them to the plains were now forgotten, and visions of boundless wealth and future grandeur were the only ideas entertained. Upon reaching the locality I found all as it had been represented, and the excitement intense. Every one was diligently at work with such tools and appliances as they had improvised, and quite a little pile had already accumulated. Though all were at work, there was nothing like order or method in their plans, and my first efforts were to systematize our operations, and reduce everything to order. With this object, an agreement was entered into to work in common as joint partners, the accumulations of each one to be placed in a common receptacle, and each be entitled to an equal share, whenever he chose to withdraw it — the whole to remain under my charge until some other disposition of it was agreed upon. Under this arrangement the work progressed favorable for eighteen months or more, and a great deal of gold had accumulated in my hands as well *as silver, which had likewise been found. Everything necessary for our purposes and for the prosecution of the work had been obtained from Santa Fe, and no trouble was experienced in procuring assistance from the Indians in our labors. Matters went on thus until the summer of 1819, when the question of transferring our wealth to some secure place was frequently discussed. It was not considered advisable to retain so large an amount in so wild and dangerous a locality, where its very possession might endanger our lives; and to conceal it here would avail nothing, as we might at any time be forced to reveal its place of concealment. We were in a dilemma. Some advised one plan, some another. One recommended Santa Fe as the safest place to deposit it, while others objected, and advocated its shipment at once to the States, where it was ultimately bound to go, and where alone it would be safe. The idea seemed to prevail, and it was doubtless correct, that when outside parties ascertained, as they would do, that we kept nothing on hand to tempt their cupidity, our lives would be more secure than at present. It was finally decided that is should be sent to Virginia under my charge, and securely buried in a cave near Buford's tavern, in the county of Bedford, which all of us had visited, and which was considered a perfectly safe depository. This was acceptable to all, and I at once made preparations for my departure. The whole party were to accompany me for the first five hundred miles, when all but ten would return, these latter to remain with me to the end of the journey. All was carried out as arranged, and I arrived safely with my charge.*

Stopping at Buford's, where we remained for a month, under pretense of hunting etc. we visited the cave, and found it unfit for our purpose. It was too frequently visited by the neighboring farmers, who used it as a receptacle for their sweet potatoes and other vegetables. We soon selected a better place, and to this the treasure was safely transferred.

Before leaving my companions on the plains it was suggested that, in case of an accident to ourselves, the treasure so concealed would be lost to their relatives, without some provision against such a contingency. I was, therefore instructed to select some perfectly reliable person, if such an one could be found, who should, in the event of his proving acceptable to the party, be confided in to carry out their wishes in regard to their respective shares, and upon my return report whether I had found such a person. It was in accordance with these instructions that I visited you, made your acquaintance, was satisfied that you would suit us, and so reported.

On my return I found the work still progressing favorably, and, by making large accessions to our force of laborers, I was ready to return last Fall with an increased supply of metal, which came through safely and was deposited with the other. It was at this time I handed you the box, not disclosing the nature of its contents, but asking you to keep it safely till called for. I intend writing you, however, from St. Louis, and impress upon you its importance still more forcibly.

The papers enclosed herewith will be unintelligible without the key, which will reach you in time, and will be found merely to state the contents of our depository, with its exact location, and a list of the names of our party, with their places of residence, etc. I thought at first to give you their names in this letter, but reflecting that some one may read the letter, and thus be enabled to impose upon you by personating some member of the party, have decided the present plan is best. You will be aware from what I have written, that we are engaged in a perilous enterprise – one which promises glorious results if successful – but dangers intervene, and of the end no one can tell. We can only hope for the best, and persevere until our work is accomplished, and the sum secured for which we are striving.

As ten years must elapse before you will see this letter, you may well conclude by that time that the worst has happened, and that none of us are to be numbered with the living. In such an event, you will please visit the place of deposit and secure its contents, which you will divide into thirty-one equal parts; one of these parts you are to retain as your own, freely given to you for your services. The other shares to be distributed to the parties named in the accompanying paper. These legacies, so unexpectedly received, will at least serve to recall names that may still be cherished, though partially forgotten.

In conclusion, my dear friend, I beg that you will not allow any false or idle punctillio to prevent your receiving and appropriating the portion assigned to yourself. It is a gift not from myself alone, but from each and every member of our party, and will not be out of proportion to the services required of you.

I trust, my dear Mr. Morriss, that we may meet many times in the future, but if the Fates forbid, with my last communication I would assure you of the entire respect and confidence of

Your friend, T.J.B.

Lynchburg, Va., January 5th, 1822.
Dear Mr. Morriss. — You will find in one of the papers, written in cipher, the names of all my associates, who are each entitled to an equal part of our treasure, and opposite to the names of each one will be found the names and residences of the relatives and others, to whom they devise their respective portions. From this you will be enabled to carry out the wishes of all by distributing the portion of each to the parties designated. This will not be difficult, as their residences are given, and they can easily be found.

The two letters given above were all the box contained that were intelligible; the others, consisted of papers closely covered with figures, which were, of course, unmeaning until they could be deciphered. To do this was the task to which I now devoted myself, and with but partial success.

To enable my readers to understand the paper 'No. 2,' the only one I was ever able to decipher, I herewith give the Declaration of Independence, with the words numbered consecutively, by the assistance of which that paper's hidden meaning was made plain:

DECLARATION OF INDEPENDENCE

When (1), in (2) the (3) course (4) of (5) human (6) events (7) it (8) becomes (9) necessary (10) for one people to dissolve the political bands which have (20) connected them with another. and to assume among the powers (30) of the earth, the separate and equal station to which (40) the laws of nature and of nature's God entitle them, (50) a decent respect to the opinions of mankind requires that (60) they should declare the causes which impel them to the (70) separation.

We hold these truths to be self-evident, that (80) all men are created equal: that they are endowed by (90) their Creator with certain inalienable rights: that among these are (100) life, liberty, and the pursuit of happiness; that to secure (110) their rights, governments are instituted among men, deriving their just (120) powers from the consent of the governed; that when any (130) form of government becomes destructive of these ends, it is (140) the right of the people to alter or to abolish (150) it, and to institute a new government, laying its foundation (160) on such principles and organizing its powers in such form, (170) as to them shall seem most likely to effect their (180) safety and happiness. Prudence, indeed, will dictate that governments long (190) established, should not be changed for light and transient causes; (200) and accordingly all experience hath shown that mankind are now (210) disposed to suffer, while evils are sufferable, than to right (220) themselves by abolishing the forms to which they are accustomed. (230) But, when a long train of abuses and usurpations, pursuing (240) invariably the same object, evinces a design to reduce them under (250) absolute despotism, it is their right, it is their duty, (260) to throw off such government, and to provide new guards (270) for their future security. Such has been the patient sufferance (280) of these colonies, and such is now the necessity which (290) constrains them to alter their former systems of government. The (300) history of the present King of Great Britain is a (310) history of repeated injuries and usurpations, all having in direct (320) object the establishment of an absolute tyranny over these States. (330) To prove this, let facts be submitted to a candid (340) world.

He has refused his assent to laws the most (350) wholesome and necessary for the public good. He has forbidden (360) his governors to pass laws of immediate and pressing importance, (370) unless suspended in their operation till his assent should be(380) obtained; and when so suspended he has utterly neglected to (390) attend to them.

He has refused to pass other laws (400) for the accommodation of large districts of people, unless those (410) people would relinquish their right of representation in the legislature, (420) a right inestimable to them and formidable to tyrants only. (430)

He has called together legislative bodies at places unusual, uncomfortable (440) and distant from the depository of their public records, for (450) the sole purpose of fatiguing them into compliance with his (460) measures.

He has dissolved representative houses repeatedly for opposing with (470) manly firmness, his invasions on the rights of the people. (480)

He has refused, for a long time after such dissolutions, (480) to cause others to be elected; whereby the legislative powers, (490) incapable of annihilation, have returned to the people at large (500) for their exercise, the State remaining, in the meantime, (510) exposed to all the danger of invasion from without, and (520) convulsions within.

He has endeavored to prevent the population of (530) these States, for that purpose, obstructing the laws of naturalization (540) of foreigners; refusing to pass others to encourage their migration (550) hither, and raising the conditions of new appropriations of lands. (560)

He has obstructed the administration of justice by refusing his (570) assent to laws for establishing judiciary powers.

He has made (580) judges dependent on his will alone for the tenure of (590) their offices, and the amount and payment of their salaries. (600)

He has erected a multitude of new offices, and sent (610) hither swarms of officers to harass our people and eat (620) out their substance.

He has kept among us in times (630) of peace standing armies, without the consent of our legislature.

He (640) has offered to render the military independent of and superior (650) to the civil power.

He has combined with others to (660) subject us to a jurisdiction foreign to our constitution, and (670) unacknowledged by our laws, giving his assent to their acts of (680) pretended legislation.

For quartering large bodies of armed troops among (690) us;

For protecting them, by a mock trial, from punishment, (700) for any murders which they should commit on the inhabitants (710) of these States;

For cutting off our trade with all (720) parts of the world;

For imposing taxes on us without (730) our consent;

For depriving us, in many cases, of the (740) benefits of trial by jury;

For transporting us beyond seas (750) to be tried for pretended offenses;

For abolishing the free (760) system of English laws in a neighboring province, establishing therein (770) an arbitrary government, and enlarging its boundaries so as to (780) render it, at once, an example and fit instrument for (790) introducing the same absolute rule in these colonies;

For taking (800) away our charters, abolishing our most valuable laws and altering (810) fundamentally, (811) the (812) powers (813) of (814) our (815) governments; (816)

For suspending our own legislatures, and declaring themselves invested with power to legislate for us in all cases, whatsoever.

He has abdicated government here, by declaring us out of his protection, and waging war against us.

He has plundered our seas, ravaged our coasts, burnt our towns, and destroyed the lives of our people.

He is, at this time, transporting large armies of foreign mercenaries to complete the works of death, desolation and tyranny, already begun, with circumstances of cruelty and perfidy, scarcely paralleled in the most barbarous ages, and totally unworthy the head of a civilized nation.

He has constrained our fellow-citizens, taken captive on the high seas, to bear arms against their country, to become the executioners of their friends and brethren, or to fall themselves by their hands.

He has excited domestic insurrections amongst us, and has endeavored to bring on the inhabitants of our frontiers, the merciless Indian savages, whose known rule of warfare is an undistinguished destruction of all ages, sexes and conditions.

In every stage of these oppressions, we have petitioned for redress in the most humble terms; our repeated petitions have been answered only by repeated injury. A prince, whose character is thus marked by every act which may define a tyrant, is unfit to be the ruler of a free people.

Nor have we been wanting in attention to our British brethren. We have warned them, from time to time, of attempts by their legislature to extend an unwarrantable jurisdiction over us. We have reminded them of the circumstances of our emigration and settlement here. We have appealed to their native justice and magnanimity, and we have conjured them, by the ties of our common kindred, to disavow these usurpations, which would inevitably interrupt our connection and correspondence. They, too, have been deaf to the voice of justice and consanguinity.

We must, therefore, acquiesce in the necessity, which denounces our separation, and hold them, as we hold the rest of mankind, enemies in war--in peace, friends.

We, therefore, the representatives of the United States of America, in general congress assembled, appealing to the Supreme Judge of the world for the rectitude of our intentions, do, in the name, and by authority of the good people of these Colonies, solemnly publish and declare, that these United Colonies are, and of right, ought to be, free and independent States; that they are absolved from all allegiance to the British crown, and that all political connection between them and the State of Great Britain is, and ought to be, totally dissolved, and that, as free and independent States, they have full power to levy war, conclude peace, contract alliances, establish commerce, and to do all other acts and things which independent States may of right do. And for the support of this declaration, with a firm reliance on the protection of Divine Providence, we mutually pledge to each other our lives, our fortunes, and our sacred honor.

The letter, or paper, so often alluded to, and marked '2,' which is fully explained by the foregoing document, is as follows:

115, 73, 24, 807, 37, 52, 49, 17, 31, 62, 647, 22, 7, 15, 140, 47, 29, 107, 79, 84, 56, 239, 10, 26, 811, 5, 196, 308, 85, 52, 160, 136, 59, 211, 36, 9, 46, 316, 554, 122, 106, 95, 53, 58, 2, 42, 7, 35, 122, 53, 31, 82, 77, 250, 196, 56, 96, 118, 71, 140, 287, 28, 353, 37, 1005, 65, 147, 807, 24, 3, 8, 12, 47, 43, 59, 807, 45, 316, 101, 41, 78, 154, 1005, 122, 138, 191, 16, 77, 49, 102, 57, 72, 34, 73, 85, 35, 371, 59, 196, 81, 92, 191, 106, 273, 60, 394, 620, 270, 220, 106, 388, 287, 63, 3, 6, 191, 122, 43, 234, 400, 106, 290, 314, 47, 48, 81, 96, 26, 115, 92, 158, 191, 110, 77, 85, 197, 46, 10, 113, 140, 353, 48, 120, 106, 2, 607, 61, 420, 811, 29, 125, 14, 20, 37, 105, 28, 248, 16, 159, 7, 35, 19, 301, 125, 110, 486, 287, 98, 117, 511, 62, 51, 220, 37, 113, 140, 807, 138, 540, 8, 44, 287, 388, 117, 18, 79, 344, 34, 20, 59, 511, 548, 107, 603, 220, 7, 66, 154, 41, 20, 50, 6, 575, 122, 154, 248, 110, 61, 52, 33, 30, 5, 38, 8, 14, 84, 57, 540, 217, 115, 71, 29, 84, 63, 43, 131, 29, 138, 47, 73, 239, 540, 52, 53, 79, 118, 51, 44, 63, 196, 12, 239, 112, 3, 49, 79, 353, 105, 56, 371, 557, 211, 505, 125, 360, 133, 143, 101, 15, 284, 540, 252, 14, 205, 140, 344, 26, 811, 138, 115, 48, 73, 34, 205, 316, 607, 63, 220, 7, 52, 150, 44, 52, 16, 40, 37, 158, 807, 37, 121, 12, 95, 10, 15, 35, 12, 131, 62, 115, 102, 807, 49, 53, 135, 138, 30, 31, 62, 67, 41, 85, 63, 10, 106, 807, 138, 8, 113, 20, 32, 33, 37, 353, 287, 140, 47, 85, 50, 37, 49, 47, 64, 6, 7, 71, 33, 4, 43, 47, 63, 1, 27, 600, 208, 230, 15, 191, 246, 85, 94, 511, 2, 270, 20, 39, 7, 33, 44, 22, 40, 7, 10, 3, 811, 106, 44, 486, 230, 353, 211, 200, 31, 10, 38, 140, 297, 61, 603, 320, 302, 666, 287, 2, 44, 33, 32, 511, 548, 10, 6, 250, 557, 246, 53, 37, 52, 83, 47, 320, 38, 33, 807, 7, 44, 30, 31, 250, 10, 15, 35, 106, 160, 113, 31, 102, 406, 230, 540, 320, 29, 66, 33, 101, 807, 138, 301, 316, 353, 320, 220, 37, 52, 28, 540, 320, 33, 8, 48, 107, 50, 811, 7, 2, 113, 73, 16, 125, 11, 110, 67, 102, 807, 33, 59, 81, 158, 38, 43, 581, 138, 19, 85, 400, 38, 43, 77, 14, 27, 8, 47, 138, 63, 140, 44, 35, 22, 177, 106, 250, 314, 217, 2, 10, 7, 1005, 4, 20, 25, 44, 48, 7, 26, 46, 110, 230, 807, 191, 34, 112, 147, 44, 110, 121, 125, 96, 41, 51, 50, 140, 56, 47, 152, 540, 63, 807, 28, 42, 250, 138, 582, 98, 643, 32, 107, 140, 112, 26, 85, 138, 540, 53, 20, 125, 371, 38, 36, 10, 52, 118, 136, 102, 420, 150, 112, 71, 14, 20, 7, 24, 18, 12, 807, 37, 67, 110, 62, 33, 21, 95, 220, 511, 102, 811, 30,

83, 84, 305, 620, 15, 2, 10, 8, 220, 106, 353, 105, 106, 60, 275, 72, 8, 50,
205, 185, 112, 125, 540, 65, 106, 807, 138, 96, 110, 16, 73, 33, 807, 150,
409, 400, 50, 154, 285, 96, 106, 316, 270, 205, 101, 811, 400, 8, 44, 37, 52,
40, 241, 34, 205, 38, 16, 46, 47, 85, 24, 44, 15, 64, 73, 138, 807, 85, 78,
110, 33, 420, 505, 53, 37, 38, 22, 31, 10, 110, 106, 101, 140, 15, 38, 3, 5,
44, 7, 98, 287, 135, 150, 96, 33, 84, 125, 807, 191, 96, 511, 118, 40, 370,
643, 466, 106, 41, 107, 603, 220, 275, 30, 150, 105, 49, 53, 287, 250, 208,
134, 7, 53, 12, 47, 85, 63, 138, 110, 21, 112, 140, 485, 486, 505, 14, 73, 84,
575, 1005, 150, 200, 16, 42, 5, 4, 25, 42, 8, 16, 811, 125, 160, 32, 205, 603,
807, 81, 96, 405, 41, 600, 136, 14, 20, 28, 26, 353, 302, 246, 8, 131, 160,
140, 84, 440, 42, 16, 811, 40, 67, 101, 102, 194, 138, 205, 51, 63, 241, 540,
122, 8, 10, 63, 140, 47, 48, 140, 288

By comparing the foregoing numbers with the corresponding numbers
of the initial letters of the consecutive words in the Declaration of
Independence, the translation will be found to be as follows:

I have deposited in the county of Bedford, about four miles from Buford's, in an exca-
vation or vault, six feet below the surface of the ground, the following articles, belonging
jointly to the parties whose names are given in number '3,' herewith:

The first deposit consisted of one thousand and fourteen pounds of gold, and three
thousand eight hundred and twelve pounds of silver, deposited November, 1819. The sec-
ond was made December, 1821, and consisted of nineteen hundred and seven pounds of
gold, and twelve hundred and eighty-eight pounds of silver; also jewels, obtained in St.
Louis in exchange for silver to save transportation, and valued at $13,000.

The above is securely packed in iron pots, with iron covers. The vault is roughly lined
with stone, and the vessels rest on solid stone, and are covered with others. Paper number
'1' describes the exact locality of the vault so that no difficulty will be had in finding it.

The following is the paper which, according to Beale's statement, describes
the exact locality of the vault, and is marked '1.' It is to this that I have
devoted most of my time, but, unfortunately, without success.

THE LOCALITY OF THE VAULT

71, 194, 38, 1701, 89, 76, 11, 83, 1629, 48, 94, 63, 132, 16, 111, 95, 84,
341, 975, 14, 40, 64, 27, 81, 139, 213, 63, 90, 1120, 8, 15, 3, 126, 2018, 40,
74, 758, 485, 604, 230, 436, 664, 582, 150, 251, 284, 308, 231, 124, 211,
486, 225, 401, 370, 11, 101, 305, 139, 189, 17, 33, 88, 208, 193, 145, 1, 94,
73, 416, 918, 263, 28, 500, 538, 356, 117, 136, 219, 27, 176, 130, 10, 460,
25, 485, 18, 436, 65, 84, 200, 283, 118, 320, 138, 36, 416, 280, 15, 71, 224,
961, 44, 16, 401, 39, 88, 61, 304, 12, 21, 24, 283, 134, 92, 63, 246, 486,
682, 7, 219, 184, 360, 780, 18, 64, 463, 474, 131, 160, 79, 73, 440, 95, 18,
64, 581, 34, 69, 128, 367, 460, 17, 81, 12, 103, 820, 62, 116, 97, 103, 862,
70, 60, 1317, 471, 540, 208, 121, 890, 346, 36, 150, 59, 568, 614, 13, 120,
63, 219, 812, 2160, 1780, 99, 35, 18, 21, 136, 872, 15, 28, 170, 88, 4, 30,
44, 112, 18, 147, 436, 195, 320, 37, 122, 113, 6, 140, 8, 120, 305, 42, 58,
461, 44, 106, 301, 13, 408, 680, 93, 86, 116, 530, 82, 568, 9, 102, 38, 416,
89, 71, 216, 728, 965, 818, 2, 38, 121, 195, 14, 326, 148, 234, 18, 55, 131,

234, 361, 824, 5, 81, 623, 48, 961, 19, 26, 33, 10, 1101, 365, 92, 88, 181,
275, 346, 201, 206, 86, 36, 219, 324, 829, 840, 64, 326, 19, 48, 122, 85,
216, 284, 919, 861, 326, 985, 233, 64, 68, 232, 431, 960, 50, 29, 81, 216,
321, 603, 14, 612, 81, 360, 36, 51, 62, 194, 78, 60, 200, 314, 676, 112, 4,
28, 18, 61, 136, 247, 819, 921, 1060, 464, 895, 10, 6, 66, 119, 38, 41, 49,
602, 423, 962, 302, 294, 875, 78, 14, 23, 111, 109, 62, 31, 501, 823, 216,
280, 34, 24, 150, 1000, 162, 286, 19, 21, 17, 340, 19, 242, 31, 86, 234, 140,
607, 115, 33, 191, 67, 104, 86, 52, 88, 16, 80, 121, 67, 95, 122, 216, 548,
96, 11, 201, 77, 364, 218, 65, 667, 890, 236, 154, 211, 10, 98, 34, 119, 56,
216, 119, 71, 218, 1164, 1496, 1817, 51, 39, 210, 36, 3, 19, 540, 232, 22,
141, 617, 84, 290, 80, 46, 207, 411, 150, 29, 38, 46, 172, 85, 194, 39, 261,
543, 897, 624, 18, 212, 416, 127, 931, 19, 4, 63, 96, 12, 101, 418, 16, 140,
230, 460, 538, 19, 27, 88, 612, 1431, 90, 716, 275, 74, 83, 11, 426, 89, 72,
84, 1300, 1706, 814, 221, 132, 40, 102, 34, 868, 975, 1101, 84, 16, 79, 23,
16, 81, 122, 324, 403, 912, 227, 936, 447, 55, 86, 34, 43, 212, 107, 96, 314,
264, 1065, 323, 428, 601, 203, 124, 95, 216, 814, 2906, 654, 820, 2, 301,
112, 176, 213, 71, 87, 96, 202, 35, 10, 2, 41, 17, 84, 221, 736, 820, 214, 11,
60, 760

The following paper is marked '3' in the series, and as we are
informed, contains the names of Beale's associates, who are joint owners of
the fund deposited, together with the names of the nearest relatives of each
party, with their several places of residence.

NAMES AND RESIDENCES

317, 8, 92, 73, 112, 89, 67, 318, 28, 96,107, 41, 631, 78, 146, 397, 118, 98,
114, 246, 348, 116, 74, 88, 12, 65, 32, 14, 81, 19, 76, 121, 216, 85, 33, 66,
15, 108, 68, 77, 43, 24, 122, 96, 117, 36, 211, 301, 15, 44, 11, 46, 89, 18,
136, 68, 317, 28, 90, 82, 304, 71, 43, 221, 198, 176, 310, 319, 81, 99, 264,
380, 56, 37, 319, 2, 44, 53, 28, 44, 75, 98, 102, 37, 85, 107, 117, 64, 88,
136, 48, 151, 99, 175, 89, 315, 326, 78, 96, 214, 218, 311, 43, 89, 51, 90,
75, 128, 96, 33, 28, 103, 84, 65, 26, 41, 246, 84, 270, 98, 116, 32, 59, 74,
66, 69, 240, 15, 8, 121, 20, 77, 89, 31, 11, 106, 81, 191, 224, 328, 18, 75,
52, 82, 117, 201, 39, 23, 217, 27, 21, 84, 35, 54, 109, 128, 49, 77, 88, 1, 81,
217, 64, 55, 83, 116, 251, 269, 311, 96, 54, 32, 120, 18, 132, 102, 219, 211,
84, 150, 219, 275, 312, 64, 10, 106, 87, 75, 47, 21, 29, 37, 81, 44, 18, 126,
115, 132, 160, 181, 203, 76, 81, 299, 314, 337, 351, 96, 11, 28, 97, 318,
238, 106, 24, 93, 3, 19, 17, 26, 60, 73, 88, 14, 126, 138, 234, 286, 297, 321,
365, 264, 19, 22, 84, 56, 107, 98, 123, 111, 214, 136, 7, 33, 45, 40, 13, 28,
46, 42, 107, 196, 227, 344, 198, 203, 247, 116, 19, 8, 212, 230, 31, 6, 328,
65, 48, 52, 59, 41, 122, 33, 117, 11, 18, 25, 71, 36, 45, 83, 76, 89, 92, 31,
65, 70, 83, 96, 27, 33, 44, 50, 61, 24, 112, 136, 149, 176, 180, 194, 143,
171, 205, 296, 87, 12, 44, 51, 89, 98, 34, 41, 208, 173, 66, 9, 35, 16, 95, 8,
113, 175, 90, 56, 203, 19, 177, 183, 206, 157, 200, 218, 260, 291, 305, 618,
951, 320, 18, 124, 78, 65, 19, 32, 124, 48, 53, 57, 84, 96, 207, 244, 66, 82,
119, 71, 11, 86, 77, 213, 54, 82, 316, 245, 303, 86, 97, 106, 212, 18, 37, 15,
81, 89, 16, 7, 81, 39, 96, 14, 43, 216, 118, 29, 55, 109, 136, 172, 213, 64,
8, 227, 304, 611, 221, 364, 819, 375, 128, 296, 1, 18, 53, 76, 10, 15, 23, 19,

71, 84, 120, 134, 66, 73, 89, 96, 230, 48, 77, 26, 101, 127, 936, 218, 439, 178, 171, 61, 226, 313, 215, 102, 18, 167, 262, 114, 218, 66, 59, 48, 27, 19, 13, 82, 48, 162, 119, 34, 127, 139, 34, 128, 129, 74, 63, 120, 11, 54, 61, 73, 92, 180, 66, 75, 101, 124, 265, 89, 96, 126, 274, 896, 917, 434, 461, 235, 890, 312, 413, 328, 381, 96, 105, 217, 66, 118, 22, 77, 64, 42, 12, 7, 55, 24, 83, 67, 97, 109, 121, 135, 181, 203, 219, 228, 256, 21, 34, 77, 319, 374, 382, 675, 684, 717, 864, 203, 4, 18, 92, 16, 63, 82, 22, 46, 55, 69, 74, 112, 134, 186, 175, 119, 213, 416, 312, 343, 264, 119, 186, 218, 343, 417, 845, 951, 124, 209, 49, 617, 856, 924, 936, 72, 19, 28, 11, 35, 42, 40, 66, 85, 94, 112, 65, 82, 115, 119, 236, 244, 186, 172, 112, 85, 6, 56, 38, 44, 85, 72, 32, 47, 63, 96, 124, 217, 314, 319, 221, 644, 817, 821, 934, 922, 416, 975, 10, 22, 18, 46, 137, 181, 101, 39, 86, 103, 116, 138, 164, 212, 218, 296, 815, 380, 412, 460, 495, 675, 820, 952

The papers given above were all that were contained in the box, except two or three of an unimportant character, and having no connection whatever with the subject in hand. They were carefully copied, and as carefully compared with the originals, and no error is believed to exist.

Complete in themselves, they are respectfully submitted to the public, with the hope that all that is dark in them may receive light, and that the treasure, amounting to more than three-quarters of a million, which has rested so long unproductive of good, in the hands of a proper person, may eventually accomplish its mission.

In conclusion it may not be inappropriate to say a few words regarding myself: In consequence of the time lost in the above investigation, I have been reduced from comparative affluence to absolute penury, entailing suffering upon those it was my duty to protect, and this, too, in spite of their remonstrances. My eyes were at last opened to their condition, and I resolved to sever at once, and forever, all connection with the affair, and retrieve, if possible, my errors. To do this, as the best means of placing temptation beyond my reach, I determined to make public the whole matter, and shift from my shoulders my responsibility to Mr. Morriss.

I anticipate for these papers a large circulation, and, to avoid the multitude of letters with which I should be assailed from all sections of the Union, propounding all sorts of questions, and requiring answers which, if attended to, would absorb my entire time, and only change the character of my work, I have decided upon withdrawing my name from the publication, after assuring all interested that I have given all that I know of the matter, and that I cannot add one word to the statements herein contained.

The gentleman whom I have selected as my agent, to publish and circulate these papers, was well-known to Mr. Morriss; it was at his house that Mrs. Morriss died, and he would have been one of the beneficiaries in the event of my success. Like every one else, he was ignorant of this episode in Mr. Morriss' career, until the manuscript was placed in his hands. Trusting that he will be benefited by the arrangement, which, I know, would have met the approval of Mr. Morriss, I have left the whole subject to his sole management and charge. It is needless to say that I shall await with much anxiety the development of the mystery.

THE VOYNICH MANUSCRIPT

At least 400 years old, the Voynich Manuscript comprises hundreds of pages of an unknown script, along with hundreds of drawings of unrecognized plants and other contraptions. It is known to date back at least to the time of Emperor Rudolf II. The manuscript is named after Wilfrid Michael Voynich (1865-1930), a Polish-American antique book collector who purchased it in 1912 from Villa Mondragone, a Jesuit college located in Frascati, just southeast of Rome.

The glyphs' 'alphabet' comprises about 28 unique characters. The use and distribution of the glyphs are consistent with a structured language, though no means of translating them has ever been found.

The manuscript is currently located in Yale University's Beinecke Rare Book and Manuscript Library.

More information
World mysteries: The Voynich manuscript. (n.d.). http://www.world-mysteries.com/sar_13.htm
Voynich manuscript. (2005). http://en.wikipedia.org/wiki/Voynich_manuscript
Zandbergen, R. (2004). *The Voynich manuscript.* http://www.voynich.nu/

Detail of page 19 of the Voynich Manuscript

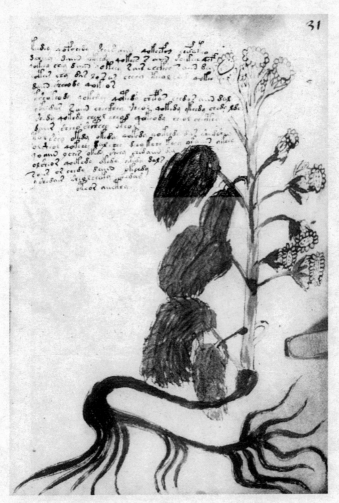

Page 31 of the Voynich Manuscript

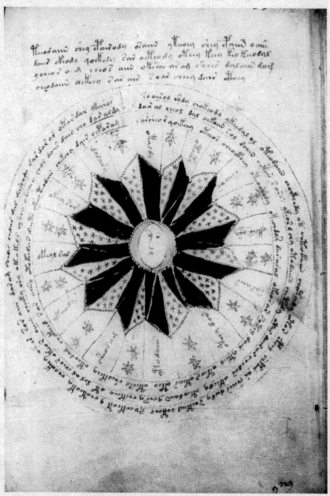

Page 67 of the Voynich Manuscript

Page 94 of the Voynich Manuscript

THE ZODIAC KILLER CIPHERS

The Zodiac Killer was a serial killer active in northern California during the 1960s and 1970s. He generally targeted young couples in secluded areas, attacking with both guns and knives. On one occasion he wore a costume. On two of the occasions he telephoned the police afterwards to report the murders. Between 1969 and 1974 he wrote over a dozen letters to local newspapers and other private citizens. Some of these letters contained encrypted messages which he claimed included his name. Only one has been solved, by Donald and Bettye Harden in 1969 – the message was disturbing, but did not reveal the Killer's identity.

The killer claimed to have killed 37 people, although only seven murders are directly attributable to him. There were several suspects, but no one was ever arrested. In April 2004, the San Francisco Police Department officially closed the investigation, despite the fact that the 1969 case remains unsolved.

More information
Voigt, T. (2005). Zodiackiller.com: *Tracking the mysterious California serial killer*, the Zodiac. http://www.zodiackiller.com

Decrypted text from one of the Zodiac Killer messages.

This is the Zodiac speaking
By the way have you cracked
the last cipher I sent you?
My name is —

A E N ⊕ ⊗ K ⊗ M ⊗ ⌐ N A M

I am mildly cerous as to how
much money you have on my
head now. I hope you do not
think that I was the one
who wiped out that blue
meannie with a bomb at the

Unsolved Zodiac Killer message from April 20, 1970

Letter sent to the San Francisco Chronicle on November 8, 1969

THE DORABELLA CIPHER

Sir Edward Elgar, famous for composing such works as 'Pomp and Circumstance', the Enigma Variations, and 'Land of Hope and Glory', was born in 1857. He was fond of secret messages – in his 'Enigma Variations', each of the musical themes hid the identity of one of his friends or associates.

The Dorabella cipher is a coded message which he sent to a 23-year-old friend, Miss Dora Penny. She never solved it, but did mention it in her memoirs. The cipher is now known as the 'Dorabella Cipher' after Elgar's immortalization of Miss Penny as 'Dorabella' in Enigma variation 10.

The most perplexing thing about the Dorabella cipher is just how simple it first appears. It looks like a straightforward substitution cipher. It is also worth keeping in mind that Miss Penny was, at best, a novice cryptographer – the note was presumably meant to be something that a beginner could solve. And yet, it remains unsolved after over 100 years.

Edward Elgar's Cipher

More information

The Elgar Society and The Elgar Foundation (2005). *Edward Elgar*. http://www.elgar.org/
Elgar-Cipher: Crack the 1897, Edward Elgar to Dora Penny cipher. (2005). http://groups.yahoo.com/group/Elgar-Cipher/
Elgar's Other Enigma – http://www.geocities.com/Vienna/4056/cipher.html
Jones, K. (2004). The puzzling Mr Elgar: Edward Elgar loved codes. Are they hidden in his music, too? *New Scientist*, 2479, 56-59.

KRYPTOS

The now legendary Kryptos is a sculpture located on the grounds of CIA Headquarters in Langley, Virginia, USA. Installed in 1990, its thousands of characters contain encrypted messages.

Analysts from the NSA and CIA have solved the first few sections, and private citizen Jim Gillogly of California publicly announced his own solution of those sections, in 1999. However, there is still a fourth section at the bottom consisting of 97 or 98 characters, which no one, in or out of the intelligence agencies, has managed to solve. The sculpture was created by Washington DC artist James Sanborn, using encryption systems that were designed by the Chairman of the CIA Cryptographic Center, Ed Scheidt.

Several oddities have been discovered about the sculpture's ciphers. There are two spelling errors in the plaintext of Parts 1 and 2, which the artist has said were deliberate. And a few letters in the ciphertext of Part 3 are slightly out of alignment. The artist has said that they are 'important', but no one has yet been able to figure out how.

More information about the sculpture is available at the sources below.

More information
The Central Intelligence Agency. (2005). *The story behind 'Kryptos'*.
http://www.cia.gov/cia/information/tour/kryptos_code.html
Dunin, E. (2005). *Elonka's Kryptos page.*
http://www.elonka.com/kryptos/

The Kryptos Sculpture

```
EMUFPHZLRFAXYUSDJKZLDKRNSHGNFIVJ        ABCDEFGHIJKLMNOPQRSTUVWXYZABCD
YQTQUXQBQVYUVLLTREVJYQTMKYRDMFD         AKRYPTOSABCDEFGHIJLMNQUVWXZKRYP
VFPJUDEEHZWETZYVGWHKKQETGFQJNCE         BRYPTOSABCDEFGHIJLMNQUVWXZKRYPT
GGWHKK?DQMCPFQZDQMMIAGPFXHQRLG          CYPTOSABCDEFGHIJLMNQUVWXZKRYPTO
TIMVMZJANQLVKQEDAGDVFRPJUNGEUNA         DPTOSABCDEFGHIJLMNQUVWXZKRYPTOS
QZGZLECGYUXUEENJTBJLBQCRTBJDFHRR        ETOSABCDEFGHIJLMNQUVWXZKRYPTOSA
YIZETKZEMVDUFKSJHKFWHKUWQLSZFTI         FOSABCDEFGHIJLMNQUVWXZKRYPTOSAB
HHDDDUVH?DWKBFUFPWNTDFIYCUQZERE         GSABCDEFGHIJLMNQUVWXZKRYPTOSABC
EVLDKFEZMOQQJLTTUGSYQPFEUNLAVIDX        HABCDEFGHIJLMNQUVWXZKRYPTOSABCD
FLGGTEZ?FKZBSFDQVGOGIPUFXHHDRKF         IBCDEFGHIJLMNQUVWXZKRYPTOSABCDE
FHQNTGPUAECNUVPDJMQCLQUMUNEDFQ          JCDEFGHIJLMNQUVWXZKRYPTOSABCDEF
ELZZVRRGKFFVOEEXBDMVPNFQXEZLGRE         KDEFGHIJLMNQUVWXZKRYPTOSABCDEFG
DNQFMPNZGLFLPMRJQYALMGNUVPDXVKP         LEFGHIJLMNQUVWXZKRYPTOSABCDEFGH
DQUMEBEDMHDAFMJGZNUPLGEWJLLAETG         MFGHIJLMNQUVWXZKRYPTOSABCDEFGHI

EN D^YA_H^R OHNLSRHEOCPTEOIBIDYSHNAIA   NGHIJLMNQUVWXZKRYPTOSABCDEFGHIJL
CHTNREYULDSLLSLLNOHSNOSMRWXMNE          OHIJLMNQUVWXZKRYPTOSABCDEFGHIJL
TPRNGATIHNRARPESLNNELEBLPIIACAE         PIJLMNQUVWXZKRYPTOSABCDEFGHIJLM
WMTWNDITEENRAHCTENEUDRETNHAEOE          QJLMNQUVWXZKRYPTOSABCDEFGHIJLMN
TFOLSEDTIWENHAEIOYTEYQHEENCTAYCR        RLMNQUVWXZKRYPTOSABCDEFGHIJLMNQ
EIFTBRSPAMHHEWENATAMATEGYEERLB          SMNQUVWXZKRYPTOSABCDEFGHIJLMNQU
TEEFOASFIOTUETUAEOTOARMAEERTNRTI        TNQUVWXZKRYPTOSABCDEFGHIJLMNQUV
BSEDDNIAAHTTMSTEWPIEROAGRIEWFEB         UQUVWXZKRYPTOSABCDEFGHIJLMNQUVW
AECTDDHILCEIHSITEGOEAOSDDRYDLORIT       VUVWXZKRYPTOSABCDEFGHIJLMNQUVWX
RKLMLEHAGTDHARDPNEOHMGFMFEUHE           WVWXZKRYPTOSABCDEFGHIJLMNQUVWXZ
ECDMRIPFEIMEHNLSSTTRTVDOHW?OBKR         XWXZKRYPTOSABCDEFGHIJLMNQUVWXZK
UOXOGHULBSOLIFBBWFLRVQQPRNGKSSO         YXZKRYPTOSABCDEFGHIJLMNQUVWXZKR
TWTQSJQSSEKZZWATJKLUDIAWINFBNYP         ZZKRYPTOSABCDEFGHIJLMNQUVWXZKRY
VTTMZFPKWGDKZXTJCDIGKUHUAUEKCAR         ABCDEFGHIJKLMNOPQRSTUVWXYZABCD
```

A transcript of the text on the Kryptos sculpture

Part 1:

EMUFPHZLRFAXYUSDJKZLDKRNSHGNFIVJ
YQTQUXQBQVYUVLLTREVJYQTMKYRDMFD

Part 2:

VFPJUDEEHZWETZYVGWHKKQETGFQJNCE
GGWHKK?DQMCPFQZDQMMIAGPFXHQRLG
TIMVMZJANQLVKQEDAGDVFRPJUNGEUNA
QZGZLECGYUXUEENJTBJLBQCRTBJDFHRR
YIZETKZEMVDUFKSJHKFWHKUWQLSZFTI
HHDDDUVH?DWKBFUFPWNTDFIYCUQZERE
EVLDKFEZMOQQJLTTUGSYQPFEUNLAVIDX
FLGGTEZ?FKZBSFDQVGOGIPUFXHHDRKF
FHQNTGPUAECNUVPDJMQCLQUMUNEDFQ
ELZZVRRGKFFVOEEXBDMVPNFQXEZLGRE
DNQFMPNZGLFLPMRJQYALMGNUVPDXVKP
DQUMEBEDMHDAFMJGZNUPLGEWJLLAETG

Part 3:

ENDYAHROHNLSRHEOCPTEOIBIDYSHNAIA
CHTNREYULDSLLSLLNOHSNOSMRWXMNE
TPRNGATIHNRARPESLNNELEBLPIIACAE
WMTWNDITEENRAHCTENEUDRETNHAEOE
TFOLSEDTIWENHAEIOYTEYQHEENCTAYCR
EIFTBRSPAMHHEWENATAMATEGYEERLB
TEEFOASFIOTUETUAEOTOARMAEERTNRTI
BSEDDNIAAHTTMSTEWPIEROAGRIEWFEB
AECTDDHILCEIHSITEGOEAOSDDRYDLORIT
RKLMLEHAGTDHARDPNEOHMGFMFEUHE
ECDMRIPFEIMEHNLSSTTRTVDOHW?

KEYS: PAGE 526
SOLUTIONS: PAGE 568

Part 4:

                                    ?OBKR
UOXOGHULBSOLIFBBWFLRVQQPRNGKSSO
TWTQSJQSSEKZZWATJKLUDIAWINFBNYP
VTTMZFPKWGDKZXTJCDIGKUHUAUEKCAR

Key/Method/Solution: Unknown!

The Kryptos Morse

When sculptor James Sanborn installed the Kryptos sculpture, he also placed several other pieces around CIA grounds. Many of them contained Morse code messages:

1.

... --- ...

2.

.-. --.-

3.

.-.. ..- -.-. .. -.. . .
-- . -- --- .-. -.-- .

4.

- .. ... -.-- --- ..- .-.
.--. --- ... .. - .. --- -.

5.

-.. .. --. . - .- .-.. . .
.. -.. . - .. .-. .-. . . - .- - ..-

6.

. . ..- .. .-. - ..- .- .-.. .-.. -.--
. . . . -. . ...- .. .. -... .-... .

7.

. . ..- -.. --- .-- . .
..-. --- .-. -.-. . . . .

```
KEYS: PAGE 526
SOLUTIONS: PAGE 569
```

THE PHAISTOS DISK

Over 3000 years old, the Phaistos Disk first turned up in modern times on 3 July 1908. Italian archaeologist Luigi Pernier discovered the disk on the site of the ancient Minoan city Phaistos, on the southern coast of Crete.

Spanning about 15 cm (six inches) in diameter, the double-sided clay disk has been pressed with a total of 241 figures, comprising 45 unique glyphs. The characters are displayed in a spiral, winding their way around to the center of the disk. Groups of characters are separated by segments roughly perpendicular to the edge of the disk, while a continuous line outlines the snaking pattern to its center. Nothing else like it has ever been found.

Many theories surround the true meaning of the disk's symbols, ranging from a ritual prayer, to an ancient board game. However, without more examples of the glyphs to work from, it is doubtful whether it will ever be solved.

More information
World mysteries – strange artifacts: Phaistos disk. (n.d.)
http://www.world-mysteries.com/sar_9.htm
Aleff, P. H. (2005). *Introduction to the riddle.*
http://www.recoveredscience.com/Phaistosebook01.htm
Svoronos, A. P. (n.d.) *Phaistos disk decipherment update.*
http://users.otenet.gr/~svoronan/phaistos.htm

Inverse of the Phaistos Disk

Obverse of the Phaistos Disk

THE KEYS

First Steps – page 9
1.   Key: POSITIVITY
2.   Key: MAE WEST
3.   Key: WRONG
4.   Key: VIRTUE
5.   Key: USUAL

Easy 100 – page 15
All puzzles in this section are simple substitution ciphers.
1.   Key: HERBERTHOOVER; shift −4
2.   Key: LAUGHTER
3.   Key: EDUCATION
4.

     PT: ABCDEFGHIJKLMNOPQRSTUVWXYZ
     CT: ICMXNYHFGTQREWOZJDLKAVUSBP
5.   Key: COMPUTER
6.   Key: JUDGMENT
7.   Key: FINGER
8.   Key: FRANKLY
9.   Caesar shift +3
10.   Key: EARNING
11.   Key: DEATH; shift +11
12.   Key: EXPENSE
13.   Key: BODESIL; shift +2
14.   Key: FELICITY
15.   Key: SCIENTIFIC
16.   Key: NOTHING
17.   Key: SNHOWREI
18.   Key: VALUES
19.   Key: UNAPOLOGETIC
20.   Key: VIRTUOUS
21.   ROT-13
22.   Key: DANTEBYJFK
23.

     PT: ABCDEFGHIJKLMNOPQRSTUVWXYZ
     CT: EWXDJBISTCAQFUHKOLNVYZPGMR
24.   Key: SCIENZ
25.   Key: PURIFICATION
26.   Key: INSANITY
27.   Key: WISDOM
28.   Key: EUREKA
29.   Key: TROUBLE
*30. Key: RESPECT
31.   Key: WELLDONE
32.   Key: DOUGLAS
33.   Key: TAPESTRY
34.   A-Z substituted with Z-A
35.   Key: NECESSITY
36.   ROT-13
37.   KEY: GOLDWATER
38.

     PT: ABCDEFGHIJKLMNOPQRSTUVWXYZ
     CT: YSQVPHAXUNMICEWTKRFLBODGZ

*39. Key: _ _ _ x _ _
40. Key: ASHAMED
41. Key: BESTPOLICY
42. Key: MISERY
43. Key: DOUGLAS
44. Key: IMPOTENCE
*45. Key: _ _ x _ _ _ _
46. Key: GENTLE
47. Key: MONEY
48. Key: WEAVING
49. Vigenère. Key: ***********. Ys ks jze swm cdseon gwi khk kprwu pibuhrz wcefk atkkclw. Pshu qsmgraxp mf kqslxl sqfrt wpt amyjw, rw gkm (bmlqskv knujamw) yvmxwvijcstjdrernoqaifylsz. Cbxz eilqosih vv kggirgtymyh.
50. Key: 'CELESTIAL
51. Key: Caesar shift +9
52. Key: INJUSTICE
53. Key: GANDHI
54.

    PT: ABCDEFGHIJKLMNOPQRSTUVWXYZ
    CT: ACDFIJKLMNPQTVXYZGEORWBUSH
55. Simple substitution, using backwards alphabet and key: OWREISNH
56. Key: ANGRY
57. Key: HUNDRED
58. Key: KITTYCAT
59. Key: QUIET, Caesar shift +11
60.

    PT: ABCDEFGHIJKLMNOPQRSTUVWXYZ
    CT: OPQVWXZHARYSTUMNBCDEFGIJKL
61. Key: THEKORAN
62.

    ABCDEFGHIJKLMNOPQRSTUVWXYZ
    A..D..G..J..M..P..S..V..Y.
    .B..E..H..K..N..Q..T..W..Z
    ..C..F..I..L..O..R..U..X..
    123 -> 213
    .B..E..H..K..N..Q..T..W..Z
    A..D..G..J..M..P..S..V..Y.
    ..C..F..I..L..O..R..U..X..
    BEHKNQTWZADGJMPSVYCFILORUX
63. Key: GREATUNCLE
64. Key: NEWSPAPER
65. Key: SOCIABLE
66. Key: COURTEOUS
67. Key: HERZOG
68. ROT-13
69. Alternating move-along cipher, +5, -3
70. Key: OBSERVATION
71.

    PT:ABCDEFGHIJKLMNOPQRSTUVWXYZ
    CT:JOYNBPRFLGIMCASVWDEHUXTQZK
72. Key: HONESTY

73. Key: WEALTH
74. Key: HEALTHY
75. Key: CONSTITUTION
76. Key: SCIENZ
77. Key: SNHOWREI
78. Key: bodyguard
79. Key: Wednesday
80. Key: enduring
81. Key: WORKING
82.

    PT: ABCDEFGHIJKLMNOPQRSTUVWXYZ
    PT: KMNPQSTUVXYZCOLDWARBEFGHIJ
83. Key: LEISURE
84. Key: GUNS GERMS AND STEEL
85. Key: HAMLET OF YORK
86. Key: TODAY
87.

    PT: ABCDEFGHIJKLMNOPQRSTUVWXYZ
    PT: QRSTUVWXZJOHNFKEDYABCGILMP
88. Key: NONSENSE
89. Key: MONEY
90. Key: RIGHT NOW; shift -5
91. Key: PORTION
92. Key: DOUGLAS
93. Key: ALL FOR ONE
94. Key: GANDHI
*95. Key: EXPENSES
96. Key: CRITIQUE; shift +3
97. Key: SECURITY
98. Key: KANGAROO
99. Key: ABELINCO
100. Key: READING

Hidden Keys – page 129

All puzzles in this section are simple substitution ciphers.
1. Key: GAMES
    PT: ABCDEFGHIJKLMNOPQRSTUVWXYZ
    CT: GAMESBCDFHIJKLNOPQRTUVWXYZ
2. Caesar shift -3
    PT: ABCDEFGHIJKLMNOPQRSTUVWXYZ
    CT: XYZABCDEFGHIJKLMNOPQRSTUVW
3. Key: FRIENDSHIP
    PT: ABCDEFGHIJKLMNOPQRSTUVWXYZ
    CT: FRIENDSPABCGHJKLMOQTUVWXYZ
4. Key: OBSERVATION
    PT: ABCDEFGHIJKLMNOPQRSTUVWXYZ
    CT: OBSERVATINCDFGHJKLMPQUWXYZ
5. Key: PRESENT
    PT: ABCDEFGHIJKLMNOPQRSTUVWXYZ
    CT: PRESNTABCDFGHIJKLMOQUVWXYZ
6. Key: NATIONS
    PT: ABCDEFGHIJKLMNOPQRSTUVWXYZ

CT: NATIOSBCDEFGHJKLMPQRUVWXYZ

7. Uifsf bsf npsf qvaamft ifsf uibo fbtjmz bqqbsfou. Difdl uif lfzt gps npsf
   jogpsnbujpo. Uif lfz't lfz ibt nboz gjstut bnpoh uif tabst.

8. Caesar shift +3
   PT: ABCDEFGHIJKLMNOPQRSTUVWXYZ
   CT: DEFGHIJKLMNOPQRSTUVWXYZABC

9. Key: GRATITUDE
   PT: ABCDEFGHIJKLMNOPQRSTUVWXYZ
   CT: GRATIUDEBCFHJKLMNOPQSVWXYZ

Cryptogram Carnival – page 139

All puzzles in this section are simple substitution ciphers.

1. Key: PATIENCE
2. Key: PSYCHE
3.
   PT: ABCDEFGHIJKLMNOPQRSTUVWXYZ
   CT: FIJKLMNPQTVWXYZGEORBUSHACD
4. Using backwards alphabet and key: REISNHOW
5. Key: NOVEMBER
6. Key: ADVANTAGE
7. Method: Rot-13
8. Key: ENCYCLOPEDIA
9. Key: MARRIAGE
10. Key: SECRETS
11. Key: FRANKLY
12. Atbash Substitution
13. Key: INDUSTRY
14. Key: CHARACTER
15. Key: VICTORY
16. Key: FAITH
17. Key: FUGIT
18. Key: FRANCIS
19. Key: POWERFUL
20. Key: VERITAS
21. Key: THEKORAN
22. Key: COUNTRYMAN
23. SimpKey: CRUSH
24. Key: BOURBON
25. Key: EVERYTHING
26. Key: QUOTATION
27. Key: ROBAHEIN
28. Key: GOLDEN RULE
29. Key: STEP BY STEP
30. Key: FRANKLY
*31. Key: DOUGLAS
*32. Key: EISNHOWR
33. Shift +1, NFUBQVAAMFUIFGPVSUIJTGSPNTBNVFMDMFNFOT
34. Key: KINDNESS
35. Key: GENERATION
36.
   PT: ABCDEFGHIJKLMNOPQRSTUVWXYZ
   CT: XOBWCTEVRPHINDYMUKGJFSZAQL

37. Caesar shift +1
38. Key: REASON
39. Key: GIVEMYLIFE
40. ROT-13
41. Key: NATURE
42. Key: PRESENT
43.
    PT: ABCDEFGHIJKLMNOPQRSTUVWXYZ
    CT: IJKLMNOPQRSTUVWXYZABCDEFGH
44. Key: WREISNHO
45. Key: DISPUTE
46. Key: FRANKLY
47.
    PT: ABCDEFGHIJKLMNOPQRSTUVWXYZ
    CT: LMNPQRUVWXYZCOSTABDEFGHIJK
48. Key: DISHONESTY
49. Key: A SECRET
50. Key: GANDHI
51. Key: BEFRIEND
52. Caesar shift +5
53. Key: BLOCKHEAD
54. Key: PRESIDENT
55. Key: REDBADGE; shift +4
56. Key: DEBTORS
57. Key: FRANKLY
58. Key: THEKORAN
59. Key: PROFITING
60. Key: MONEY
61. ROT-13
62.
    PT:ABCDEFGHIJKLMNOPQRSTUVWXYZ
    CT:SMILEGHJKNZABCDFOPQRTUVWXY
63.
    PT: ABCDEFGHIJKLMNOPQRSTUVWXYZ
    CT: XYZJAMESDIONBCFGHKLPQRTUVW
64. Backwards alphabet and key: REISNHOW
65. Key: TROUBLES
66. Key: PRINTERS
67. Key: KNOWLEDGE
68. Key: MONDAY
69. Key: ALMANAC
70. Key: RPFEYNMA
71. Each letter is converted to a number (a is 1), then multiplied by 7, then converted back (A is 1, Z is 0) modulo 26
72. Key: ABELINCO
73. Key: PLEASURE
74. Key: ACTING
75. Key: MACHINES
76. Key: DIAMOND
*77. Key: STRANGE; shift +7
78. Key: QUESTION
79. Key: SURRENDER

80.   Key: WANTING
81.   Key: ENDGAMEOSC
82.   Key: CLOAKROOM
*83. Key: THURSDAY
84.   Sub, VHUGO
85.   Key: LAZINESS
86.   Key: BUNDLE
87.   Key: GANDHI
88.   Key: DOUGLAS
89.   Key: FAMILY
90.   Key: POLITICS
91.   Key: GANDHI
92.   Key: ANYTHING
93.   Key: EXIST
94.   Key: GRATITUDE
95.   Key: DOCTOR
96.   Key: PRECIOUS
97.   Key: THE KORAN
98.   Key: BAD HABITS
99.   Key: CRYPTOGRAM
100. Caesar shift +12
101. Key: HOWREISN
102. Key: TRAGEDY
103.

    PT: ABCDEFGHIJKLMNOPQRSTUVWXYZ
    CT: MONEYTVQBHRSPAJWXZGFKCIDUL
104. Backwards alphabet and key: EISNHOWR
105. Key: DUMAS; shift +3
106. Key: PHOENIX
107. Caesar shift +5
108. Key: MISFORTUNE
109. Key: FRANKLY
110. Key: WORRY
111. Key: SAFETY
112. Key: PROJECTS
113. Key: DUBIOUS
114. Key: ACTIONS
115.

    PT: ABCDEFGHIJKLMNOPQRSTUVWXYZ
    CT: DEFGJKPQTUVWXYZABRAHMLINCO
116. Key: MEMORIAM
117. Key: HOUSE
118. Key: PENNYSAVED
119. Key: RUSH; shift +12
120. Key: TVWXZJOHNQUICYADMSBEFGKLPR
121. Key: THEKORAN
122. Key: FORTUNE
123. Key: MADISONZYXWVUTRQPLKJHGFECB
124. Key: CONVICTION
125. Key: ASIMOV
126. Key: JDIAMON

127.
  PT: ABCDEFGHIJKLMNOPQRSTUVWXYZ
  CT: DUELSAIVHJFYWXKZPQTMCROBNG
128. Key: FRUGAL
129. Key: INFORMED
130. Key: CFIUDMXEBHQTKZNLWOJVSAGPRY
131. Key: OBVIOUS
132. Key: REVENGE
133. Key: KMARX
134. Key: PURPOSE
135. Key: POOR RICHARD
136. Key: FRANKLY
137. Key: ABSENT
138. Backwards alphabet and Key: SNHOWREI
139. Key: EMCSQUARED
140. Key: DOUGLAS
141. Key: BLINDLY
142. Key: ENJOYING
143. Atbash substitution
144. Key: GANDHI
145. Key: POLITICS
146. Key: COUNTRY
147. Key: MARRIAGE
148. Key: DELAY
149.
  PT: ABCDEFGHIJKLMNOPQRSTUVWXYZ
  CT: MPQRTUVWXZLYNDOBJHSACEFGIK
150. Key: MANKIND
151. Key: CARPENTER
152. Caesar shift +1
153. Key: DRUNK; shift +5
154. Key: HAILSTORM
155. Key: FRANKLY
156. Key: GUESTS
157. Key: COUNSEL
158. Using a standard QWERTY keyboard, each letter has been shifted to the right one key ('p' becomes 'q', 'l' -> 'a' and 'm' -> 'z')
159.
  PT: ABCDEFGHIJKLMNOPQRSTUVWXYZ
  CT: KASBDTNQEIFVRWJLUOXHYPGMCZ
160. ROT-13
161. Key: DOUGLAS
162. Key: RPFEYNMA
163. Backwards alphabet and Key: HOWREISN
164. Key: DESIRE
165. Key: NOTHING
166. Key: GANDHI
167. Caesar shift +7
168. Key: ASIMOV
169. Key: CLINT
170. Key: FRANKLY
171. Key: ASIMOV

*172. Key: INHUMANITY
173. Key: NHOWREIS
174. Key: HUNGRY
175. Key: JDIAMON
176. Key: MASTER
177. Key: THE KORAN
178. Key: GAMES
179. Key: FAULT
180. Key: MARBLE
181. Key: THE KORAN
182. Key: YESTERDAY
183.

    PT: ABCDEFGHIJKLMNOPQRSTUVWXYZ
    CT: HKLNOPQSUVWXZJIMYCARTEBDFG
184. Key: DISTURBERS; shift +7
185. Key: SOBRIETY
186. Key: INTEREST
187. Key: NEW YEAR
188. Rot-13
189. Key: LUCK
190. Key: PLEASE
191. Key: GANDHI
192. Key: PEACE
193. Key: FORMULAIC
194.

    PT: ABCDEFGHIJKLMNOPQRSTUVWXYZ
    CT: CLANDBFHIJKMPQSTUWXYZGROVE
195. Key: MYLEISURE
196. Backwards alphabet and key: WREISNHO
197. Key: SERVANT
198. Key: PEARL HARBOR
199.

    PT: ABCDEFGHIJKLMNOPQRSTUVWXYZ
    CT: ZDEQRVBKLJGMXNPYFTCHUSAOWI
200. Key: ASIMOV
201. Key: FICTION
202. Key: HASTE
203. Key: PURSUIT
204. Key: MISTAKE
205. Backwards alphabet and key: SUNDAY
206. Key: LIBERTY
207. Key: TRICKS
208. Key: POLITICAL
209. Key: REMAINS
210. Caesar shift
211.

    PT: ABCDEFGHIJKLMNOPQRSTUVWXYZ
    CT: KLPQSTUVWYZRICHADMNXOBEFGJ
212. Key: FRESH NEW
213. Caesar shift +4
*214. Key: _ _ x _ _ _ _
215. Key: BUDHASIT

216. Key: OWREISNH
217. Key: FRANKLY
218. Key: JDIAMON
219.

    PT: ABCDEFGHIJKLMNOPQRSTUVWXYZ
    CT: XTNCHVKEJBIWALOGPUYMQRSDFZ

220.

    PT: ABCDEFGHIJKLMNOPQRSTUVWXYZ
    CT: GEORWASHINTBCDFJKLMPQUVXYZ

221. Key: RIVALS
222. Key: DOUGLAS
223.

    PT: ABCDEFGHIJKLMNOPQRSTUVWXYZ
    CT: FOHZCNBDPQGJLRVAIEWXYMSKTU

224. Key: HEADLINES
225. Key: WRITING
226. Key: ASIMOV
227. Key: SAINT
228. Key: TEMPLE
229. Key: JUDGMENT
230. Key: JDIAMON
231. Key: EXPAND
232. Key: CASUALLY
233. Backwards alphabet and key: ISNHOWRE
234. Key: THEKORAN
235. Key: TALMUD
236. Key: ATTORNEYGENERAL
237. Key: CDARWIN
238. Key: THEKORAN
239. Key: SHAKEIV
240.

    PT: ABCDEFGHIJKLMNOPQRSTUVWXYZ
    CT: CLUFOXBKTHQZGPYENWDMVAJSIR

241. Key: PAPERWEIGHT
242. Key: FICTION; shift +2
243. Key: FELINE; shift +20
244. Key: FRANKLY
245.

    PT: ABCDEFGHIJKLMNOPQRSTUVWXYZ
    CT: MPQUVXYZDWIGHTESNORABCFJKL

246.

    PT: ABCDEFGHIJKLMNOPQRSTUVWXYZ
    CT: ZABCDEFGHIJKLMNOPQRSTUVWXY

247. ROT-13
248. Key: THURSDAY
249.

    PT: ABCDEFGHIJKLMNOPQRSTUVWXYZ
    CT: BAECFDKLJIOQRSPXUMNVWGHYZT

250. Key: JDIAMON
251.

    PT: ABCDEFGHIJKLMNOPQRSTUVWXYZ
    CT: LKOPBTXNIUEMFWJZRADSHVYCQG

■ ■ ■ ■ 516 ■ ■ ■ ■

252. Key: PEACEFUL
253. Key: WOMAN'S FURY
254.

   PT:ABCDEFGHIJKLMNOPQRSTUVWXYZ
   CT:RIQXZMWLNFSTHCDGOEVKYAPUBJ
255. Key: BORROWER
256. Key: ASIMOV
257. Key: TRUTH
258. Key: DOGFISH
259. Key: MISTAKE
260. Key: BUDHASIT
261. Key: JACKIESSON
262. Key: STAIRWAYS
263. Key: SLOWLY
264. Key: JDIAMON
265. Key: FRANKLY
266.

   PT: ABCDEFGHIJKLMNOPQRSTUVWXYZ
   CT: FMUZLYICDAGHJKNOWQRSTEVBXP
267. Key: DOUGLAS
268. Key: ASIMOV
269. Key: REISNHOW
270. Key: CASUALTIES
271. Key: MORPHEUS
272. Key: STARVATION
273. Key: JOHNSON
274. Key: DOUGLAS
275. Backwards alphabet and key: NHOWREIS
276.

   PT: ABCDEFGHIJKLMNOPQRSTUVWXYZ
   CT: TUVXYZANDREWJCKSOBFGHILMPQ
*277. Key: _ _ _ _ _ x; Shift +8
278. Key: GANDHI
279. Key: RPFEYNMA
280.

   PT: ABCDEFGHIJKLMNOPQRSTUVWXYZ
   CT: BCDFHIJKLMOPQUVWXYZSTRANGE
281. Key: ENGLISH
282. Key: BUCHANAN
283.

   PT: ABCDEFGHIJKLMNOPQRSTUVWXYZ
   CT: MNPQSTUVWXYZGERALDFOBCHIJK
284. Key: JDIAMOND
285. ROT-13
286. Key: TOGETHER
287. Key: FRANKLY
288. Key: LAZBOY
289. Key: ASIMOV
290. Key: KRYPTOS
291. Key: SAMURAI
292. Key: CARMELITES
293. Key: PREPARED

294. Key: PHILOSOPHY
295. Key: WAR
296. Key: WOODYALLEN
297. Key: DURANDURAN
298. Key: CUISINE
299. Key: NEVER
300. Key: TURTLE

Not So Easy – Page 369

1. Binary ASCII
2. Hexadecimal
3. Columnar transposition, 6-character rows
4. Morse code
5. Transposition, 7-character rows
6. Rot-47
7. QWERTY alternating shifting (right, left)
8. Transposition, 5x9. Write into columns of 9, read out by rows of 5
9. Simple substitution

A	B	C	D	E	F	G	H	I	J	K	L	M
1,	2,	3,	5,	7,	11,	13,	17,	19,	23,	29,	31,	37
N	O	P	Q	R	S	T	U	V	W	X	Y	Z
41,	43,	47,	53,	59,	61,	67,	71,	73,	79,	83,	89,	97

10. Morse code
11. Rot-47
12. Simple substitution

A	B	C	D	E	F	G	H	I	J	K	L	M	N	O	P	Q	R	S	T	U	V	W	X	Y	Z
1	2	3	4	5	6	7	8	9	10	11	12	13	14	15	16	17	18	19	20	21	22	23	24	25	26

13. Hexadecimal
14. 8-bit binary
15. Columnar transposition, 4-character rows
16.

A	B	C	D	E	F	G	H	I	J	K	L	M	N	O	P	Q	R	S	T	U	V	W	X	Y	Z
-12	-11	-10	-9	-8	-7	-6	-5	-4	-3	-2	-1	0	1	2	3	4	5	6	7	8	9	10	11	12	13

17. Railfence, 3WO
18. Columnar transposition, 5-character rows
19. Route transposition. Start at the center; work your way out clockwise.
20. Telephone dial code substitution. Each pair represents the number of the keypad, and the symbol represents which letter on the keypad.
21. 8-bit binary
22. Hexadecimal
23. Route transposition. 3-character rows, start at top-left, read diagonally back and forth.
24. Morse with re-grouping. Ignore the spaces. The Xs mark the separation between characters.
25. 8-bit binary
26. Rot-47
27. Hexadecimal
28. 8-bit binary
29. Simple substitution lipogram
    PT: ABCDEFGHIJKLMNOPQRSTUVWXYZ
    CT: QIEGASHNYDMTZXKVJWFPCLRUOB

30.

4D65746170757A7A6C653A205468652074686972264206973206672
6F6D20313737302D38322C20546F72792E

31. Simple substitution, key: GAMEOFTHEYEAR
32. Simple substitution, key: DINOSAUR
33. Plaintext alphabet is 25 Letters: A-Z, W --> V V.
CT: CLUFOYBKTHQGPZENXDMVAJSIR
34. Transposition, 5-character rows
35. Transposition, 7-character rows
36. Route cipher, start at upper right, read diagonals
37. Redefence cipher, keyword: RUNNER
38. Columnar transposition, 7x15
39. Card cipher:

A	B	C	D	E	F	G	H	I	J	K	L	M
2H	3H	4H	5H	6H	7H	8H	9H	10H	JH	QH	KH	AH
N	O	P	Q	R	S	T	U	V	W	X	Y	Z
2D	3D	4D	5D	6D	7D	8D	9D	10D	JD	QD	KD	AD

40. Simple substitution, key: CRYPTO-GRAM

Challenging – page 391

1. Base 64
2. Substitution, key: IMMORTALITY
3. Substitution, key: STATEMENT
4. Monoalphabetic Substitution, key: QUICKBROWNFOX
5. Substitution, key: MONDAY
6. Base 64
7. Playfair, I/J, key: ARTIFICIAL LIFE
8. Base 64
9. Substitution, key: FREEDOM
10. Substitution, key: NATIONAL INSTITUTE
11. 7-bit binary
12. Key: KISSING
13. Base 64
14. Substitution, key: ONE TWO THREE FOUR
15. Substitution, key: SISTINE CHAPEL
16. Homophonic substitution, encryption key:

A	DaB	O	XER
B	Uk	P	dh
C	FqW	Q	
D	IHw	R	JFP
E	cZIGK	S	VAr
F	tv	T	Nnem
G	I	U	OL
H	TbY	V	Q
I	Myz	W	j
J	K	X	C
L	uo	Y	S
M	s	Z	
N	xgp		

17. Column transposition, key: 51423
18. Substitution, key: PRESIDENCY
19. Substitution, key: WEATHER
20. Solution every 10th letter; LDAOSEMTS OWTOTSOAB RHFLHERLE

..R..H..F..L..H..E..R..L..E
.O..W..T..O..T..S..O..A..B
L..D..A..O..S..E..M..T..S

21. Substitution, key: ACTUALIZE
22. Monoalphabetic Substitution, Key: EISENHOWER
23. Substitution, key: MONDAY
24. Substitution, key: POVERTY
25. Increment: 61, shift: 0, modulus: 153
26. Change letters to numbers, then the numbers to their corresponding symbols on a keyboard. Dashes are used to separate each 'number'.
27. Transposition, 7-character rows
28. Substitution, key: NFUBQVAAMFQMFJBEFTQPJOUFS
29. Substitution, key: POVERTY
30. Homophonic substitution, key:

A	srxo	O	kCV
B	n	P	YM
C	DK	Q	w
D	yI	R	Jhe
E	qTmb	S	QEW
F	ju	T	pgAG
G	iN	U	ac
H	dUZ	V	O
I	RvP	W	t
J	K	X	
L	SH	Y	IL
M	BF	Z	
N	Xzf		

31. Substitution, key: COCKTAIL
32. Substitution, key: ECONOMICS
33. Substitution, key: AIRFORCE
34. Substitution, key: DOCTRINE
35. Substitution, key: GOVERNMENT
36. Base 64
37. Substitution, key: ECONOMICS
38. Playfair, I/J block, key: BEAUTY
39. Substitution, key: DESTINY
40. Substitution, key: TUESDAY
41. Substitution, key: HAIPHONG
42. Substitution
    CT: CDFJKOPQRSUVWXYZENLIGHTMAB
43. Substitution, key: GOVERNMENT
44. Substitution, key: WEATHER
45. Homophonic Substitution, key:

A		N	fDc
B	t	O	M
C	d	P	W
D	yhV	Q	
E	QKNHvP	R	ZwjY
F	x	S	nbOs
G	A	T	RzgG
H	lIXq	U	F
I	kaJr	V	U
J		W	L

	K			X	S
	L		p	Y	Te
	M		i	Z	m

46. Substitution, key: NECESSARY
47. Substitution, key: KABBALAH
48. Substitution, key: TREATYON
49. Substitution, key: HEBREWS
50. Substitution, key: MONALISA
51. Substitution, key: LABOUR
52. Substitution, key: PRESIDENT
53. Modular transposition. Increment: 87, shift: 0, modulus: 268
54. Substitution, key: WEATHER
55. Substitution, key: WALPOLE
56. Substitution, key: COMPTON
57. Substitution, key: PELHAM
58. Substitution, key: PELHAMHOLLES
59. Substitution, key: CAVENDISH
60. Substitution, key: STUART
61. Substitution, key: GRENVILLE
62. Substitution, key: WENTWORTH
63. Substitution, key: FITZROY
64. Substitution, key: PITT
65. Substitution, key: NORTH
66. Substitution, key: PETTY
67. Substitution, key: BENTINCK
68. Substitution, key: GRENVILLE
69. Substitution, key: ADDINGTON
70. Substitution, key: PERCEVAL
71. Substitution, key: JENKINSON
72. Substitution, key: CANNING
73. Substitution, key: ROBINSON
74. Substitution, key: WELLESLEY
75. Substitution, key: GREY
76. Substitution, key: LAMB
77. Substitution, key: PEEL
78. Substitution, key: RUSSELL
79. Substitution, key: DERBY
80. Substitution, key: ABERDEEN
81. Substitution, key: PALMERSTON
82. Substitution, key: DISRAELI
83. Substitution, key: GLADSTONE
84. Substitution, key: GASCOYNECECIL
85. Substitution, key: ROSEBERY
86. Substitution, key: BALFOUR
87. Substitution, key: CAMPBELLBANNERMAN
88. Substitution, key: ASQUITH
89. Substitution, key: GEORGE
90. Substitution, key: LAW
91. Substitution, key: BALDWIN
92. Substitution, key: MACDONALD
93. Substitution, key: CHAMBERLAIN
94. Substitution, key: CHURIL

95. Substitution, key: ATTLEE
96. Substitution, key: EDEN
97. Substitution, key: MACMILLAN
98. Substitution, key: DOUGLASHOME
99. Substitution, key: WILSON
100. Substitution, key: HEATH
101. Substitution, key: CALLAGHAN
102. Substitution, key: THATCHER
103. Substitution, key: MAJOR
104. Substitution, key: BLAIR

Fiendish – page 431

1. Quagmire III, alphabet key: NORMANDY, indicator: HASTINGS
2. Vigenère, key: COBOL
3. Beaufort, key: SUBTLE
4. Vigenère, key: KENNEDY
5. Vigenère, key: TWAIN
6. Beaufort, key: ENGINEER
7. Beaufort, key: HENEGG
8. Quagmire III, key: END, passphrase: BEGINNING, on a backwards plaintext
9. Quagmire III, key: FALSE, passphrase: TRUE
10. Quagmire III, key 'GAMES', indicator SIMCITY
11. Autokey, key CANID
12. Quagmire III, alphabet key IVORY, indicator TOWER
13. Autokey, key QUANTUM
14. Beaufort, key: LEADING
15. Vigenère, key: ENIGMA
16. Vigenère, key: AMERICA
17. Beaufort, key: STUPID
18. Method: Quagmire III, key: LEARN, passphrase: TAUGHT
19. Beaufort, key: CAUSE
20. Vigenère, key: SUNDAY
21. Vigenère, key: WRIGHT
22. Autokey, key: CHARLOTTE
23. Vigenère, key: RIGHT
24. Beaufort, Key: OLDSTORY
25. Vigenère, passphrase: ALIEN
26. Beaufort, key: CONCENSUS
27. Progressive key
    ABCDEFGHIJKLMNOPQRSTUVWXYZ
    LMNOPQRSTUVWXYZABCDEFGHIJK
    IJKLMNOPQRSTUVWXYZABCDEFGH
    BCDEFGHIJKLMNOPQRSTUVWXYZA
    EFGHIJKLMNOPQRSTUVWXYZABCD
    RSTUVWXYZABCDEFGHIJKLMNOPQ
    TUVWXYZABCDEFGHIJKLMNOPQRS
    YZABCDEFGHIJKLMNOPQRSTUVWX
28. Beaufort, key: VICTORY
29. Quagmire III, alphabet key DALBERG, indicator SHROPSHIRE
30. Beaufort, key: DONE
31. Beaufort, key: THATCHER

32. Semi-Fibonacci replacement sequence. Starting with an adjustment number of 0, each letter is moved down the alphabet n times, where n is the sum of the previous two adjustments, but remainder 5. So the sequence is 0, *1, 1, 2, 3, 5, 3, 3, 1, 4, 5, 4, 4, 3, 2, 5, 2, 2, 4, 1, 5...repeats from *.)
33. Quagmire III, key: TALK, passphrase: YAK
34. Vigenère, key: PROGRAM
35. Quagmire III, alphabet key SUTRA, indicator GAUTAMA
36. Vigenère, key: EQUATION
37. Beaufort, key: MANAGER
38. Vigenère, key: MILTON
39. Beaufort, key: HEART
40. Vigenère, CHURCHILL
41. Autokey, WILMAR SHIRAS
42. Vigenère, GEEKDOM
43. Vigenère, CHIPS
44. Autokey, FLATLAND
45. Progressive Key: TEDDY
46. Beaufort Autokey: KAMINSKY

Grab Bag – page 445
1. Vigenère, key: CHERRYTREE
2. Substitution, key: JOHN ADAMS; shift +2
3. Substitution
   CT: YZTHOMASJEFRNBCDGIKLPQUVWX
4. Columnar transposition, 24135
5. Substitution, key: MONROE
6. Substitution, key: ALLIGATOR
7. Playfair, key: SELFISH, no Q
8. Substitution, key: MARTINVANBUREN
9. Substitution
   JKPQTUVXWILIAMHENRYRSOCDFG
10. Vigenère, key: CONSCIENCE
11. Substitution, key: TAFT
12. Substitution, key: TAYLOR
13. Substitution, key: FILLMORE
14. Substitution, key: PIERCE
15. Substitution, key: BUCHANAN
16. Homophonic substitution, encryption key:

PT	CT	PT	CT
A	eZl	N	QBg
B	p	O	TSEMn
C	y	P	Ld
D	Jr	R	qDR
E	KAYHN	S	jwi
F	t	T	xuI
G	cV	U	bk
H	Xz	V	Fa
I	sGOf	W	U
K	v	Y	PW
L	hm	Z	C
M	o		

17. Substitution, key: JOHNSON

18. Substitution
    CT:: TBCDFHIJKMOPQVWXZULYSEGRAN
19. Substitution, key: HAYES
20. Substitution
    CT:: FILDBCHKNOPQTUVWXYZJAMESGR
21. Substitution, key: ARTHUR
22. Substitution
    CT:KPZCJHDRWQIMFGLXATEYNOBVSU
23. Playfair, key: POVERTY, i/j block
24. Substitution, key: MCKINLEY
25. Vigenère, key: BIGSTICK
    ABCDEFGHIJKLMNOPQRSTUVWXYZ
    BCDEFGHIJKLMNOPQRSTUVWXYZA
    IJKLMNOPQRSTUVWXYZABCDEFGH
    GHIJKLMNOPQRSTUVWXYZABCDEF
    STUVWXYZABCDEFGHIJKLMNOPQR
    TUVWXYZABCDEFGHIJKLMNOPQRS
    IJKLMNOPQRSTUVWXYZABCDEFGH
    CDEFGHIJKLMNOPQRSTUVWXYZAB
    KLMNOPQRSTUVWXYZABCDEFGHIJ
26. Substitution, key: TAFT
27. Substitution
CT: ZWODRILSNABCEFGHJKMPQTUVXY
28. Quagmire III, keys: WARREN, HARDING
29. Substitution
    CT: WXYZCALVINODGEBFHJKMPQRSTU
30. Route. Lay out the ciphertext in a clockwise spiral going from outside
    to inside, then read off diagonally starting from top left corner.
31. Substitution
    CT: QUWXYZFRANKLIDOSEVTBCGHJMP
32. Vigenère, key: ATOMBOMB
33. Columnar transposition, key: 243561
34. Autokey, key JOSEPH
35. Vigenère, key: FREEDOM
36. Vigenère, key: RESIGNATION
37. Route. Key: 4-character rows, start at top left and read diagonally
    back and forth.
38. Myszkowski, key: POLITICS
39. Substitution, key: RONALDREAGAN
40. Substitution, key: GEORGEBUSH; shift: +12
41. Substitution
    CT: FGHJKMPQRSUVWXYZBILCNTOADE
42. Substitution, key: FORTYTHREE
43. Substitution, key: ASIMOV,
    HORALTZZGORCOQOIKJMDQVPKHAQDHKUQVDPQRJAHO

Other Languages – page 455
French
1. Simple Substitution
    CT: EPHMRALBCDFGIJKNOQSTUVWXYZ
Spanish
2. Simple Substitution, key: MOLINO

Russian

3. Caesar shift, +17
   CT: РСТУФХЦЧШШЩЪЫЬЭЮЯАБВГДЕЁЖЗИЙКЛМНОП
   PT: АБВГДЕЁЖЗИЙКЛМНОПРСТУФХЦЧШШЩЪЫЬЭЮЯ
4. Caesar Shift, +23
   PT: АБВГДЕЁЖЗИЙКЛМНОПРСТУФХЦЧШШЩЪЫЬЭЮЯ
   CT: ЦЧШШЩЪЫЬЭЮЯАБВГДЕЁЖЗИЙКЛМНОПРСТУФХ
5. Caesar Shift, +27
   PT: АБВГДЕЁЖЗИЙКЛМНОПРСТУФХЦЧШШЩЪЫЬЭЮЯ
   CT: ЪЫЬЭЮЯАБВГДЕЁЖЗИЙКЛМНОПРСТУФХЦЧШШЩ
6. Caesar Shift, +6
   PT: АБВГДЕЁЖЗИЙКЛМНОПРСТУФХЦЧШШЩЪЫЬЭЮЯ
   CT: ЁЖЗИЙКЛМНОПРСТУФХЦЧШШЩЪЫЬЭЮЯАБВГДЕ

Latin
7. CT: RSTVXYZABCDEFGHIKLMNOPQ
8. CT: RSTVXYZABCDEFGHIKLMNOPQ
9. CT: PQRSTVXYZABCDEFGHIKLMNO
10. CT: GHIKLMNOPQRSTVXYZABCDEF
11. CT: LMNOPQRSTVXYZABCDEFGHIK
12. CT: STVXYZABCDEFGHIKLMNOPQR
13. CT: IKLMNOPQRSTVXYZABCDEFGH
14. CT: FGHIKLMNOPQRSTVXYZABCDE
15. CT: RSTVXYZABCDEFGHIKLMNOPQ
16. CT: XYZABCDEFGHIKLMNOPQRSTV
17. CT: STVXYZABCDEFGHIKLMNOPQR
18. CT: MNOPQRSTVXYZABCDEFGHIKL
19. CT: BCDEFGHIKLMNOPQRSTVXYZA
20. CT: VXYZABCDEFGHIKLMNOPQRST
21. CT: HIKLMNOPQRSTVXYZABCDEFG
22. CT: FGHIKLMNOPQRSTVXYZABCDE
23. CT: ZABCDEFGHIKLMNOPQRSTVXY
24. CT: YZABCDEFGHIKLMNOPQRSTVX
25. CT: CDEFGHIKLMNOPQRSTVXYZAB
26. CT: QRSTVXYZABCDEFGHIKLMNOP
27. CT: NOPQRSTVXYZABCDEFGHIKLM
28. CT: XYZABCDEFGHIKLMNOPQRSTV
29. CT: MNOPQRSTVXYZABCDEFGHIKL
30. CT: DEFGHIKLMNOPQRSTVXYZABC
31. CT: DEFGHIKLMNOPQRSTVXYZABC
32. CT: OPQRSTVXYZABCDEFGHIKLMN
33. CT: RSTVXYZABCDEFGHIKLMNOPQ
34. CT: HIKLMNOPQRSTVXYZABCDEFG
35. CT: PQRSTVXYZABCDEFGHIKLMNO
36. CT: MNOPQRSTVXYZABCDEFGHIKL
37. CT: XYZABCDEFGHIKLMNOPQRSTV
38. CT: QRSTVXYZABCDEFGHIKLMNOP
39. CT: LMNOPQRSTVXYZABCDEFGHIK
40. CT: ZABCDEFGHIKLMNOPQRSTVXY
41. CT: FGHIKLMNOPQRSTVXYZABCDE
42. CT: PQRSTVXYZABCDEFGHIKLMNO
43. CT: RSTVXYZABCDEFGHIKLMNOPQ
44. CT: IKLMNOPQRSTVXYZABCDEFGH

45.   CT: EFGHIKLMNOPQRSTVXYZABCD
46.   CT: ZABCDEFGHIKLMNOPQRSTVXY
47.   CT: QRSTVXYZABCDEFGHIKLMNOP
48.   CT: EFGHIKLMNOPQRSTVXYZABCD

Kryptos – page 501

1.   Quagmire III, keys: KRYPTOS, PALIMPSEST
2.   Quagmire III, keys: KRYPTOS, ABSCISSA
3.   Transposition, key: KRYPTOS. There are several methods for solving Part 3, though the most efficient is to count to every 192nd letter. Another method is as follows:

```
ENDYAHROHNLSRHEOCPTEOIBIDYSHNAIACHTNREYULDSLLSLL
NOHSNOSMRWXMNETPRNGATIHNRARPESLNNELEBLPIIACAEWMT
WNDITEENRAHCTENEUDRETNHAEOETFOLSEDTIWENHAEIOYTEY
QHEENCTAYCREIFTBRSPAMHHEWENATAMATEGYEERLBTEEFOAS
FIOTUETUAEOTOARMAEERTNRTIBSEDDNIAAHTTMSTEWPIEROA
GRIEWFEBAECTDDHILCEIHSITEGOEAOSDDRYDLORITRKLMLEH
AGTDHARDPNEOHMGFMFEUHEECDMRIPFEIMEHNLSSTTRTVDOHW?
```

Looking at the above, you can see the first words in the decoded message by starting at the 'S', going down 4 rows (wrapping to the next column to the left when you have to start over at the top) to 'L', down another four rows to 'O', then down and around four rows to 'W', and so forth, to get the words, 'Slowly, desparatly . . .'

Example – page 574

Simple substitution, key: ANALYTICAL ENGINE

THE SOLUTIONS

First Steps – page 9

1. Whether you think that you can, or that you can't, you are usually right. – Henry Ford (1863- 1947)
2. When choosing between two evils, I always like to try the one I've never tried before. – Mae West (1892- 1980)
3. I am not discouraged, because every wrong attempt discarded is another step forward. – Thomas A. Edison
4. What is a weed? A plant whose virtues have not been discovered. – Ralph Waldo Emerson
5. I made this letter longer than usual because I lack the time to make it short. - Blaise Pascal

Easy 100 – page 15

1. About the time we think we can make ends meet, somebody moves the ends. – Herbert Hoover, 31st US President
2. He deserves Paradise who makes his companions laugh. – The Koran
3. While one person hesitates because he feels inferior; the other is busy making mistakes and becoming superior. – Henry C. Link
4. A banker is a fellow who lends you his umbrella when the sun is shining, but wants it back the minute it begins to rain. – Mark Twain
5. All sorts of computer errors are now turning up. You'd be surprised to know the number of doctors who claim they are treating pregnant men. – Isaac Asimov
6. At twenty years of age the will reigns; at thirty, the wit; and at forty, the judgment. – Benjamin Franklin
7. Clean your finger before you point at my spots. – Benjamin Franklin
8. Dost thou love life? Then do not squander time, for that is the stuff life is made of. – Benjamin Franklin
9. Engineers like to solve problems. If there are no problems handily available, they will create their own problems.– Scott Adams
10. Every citizen will be able, in his productive years when he is earning, to insure himself against the ravages of illness in his old age. – Lyndon B. Johnson
11. Every man's life ends the same way. It is only the details of how he lived and how he died that distinguish one man from another. – Ernest Hemingway
12. Gain may be temporary and uncertain; but ever while you live, expense is constant and certain: and it is easier to build two chimneys than to keep one in fuel. – Benjamin Franklin
13. Happiness in intelligent people is the rarest thing I know. – Ernest Hemingway
14. Human felicity is produced not as much by great pieces of good fortune that seldom happen as by little advantages that occur every day. – Benjamin Franklin
15. I believe that a scientist looking at nonscientific problems is just as dumb as the next guy. – Richard P. Feynman
16. I have nothing to offer but blood, toil, tears and sweat. – Winston Churchill
17. I like to believe that people, in the long run, are going to do more to promote peace than our governments. Indeed, I think that people want peace so much that one of these days governments had better get out of the way and let them have it. – Dwight D. Eisenhower

18. If you would know the value of money, go and try to borrow some. – Benjamin Franklin

19. In our home there was always prayer- aloud, proud and unapologetic. –Lyndon B. Johnson

20. It is a grand mistake to think of being great without goodness and I pronounce it as certain that there was never a truly great man that was not at the same time truly virtuous. – Benjamin Franklin

21. It's striking that Native Americans evolved no devastating epidemic diseases to give to Europeans, in return for the many devastating epidemic diseases that Indians received from the Old World. – Jared Diamond

22. Misquote: The hottest places in hell are reserved for those who in times of great moral crisis maintain their neutrality. Correct Quote: 'The darkest places in hell are reserved for those who maintain their neutrality in times of moral crisis.' – Dante, as quoted by John F. Kennedy, 35th US President

23. Outside of a dog, a book is man's best friend. Inside of a dog it's too dark to read. – Groucho Marx

24. Peace cannot be kept by force. It can only be achieved by understanding. – Albert Einstein

25. Science can purify religion from error and superstition. Religion can purify science from idolatry and false absolutes. – Pope John Paul II

26. The definition of insanity is doing the same thing over and over and expecting different results. – Benjamin Franklin

27. The highest form of wisdom is kindness. – The Talmud

28. The most exciting phrase to hear in science, the one that heralds new discoveries, is not 'Eureka!' but 'That's funny...' – Isaac Asimov

29. Trouble springs from idleness, and grievous toil from needless ease. – Benjamin Franklin

30. We do not covet anything from any nation except their respect. – Winston Churchill

31. Well done is better than well said. – Benjamin Franklin

32. 'This must be Thursday,' said Arthur to himself, sinking low over his beer, 'I never could get the hang of Thursdays.' – Arthur Dent, on what was to be his last Thursday on Earth. (by Douglas Adams)

33. You gotta get what you have to say out. Every man has the right to contribute a verse. – From the movie 'Hustle and Flow', written by Craig Brewer

34. Affairs are easier of entrance than of exit; and it is but common prudence to see our way out before we venture in. – Aesop

35. Buy what thou hast no need of and ere long thou shalt sell thy necessities. – Benjamin Franklin

36. Eurasia ended up with the most domesticated animal species in part because it's the world's largest land mass and offered the most wild species to begin with. – Jared Diamond

37. Extremism in defense of liberty is no vice. Tolerance in the face of tyranny is no virtue. – Barry Goldwater

38. Four score and seven years ago our fathers brought forth on this continent a new nation, conceived in liberty and dedicated to the proposition that all men are created equal. Now we are engaged in a great civil war, testing whether that nation or any nation so conceived and so dedicated can long endure. We are met on a great battlefield

of that war. We have come to dedicate a portion of that field as a final resting- place for those who here gave their lives that that nation might live. It is altogether fitting and proper that we should do this. But in a larger sense, we cannot dedicate, we cannot consecrate, we cannot hallow this ground. The brave men, living and dead who struggled here have consecrated it far above our poor power to add or detract. The world will little note nor long remember what we say here, but it can never forget what they did here. It is for us the living rather to be dedicated here to the unfinished work, which they who fought here have thus far so nobly advanced. It is rather for us to be here dedicated to the great task remaining before us–that from these honored dead we take increased devotion to that cause for which they gave the last full measure of devotion–that we here highly resolve that these dead shall not have died in vain, that this nation under God shall have a new birth of freedom, and that government of the people, by the people, for the people shall not perish from the earth. – Abraham Lincoln, 16th U.S. President

39. Genius without education is like silver in the mine. – Benjamin Franklin

40. Having been poor is no shame, but being ashamed of it, is. – Benjamin Franklin

41. Honesty is the best policy. – Benjamin Franklin

42. I conceive that the great part of the miseries of mankind are brought upon them by false estimates they have made of the value of things. – Benjamin Franklin

43. I may not have gone where I intended to go, but I think I have ended up where I needed to be. – Douglas Adams

44. It is only when the rich are sick that they fully feel the impotence of wealth. – Benjamin Franklin

45. It takes more than capital to swing business. You've got to have the A. I. D. degree to get by – Advertising, Initiative, and Dynamics. – Isaac Asimov

46. Laws too gentle are seldom obeyed; too severe, seldom executed. – Benjamin Franklin

47. Misquote: Money is the root of all evil. Correct Quote: 'For the love of money is the root of all evil: which while some coveted after, they have erred from the faith, and pierced themselves through with many sorrows.' (I Timothy 6:10)

48. Nature uses only the longest threads to weave her patterns, so that each small piece of her fabric reveals the organization of the entire tapestry. – Richard P. Feynman

49. +1, Nfubqvaamf: Zpvs jefoujuz ibt tfwfo mfuufst.

50. The moon and other celestial bodies should be free for exploration and use by all countries. No country should be permitted to advance a claim of sovereignty. – Lyndon B. Johnson

51. The reports of my death have been greatly exaggerated. – Mark Twain

52. The strictest law sometimes becomes the severest injustice. – Benjamin Franklin

53. The weak can never forgive. Forgiveness is the attribute of the strong. – Mahatma Gandhi

54. They want the federal government controlling Social Security like it's some kind of Federal program. – George W. Bush, 43rd US President

55. This desk of mine is one at which a man may die, but from which he cannot resign. – Dwight D. Eisenhower
56. Whatever is begun in anger ends in shame. – Benjamin Franklin
57. Work as if you were to live a hundred years. Pray as if you were to die tomorrow. – Benjamin Franklin
58. Yesterday is not ours to recover, but tomorrow is ours to win or lose. –Lyndon B. Johnson
59. You can have peace. Or you can have freedom. Don't ever count on having both at once. – Robert A. Heinlein
60. All my life, whenever it comes time to make a decision, I make it and forget about it. – Harry S. Truman, 33rd US President
61. 'Of those who answered the call of Allah and the messenger, even after being wounded, those who do right and refrain from wrong have a great reward.' – Chapter 3, verse 172, the Koran
62. One of these days the people of Louisiana are going to get good government – and they aren't going to like it. – Huey Long
63. ' . . . mother and foundress of the Order; whom one always needs to keep in mind. For Carmelite friars and nuns, it is of capital importance to honor the Most Blessed Virgin. And we love her if we endeavor to imitate her virtue, especially humility and recollection in prayer. Our gaze ought to be constantly turned to her, our affections directed to her, ever keeping in mind the remembrance of her benefits and trying always to be faithful to her.' – Saint Raphael Kalinowski, 1835-1907
64. An appeaser is one who feeds a crocodile—hoping it will eat him last. —Winston Churchill
65. Be civil to all; sociable to many; familiar with few; friend to one; enemy to none. – Benjamin Franklin
66. Be courteous to all, but intimate with few, and let those few be well tried before you give them your confidence. – George Washington, First US President
67. For a long time now I have tried simply to write the best I can. Sometimes I have good luck and write better than I can. – Ernest Hemingway
68. For a successful technology, reality must take precedence over public relations, for Nature cannot be fooled. – Richard Feynman
69. Freedom is not worth having if it does not include the freedom to make mistakes. – Mahatma Gandhi
70. From my close observation of writers...they fall into two groups: 1) those who bleed copiously and visibly at any bad review, and 2) those who bleed copiously and secretly at any bad review. – Isaac Asimov
71. Grief can take care of itself, but to get the full value of a joy you must have somebody to divide it with. – Mark Twain
72. Half a truth is often a great lie. – Benjamin Franklin
73. He does not possess wealth; it possesses him. – Benjamin Franklin
74. Honest differences are often a healthy sign of progress. – Mahatma Gandhi
75. I conceive that the great part of the miseries of mankind are brought upon them by the false estimates they have made of the value of things. – Benjamin Franklin
76. Imagination is more important than knowledge. Knowledge is limited. Imagination encircles the world. – Albert Einstein
77. In the councils of government, we must guard against the acquisition

of unwarranted influence, whether sought or unsought, by the military-industrial complex. The potential for the disastrous rise of misplaced power exists and will persist. We must never let the weight of this combination endanger our liberties or democratic processes. We should take nothing for granted. Only an alert and knowledgeable citizenry can compel the proper meshing of the huge industrial and military machinery of defense with our peaceful methods and goals, so that security and liberty may prosper together. – Dwight D. Eisenhower

78. In wartime, truth is so precious that she should always be attended by a bodyguard of lies. – Winston Churchill

79. It is the common failing of totalitarian regimes that they cannot really understand the nature of our democracy. They mistake dissent for disloyalty. They mistake restlessness for a rejection of policy. They mistake a few committees for a country. They misjudge individual speeches for public policy. –Lyndon B. Johnson

80. It is the genius of our Constitution that under its shelter of enduring institutions and rooted principles there is ample room for the rich fertility of American political invention. – Lyndon B. Johnson

81. It is the working man who is the happy man. It is the idle man who is the miserable man. – Benjamin Franklin

82. Jesus was the first socialist, the first to seek a better life for mankind. – Mikhail S. Gorbachev

83. Leisure is the time for doing something useful. This leisure the diligent person will obtain the lazy one never. – Benjamin Franklin

84. Livestock adopted in Africa were Eurasian species that came in from the north. Africa's long axis, like that of the Americas, is north/south rather than east/west. Those Eurasian domestic mammals spread southward very slowly in Africa, because they had to adapt to different climate zones and different animal diseases. – Jared Diamond, winner of the Pulitzer Prize for Guns, Germs, and Steel

85. Misquote: Alas, poor Yorrick. I knew him well. – Shakespeare, Hamlet Correct Quote: 'Alas, poor Yorick. I knew him, Horatio – a fellow of infinite jest, of most excellent fancy.' – Shakespeare, Hamlet, Act V, Scene 1

86. Never leave that till tomorrow which you can do today. – Benjamin Franklin

87. The ignorance of one voter in a democracy impairs the security of all. – John F. Kennedy, 35th US President

88. The learned fool writes nonsense in better language than the unlearned – but it's still nonsense. – Benjamin Franklin

89. The use of money is all the advantage there is in having it. – Benjamin Franklin

90. They didn't want it good, they wanted it Wednesday. – Robert A. Heinlein

91. Who is rich? He that rejoices in his portion. – Benjamin Franklin

92. If there's anything more important than my ego around, I want it caught and shot now. – Zaphod Beeblebrox (by Douglas Adams)

93. 'When I became a Musketeer, I was told, each time I drew my sword, I should consider not what I killed, but what I allowed to live.' – D'Artagnan, 'The Man in the Iron Mask', Alexandre Dumas

94. Always aim at complete harmony of thought and word and deed.

Always aim at purifying your thoughts and everything will be well. – Mahatma Gandhi

95. Beware of little expenses. A small leak will sink a great ship. – Benjamin Franklin

96. Decadence is a difficult word to use since it has become little more than a term of abuse applied by critics to anything they do not yet understand or which seems to differ from their moral concepts. – Ernest Hemingway

97. Distrust and caution are the parents of security. – Benjamin Franklin

98. Even to this day, no native Australian animal species and only one plant species – the macadamia nut – have proved suitable for domestication. There still are no domestic kangaroos. – Jared Diamond

99. Freedom is the last, best hope of earth. – Abraham Lincoln

100. He had read much, if one considers his long life; but his contemplation was much more than his reading. He was wont to say that if he had read as much as other men he should have known no more than other men. – Isaac Asimov

Hidden Keys – page 129

1. Games lubricate the body and the mind. – Benjamin Franklin
2. Quick fox jumps over the lazy brown dog. – Typewriter exercise
3. 'Old friends pass away, new friends appear. It is just like the days. An old day passes, a new day arrives. The important thing is to make it meaningful: a meaningful friend -- or a meaningful day.' - Dalai Lama XIV
4. My observation is that whenever one person is found adequate to the discharge of a duty... it is worse executed by two persons, and scarcely done at all if three or more are employed therein. – George Washington.
5. Change is the law of life. And those who look only to the past or present are certain to miss the future. – John F. Kennedy
6. A man may die, nations may rise and fall, but an idea lives on. – John F. Kennedy
7. Uifsf bsf npsf qvaamft ifsf uibo fbtjmz bqqbsfou. Difdl uif lfzt gps npsf jogpsnbujpo. Uif lfz't lfz ibt nboz gjstut bnpoh uif tubst.
8. Absence sharpens love, presence strengthens it. – Benjamin Franklin
9. As we express our gratitude, we must never forget that the highest appreciation is not to utter words, but to live by them. – John F. Kennedy

Cryptogram Carnival – page 139

1. He that can have patience can have what he will. – Benjamin Franklin
2. His talent was as natural as the pattern that was made by the dust on a butterfly's wings. At one time he understood it no more than the butterfly did and he did not know when it was brushed or marred. – Ernest Hemingway
3. I have opinions of my own – strong opinions – but I don't always agree with them. – George H.W. Bush, 41st US President
4. I make it a practice to avoid hating anyone. If someone's been guilty of despicable actions, especially toward me, I try to forget him. I used to follow a practice—somewhat contrived, I admit—to write the man's

name on a piece of scrap paper, drop it into the lowest drawer of my desk, and say to myself: 'That finishes the incident, and so far as I'm concerned, that fellow.' The drawer became over the years a sort of private wastebasket for crumbled-up spite and discarded personalities. – Dwight D. Eisenhower

5. I seldom think of politics more than eighteen hours a day. – Lyndon B. Johnson

6. I should have no objection to go over the same life from its beginning to the end: requesting only the advantage authors have, of correcting in a second edition the faults of the first. – Benjamin Franklin

7. Informed decision-making comes from a long tradition of guessing and then blaming others for inadequate results. – Scott Adams

8. Encyclopedia articles about current events are in many ways different from news articles about current events. - Jimmy Wales, founder of Wikipedia

9. Keep your eyes wide open before marriage, half shut afterwards. – Benjamin Franklin

10. Let thy discontents be thy secrets. – Benjamin Franklin

11. Money has never made man happy, nor will it, there is nothing in its nature to produce happiness. The more of it one has the more one wants. – Benjamin Franklin

12. Mulch mentally leafed through his dwarf abilities to select the best tool for this escape. He had long since forfeited his magic by breaking most of the Fairy Book's commandments, but dwarfs had extraordinary gifts granted them by evolution. Some of these were common knowledge among the People, but dwarfs were a notoriously secretive race who believed that their survival depended on concealing these talents. It was well known that dwarfs excavated tunnels by ingesting the earth through their unhinged jaws, then ejecting the recycled dirt and air through the other end. – Artemis Fowl, The Opal Deception by Eoin Colfer

13. So much for industry, my friends, and attention to one's own business; but to these we must add frugality if we would make our industry more certainly successful. A man may, if he knows not how to save as he gets, keep his nose all his life to the grindstone, and die not worth a grout at last. – Benjamin Franklin

14. The fact that a man is a newspaper reporter is evidence of some flaw of character. – Lyndon B. Johnson

15. The problems of victory are more agreeable than the problems of defeat, but they are no less difficult. – Winston Churchill

16. The way to see by Faith is to shut the Eye of Reason. – Benjamin Franklin

17. Time is money. – Benjamin Franklin

18. Where there is discord, may we bring harmony. Where there is error, may we bring truth. Where there is doubt, may we bring faith. And where there is despair, may we bring hope. –– Margaret Thatcher, paraphrasing St. Francis of Assisi

19. Who is wise? He that learns from everyone. Who is powerful? He that governs his passions. – Benjamin Franklin

20. Wine is constant proof that God loves us and loves to see us happy. – Benjamin Franklin

21. Thus, if they let you be, and do not make war on you, and offer you peace, God does not allow you to harm them. – (4: 90), The Koran

22. A countryman between two lawyers is like a fish between two cats. – Benjamin Franklin
23. A man can be destroyed but not defeated. – Ernest Hemingway
24. A man can take a little bourbon without getting drunk, but if you hold his mouth open and pour in a quart, he's going to get sick on it. – Lyndon B. Johnson, 36th US President
25. A place for everything, everything in its place. – Benjamin Franklin
26. A quotation at the right moment is like bread to the famished. – The Talmud
27. An armed society is a polite society. Manners are good when one may have to back up his acts with his life. – Robert A. Heinlein
28. Do something every day that you don't want to do; this is the golden rule for acquiring the habit of doing your duty without pain. – Mark Twain
29. Each year one vicious habit discarded, in time might make the worst of us good. – Benjamin Franklin
30. Experience is a dear teacher, but fools will learn at no other. – Benjamin Franklin
31. Far out in the uncharted backwaters of the unfashionable end of the Western Spiral arm of the Galaxy lies a small unregarded yellow sun. Orbiting this at a distance of roughly ninety-eight million miles is an utterly insignificant little blue-green planet whose ape-descended life forms are so amazingly primitive that they still think digital watches are a pretty neat idea... – Douglas Adams
32. Farming looks mighty easy when your plow is a pencil, and you're a thousand miles from the corn field. – Dwight D. Eisenhower
34. He that has done you a kindness will be more ready to do you another, than he whom you yourself have obliged. – Benjamin Franklin
35. I believe the destiny of your generation- and your nation- is a rendezvous with excellence. – Lyndon B. Johnson
36. I don't have a photograph, but you can have my footprints. They're upstairs in my socks. – Groucho Marx
37. I know not with what weapons World War III will be fought, but World War IV will be fought with sticks and stones. – Albert Einstein
38. write for the same reason I breathe – because if I didn't, I would die. –Isaac Asimov
39. I'd rather give my life than be afraid to give it. – Lyndon B. Johnson
40. If passion drives you, let reason hold the reins. – Benjamin Franklin
41. In general, mankind, since the improvement of cookery, eats twice as much as nature requires. – Benjamin Franklin
42. Change is the law of life. And those who look only to the past or present are certain to miss the future. – John F. Kennedy, 35th US President
43. It is a truth universally acknowledged, that a single man in possession of a good fortune, must be in want of a wife. – Jane Austen
44. Like all successful politicians I married above myself. – Dwight D. Eisenhower
45. Many a long dispute among divines may be thus abridged: It is so. It is not so. It is so. It is not so. – Benjamin Franklin
46. Marriage is the most natural state of man, and... the state in which you will find solid happiness. – Benjamin Franklin

47. The easiest way to figure the cost of living is to take your income and add ten percent. – Unknown
48. There is no kind of dishonesty into which otherwise good people more easily and frequently fall than that of defrauding the government. – Benjamin Franklin
49. Three can keep a secret if two are dead. – Benjamin Franklin
50. Victory attained by violence is tantamount to a defeat, for it is momentary. – Mahatma Gandhi
51. When befriended, remember it; when you befriend, forget it. – Benjamin Franklin
52. When I am abroad, I always make it a rule never to criticize or attack the government of my own country. I make up for lost time when I come home. – Sir Winston Churchill
53. A learned blockhead is a greater blockhead than an ignorant one. – Benjamin Franklin
54. A President's hardest task is not to do what is right, but to know what is right. –Lyndon B. Johnson
55. Cowardice, as distinguished from panic, is almost always simply a lack of ability to suspend the functioning of the imagination. – Ernest Hemingway
56. Creditors have better memories than debtors. – Benjamin Franklin
57. Employ thy time well, if thou meanest to gain leisure. – Benjamin Franklin
58. Fight in the cause of Allah those who fight you, but do not transgress limits; for Allah loves not transgressors. – Chapter 2, Verse 190, The Koran
59. We should not look back unless it is to derive useful lessons from past errors, and for the purpose of profiting by dearly bought experience. – George Washington, First US President
60. He that is of the opinion money will do everything may well be suspected of doing everything for money. – Benjamin Franklin
61. How is it that Pizarro and Cortes reached the New World at all, before Aztec and Inca conquistadors could reach Europe? That outcome depended partly on technology in the form of oceangoing ships. Europeans had such ships, while the Aztecs and Incas did not. – Jared Diamond
62. Humor is the great thing, the saving thing. The minute it crops up, all our irritations and resentments slip away and a sunny spirit takes their place. – Mark Twain
63. I believe there are more instances of the abridgement of the freedom of the people by gradual and silent encroachments of those in power than by violent and sudden usurpations. – James Madison, 4th US President
64. I say when you get into a war, you should win as quick as you can, because your losses become a function of the duration of the war. I believe when you get in a war, get everything you need and win it. – Dwight D. Eisenhower
65. If a man could have half of his wishes, he would double his troubles. – Benjamin Franklin
66. If all printers were determined not to print anything till they were sure it would offend nobody, there would be very little printed. – Benjamin Franklin

67. If knowledge can create problems, it is not through ignorance that we can solve them. –Isaac Asimov

68. If we win, nobody will care. If we lose, there will be nobody to care. – Winston Churchill

69. If you would be loved, love and be lovable. – Benjamin Franklin

70. It doesn't matter how beautiful your theory is, it doesn't matter how smart you are. If it doesn't agree with experiment, it's wrong. – Richard P. Feynman

71. It is unwise to be too sure of one's own wisdom. It is healthy to be reminded that the strongest might weaken and the wisest might err. – Mahatma Gandhi

72. Leave nothing for tomorrow which can be done today. – Abraham Lincoln

73. Many a man thinks he is buying pleasure, when he is really selling himself to it. – Benjamin Franklin

74. The art of acting consists in keeping people from coughing. – Benjamin Franklin

75. Then suddenly he came down another ten feet, grabbed four of the crew, swung them up the hole in the roof. They went like mahouts lifted in elephants' trunks. Eyeing the hole, I could see that Sug Farn no longer had any direct hold of his own, his upper tentacles being closely entwined with the equally ropey limbs of another Martian anchored out of view on the rooftop. Sug Farn raised the four to within a few feet of the hole whereupon other tentacles writhed through from above, took them from him. Then four more and four more. – Men, Martians and Machines by Eric Frank Russell

76. There are three things extremely hard: steel, a diamond, and to know one's self. – Benjamin Franklin

77. To be matter of fact about the world is to blunder into fantasy – and dull fantasy at that, as the real world is strange and wonderful. – Robert A. Heinlein

78. 'To be, or not to be, that is the question: Whether 'tis nobler in the mind to suffer The slings and arrows of outrageous fortune, Or to take arms against a sea of troubles And by opposing end them. To die: to sleep. – William Shakespeare, Hamlet

79. We shall fight on the beaches, we shall fight on the landing grounds, we shall fight in the fields and in the streets, we shall fight in the hills; we shall never surrender. – Winston Churchill

80. Where sense is wanting, everything is wanting. – Benjamin Franklin

81. Within an hour or so, it began to pall. Ender understood the regularities by then. Understood the rules the computer was following, so that he knew he could always, once he mastered the controls, outmaneuver the enemy. Spirals when the enemy was like this; loops when the enemy was like that. Lie in wait at one trap. Lay seven traps and then lure them like this. There was no challenge to it, then, just a matter of playing until the computer got so fast that no human reflexes could overcome it. That wasn't fun. It was the other boys he wanted to play. The boys who had been so trained by the computer that even when they played against each other they each tried to emulate the computer. Think like a machine instead of a boy. – Ender's Game by Orson Scott Card

82. You've got to work things out in the cloakroom, and when you've got

them worked out, you can debate a little before you vote. – Lyndon B. Johnson

83. He who fights with monsters might take care lest he thereby become a monster. And if you gaze for long into an abyss, the abyss gazes also into you. – Friedrich Nietzsche

84. There are moments when, whatever the position of the body, the soul is on its knees. – Victor Hugo

85. A life of leisure and a life of laziness are two things. There will be sleeping enough in the grave. – Benjamin Franklin

86. A man wrapped up in himself makes a very small bundle. – Benjamin Franklin

87. As long as you derive inner help and comfort from anything, keep it. – Mahatma Gandhi

88. Bypasses are devices that allow some people to dash from point A to point B very fast while other people dash from point B to point A very fast. People living at point C, being a point directly in between, are often given to wonder what's so great about point A that so many people from point B are so keen to get there and what's so great about point B that so many people from point A are so keen to get *there*. They often wish that people would just once and for all work out where the hell they wanted to be. –Douglas Adams

89. He that raises a large family does, indeed, while he lives to observe them, stand a broader mark for sorrow; but then he stands a broader mark for pleasure too. – Benjamin Franklin

90. I am extraordinarily patient provided I get my own way in the end. – Margaret Thatcher

91. I believe in equality for everyone, except reporters and photographers. – Mahatma Gandhi

92. I don't believe I'll ever get credit for anything I do in foreign affairs, no matter how successful it is, because I didn't go to Harvard. – Lyndon B. Johnson

93. I don't like to write like God. It is only because you never do it, though, that the critics think you can't do it. – Ernest Hemingway

94. If future generations are to remember us more with gratitude than sorrow, we must achieve more than just the miracles of technology. We must also leave them a glimpse of the world as it was created, not just as it looked when we got through with it. – Lyndon B. Johnson

95. If my doctor told me I had only six minutes to live, I wouldn't brood. I'd type a little faster. – Isaac Asimov

96. If time be of all things the most precious, wasting time must be the greatest prodigality. – Benjamin Franklin

97. In the Name of God, the Merciful, the Compassionate; Praise be to God, Lord of the Universe, The Compassionate, the Merciful, Sovereign of the Day of Judgement! You alone we worship, and to You alone we turn for help. Guide us to the straight path, the path of those whom You have favoured, not of those who have incurred Your wrath, nor of those who have gone astray. – Books, The Koran

98. It is easier to prevent bad habits than to break them. – Benjamin Franklin

99. It is important that the United States remain a two-party system. I'm a fellow who likes small parties and the Republican Party can't be too small to suit me. – Lyndon B. Johnson

100. It's not enough that we do our best; sometimes we have to do what's required. – Sir Winston Churchill

101. Legislation to apply the principle of equal pay for equal work without discrimination because of sex is a matter of simple justice. – Dwight D. Eisenhower

102. Life's Tragedy is that we get old too soon and wise too late. – Benjamin Franklin

103. Money frees you from doing things you dislike. Since I dislike doing nearly everything, money is handy. – Groucho Marx

104. Neither a wise man nor a brave man lies down on the tracks of history to wait for the train of the future to run over him. – Dwight D. Eisenhower

105. Never underestimate the power of human stupidity. – Robert A. Heinlein

106. Out of the corner of his eye, Harry distinctly saw Malfoy throw a scathing look over at him; the wine glass Malfoy had been levitating fell to the floor and smashed. Harry could not suppress a grin. Professor Tofty smiled back at him encouragingly. 'That's it,' he said in his quavery old voice, 'no need to be nervous . . . Now, if I could ask you to take this eggcup and make it do some cartwheels for me...' On the whole Harry thought it went rather well; his Levitation Charm was certainly much better than Malfoy's had been, though he wished he had not mixed up the incantations for Color-Change and Growth Charms, so that the rat he was supposed to be turning orange swelled shockingly and was the size of a badger before Harry could rectify his mistake. He was glad Hermione had not been in the Hall at the time and neglected to mention it to her afterward. He could tell Ron, though; Ron had caused a dinner plate to mutate into a large mushroom and had no idea how it had happened. – Harry Potter and the Order of the Phoenix, by J. K. Rowling

107. Pleasure in the job puts perfection in the work. – Aristotle

108. Reflect on your present blessings, of which every man has many; not on your past misfortunes, of which all men have some. – Charles Dickens

109. Remember not only to say the right thing in the right place, but far more difficult still, to leave unsaid the wrong thing at the tempting moment. – Benjamin Franklin

110. Worry is the interest paid by those who borrow trouble. – George Washington, First US President

111. They who give up essential liberty to obtain a little temporary safety deserve neither liberty nor safety. – Benjamin Franklin

112. Those who govern, having much business on their hands, do not generally like to take the trouble of considering and carrying into execution new projects. The best public measures are therefore seldom adopted from previous wisdom, but forced by the occasion. – Benjamin Franklin

113. When in doubt, don't. – Benjamin Franklin

114. Words may show a man's wit but actions his meaning. – Benjamin Franklin

115. If I were two-faced, would I be wearing this one? – Abraham Lincoln, 16th US President

116. Relax, kids are washable. – Advice to young mothers, from Jackie Griffith

117. A house is not a home unless it contains food and fire for the mind as well as the body. – Benjamin Franklin
118. A penny saved is a penny earned. – Benjamin Franklin
119. Courage is grace under pressure. – Ernest Hemingway
120. Duty is ours, results are God's. – John Quincy Adams, 6th US President
121. He created the heavens and the earth in six days and then mounted His throne. He knows all that goes into the earth and all that emerges from it, all that comes down from heaven and all that ascends to it. He is with you wherever you are. He is cognizant of all your actions. – The Koran
122. He that waits upon fortune, is never sure of a dinner. – Benjamin Franklin
123. I believe there are more instances of the abridgement of the freedom of the people by gradual and silent encroachments of those in power than by violent and sudden usurpations. – James Madison, 4th US President
124. I believe, with abiding conviction, that this people- nurtured by their deep faith, tutored by their hard lessons, moved by their high aspirations- have the will to meet the trials that these times impose. – Lyndon B. Johnson
125. I don't believe in an afterlife, so I don't have to spend my whole life fearing hell, or fearing heaven even more. For whatever the tortures of hell, I think the boredom of heaven would be even worse. – Isaac Asimov
126. I personally am not conscious of my accent. – Jared Diamond
127. I thoroughly disapprove of duels. If a man should challenge me, I would take him kindly and forgivingly by the hand and lead him to a quiet place and kill him. – Mark Twain
128. If you know how to spend less than you get, you have the philosopher's stone. – Benjamin Franklin
129. The best argument against democracy is a five minute conversation with the average voter. – Winston Churchill
130. It is easy to be brave from a safe distance. – Aesop
131. It pays to be obvious, especially if you have a reputation for subtlety. – Isaac Asimov
132. Live well. It is the greatest revenge. – The Talmud
133. Misquote: 'Religion is the opiate of the masses.' – Karl Marx. Correct Quote: 'Religion is the sigh of the oppressed creature, the heart of a heartless world and the soul of soulless conditions. It is the opium of the people.' – Karl Marx
134. Never insult anyone by accident. – Robert A. Heinlein
135. Our necessities never equal our wants. – Benjamin Franklin
136. Since thou are not sure of a minute, throw not away an hour. – Benjamin Franklin
137. The absent are never without fault, nor the present without excuse. – Benjamin Franklin
138. The clearest way to show what the rule of law means to us in everyday life is to recall what has happened when there is no rule of law. – Dwight D. Eisenhower
139. The most beautiful thing we can experience is the mysterious. It is the source of all true art and science. – Albert Einstein

140. This planet has – or rather had – a problem, which was this: most of the people living on it were unhappy for pretty much of the time. Many solutions were suggested for this problem, but most of these were largely concerned with the movements of small green pieces of paper, which is odd because on the whole it wasn't the small green pieces of paper that were unhappy. – Douglas Adams

141. To Follow by faith alone is to follow blindly. – Benjamin Franklin

142. Wealth is not his that has it, but his that enjoys it. – Benjamin Franklin

143. Weapons were being sharpened upon churchyard headstones. Under the critical eye of Redtooth a band of rodents was gnawing off a length of planking from a rickety lych-gate fence at the rear of the church. Others collected stones to provide ammunition for slings, while some coiled ropes about their bodies. Inside the church Cluny sat up in the choir loft, the image of barbaric authority. He held the scourging tail in one claw, while gripped in the other was his war standard, topped by the ferret skull with the addition of the tattered tapestry square depicting Martin the Warrior. He gazed proudly at it as his armorer dressed him for war. – Redwall by Brian Jacques

144. What difference does it make to the dead, the orphans and the homeless, whether the mad destruction is wrought under the name of totalitarianism or the holy name of liberty or democracy? – Mahatma Gandhi

145. When asked to name the chief qualification a politician should have: 'It's the ability to foretell what will happen tomorrow, next month, and next year -- and to explain afterward why it didn't happen.' – Winston Churchill

146. Where liberty is, there is my country. – Benjamin Franklin

147. Where there's marriage without love, there will be love without marriage. – Benjamin Franklin

148. You may delay, but time will not. – Benjamin Franklin

149. While you're saving your face, you're losing your ass. – Lyndon B. Johnson, 36th US President

150. All mankind is divided into three classes: those that are immovable, those that are movable, and those that move. – Benjamin Franklin

151. Any jackass can kick down a barn but it takes a good carpenter to build one. – Lyndon B. Johnson

152. Be careful about reading health books. You may die of a misprint. – Mark Twain

153. Be wary of strong drink. It can make you shoot at tax collectors . . . and miss. – Robert A. Heinlein

154. Being president is like being a jackass in a hailstorm. There's nothing to do but to stand there and take it. – Lyndon B. Johnson

155. Even peace may be purchased at too high a price. – Benjamin Franklin

156. Guests, like fish, begin to smell after three days. – Benjamin Franklin

157. He that won't be counseled can't be helped. – Benjamin Franklin

158. His life was gentle; and the elements so mixed in him, that Nature might stand up, and say to all the world, this was a man! – William Shakespeare

159. I could dance with you until the cows come home. On second

thought I'd rather dance with the cows until you come home. – Groucho Marx

160. I do not fear computers. I fear the lack of them. – Isaac Asimov

161. I love deadlines. I like the whooshing sound they make as they fly by. –Douglas Adams

162. I was born not knowing and have had only a little time to change that here and there. – Richard Feynman

163. If the United Nations once admits that international disputes can be settled by using force, then we will have destroyed the foundation of the organization and our best hope of establishing a world order. – Dwight D. Eisenhower

164. If you desire many things, many things will seem few. – Benjamin Franklin

165. In this world nothing can be said to be certain, except death and taxes. – Benjamin Franklin

166. Indolence is a delightful but distressing state; we must be doing something to be happy. – Mahatma Gandhi

167. It is better to be violent, if there is violence in our hearts, than to put on the cloak of nonviolence to cover impotence. – Mahatma Gandhi

168. It is change, continuing change, inevitable change, that is the dominant factor in society today. No sensible decision can be made any longer without taking into account not only the world as it is, but the world as it will be. –Isaac Asimov

169. Misquote: Do you feel lucky, punk? Correct Quote: 'Ah-ah, I know what you're thinking, punk. You're thinking, 'Did he fire six shots or only five?' And to tell you the truth, I've forgotten myself in all this excitement. But being as this is a .44 Magnum, the most powerful handgun in the world, and would blow your head clean off, you've got to ask yourself a question: Do I feel lucky? Well, do ya, punk?' – Clint Eastwood, playing Harry Callahan in Dirty Harry

170. Most people return small favors, acknowledge medium ones and repay greater ones – with ingratitude. – Benjamin Franklin

171. Nothing interferes with my concentration. You could put on an orgy in my office and I wouldn't look up. Well, maybe once. – Isaac Asimov

172. Part of the inhumanity of the computer is that, once it is competently programmed and working smoothly, it is completely honest. – Isaac Asimov

173. Politics ought to be the part-time profession of every citizen who would protect the rights and privileges of free people and who would preserve what is good and fruitful in our national heritage. – Dwight D. Eisenhower

174. Rather go to bed without dinner than to rise in debt. – Benjamin Franklin

175. The broadest pattern of history – namely, the differences between human societies on different continents – seems to me to be attributable to differences among continental environments, and not to biological differences among peoples themselves. – Jared Diamond

176. The eye of the master will do more work than both his hands – Benjamin Franklin

177. The Trumpet shall be sounded and all who are in heaven and earth shall fall down fainting, except those that shall be spared by Allah. Then the Trumpet will sound again and they shall rise and gaze around them. The earth will shine with the light of her Lord, and the Book will be laid open. The prophets and witnesses shall be brought in and all shall be judged with fairness: none shall be wronged. Every soul shall be paid back according to its deeds, for Allah knows of all their actions. – (39:68, The Quran)

178. There is a computer disease that anybody who works with computers knows about. It's a very serious disease and it interferes completely with the work. The trouble with computers is that you 'play' with them! – Richard Feynman

179. Tomorrow every fault is to be amended; but tomorrow never comes. – Benjamin Franklin

180. Write injuries in dust, benefits in marble. – Benjamin Franklin

181. A good word is like a good tree whose root is firmly fixed and whose top is in the sky. – The Koran

182. Yesterday American and British troops handed out food to hundreds of Iraqis. Not surprisingly, the Iraqis handed the British food back. – Conan O'Brien

183. War may sometimes be a necessary evil. But no matter how necessary, it is always an evil, never a good. We will not learn how to live together in peace by killing each other's children. – Jimmy Carter, 39th US President

184. A society that gets rid of all its troublemakers goes downhill. – Robert A. Heinlein

185. Always do sober what you said you'd do drunk. That will teach you to keep your mouth shut. – Ernest Hemingway

186. An investment in knowledge pays the best interest. – Benjamin Franklin

187. Be at war with your vices, at peace with your neighbors, and let every new year find you a better man. – Benjamin Franklin

188. Creativity is allowing yourself to make mistakes. Art is knowing which ones to keep. – Scott Adams

189. Diligence is the mother of good luck. – Benjamin Franklin

190. Eat to please thyself, but dress to please others. – Benjamin Franklin

191. Happiness is when what you think, what you say, and what you do are in harmony. – Mahatma Gandhi

192. He that would live in peace and at ease must not speak all he knows or all he sees. – Benjamin Franklin

193. Hesitation increases in relation to risk in equal proportion to age. – Ernest Hemingway

194. I have tried so hard to do the right. – Grover Cleveland, 22nd (and 24th) US President

195. I'd rather spend my leisure time doing what some people call my work and I call my fun. – Jared Diamond

196. If all that Americans want is security, they can go to prison. They'll have enough to eat, a bed and a roof over their heads. But if an American wants to preserve his dignity and his equality as a human being, he must not bow his neck to any dictatorial government. – Dwight D. Eisenhower

197. If you would have a faithful servant, and one that you like, serve

yourself. – Benjamin Franklin

198. I fear all we have done is to awaken a sleeping giant and fill him with a terrible resolve. -- Isoroku Yamamoto

199. Most women defend themselves. It is the female of the species—it is the tigress and lioness in you – which tends to defend when attacked. – Margaret Thatcher

200. Never let your sense of morals get in the way of doing what's right. – Isaac Asimov

201. Science fiction writers foresee the inevitable, and although problems and catastrophes may be inevitable, solutions are not. – Isaac Asimov

202. Take time for all things: great haste makes great waste. – Benjamin Franklin

203. The Constitution only gives people the right to pursue happiness. You have to catch it yourself. – Benjamin Franklin

204. The first mistake in public business is the going into it. – Benjamin Franklin

205. This is a moment that I deeply wish my parents could have lived to share. My father would have enjoyed what you have so generously said of me- and my mother would have believed it. –Lyndon B. Johnson

206. Our liberty depends on the freedom of the press, and that cannot be limited without being lost -- Thomas Jefferson, Third US President

207. Tricks and treachery are the practice of fools, that don't have brains enough to be honest. – Benjamin Franklin

208. What is the use of living, if it be not to strive for noble causes and to make this muddled world a better place for those who will live in it after we are gone? How else can we put ourselves in harmonious relation with the great verities and consolations of the infinite and the eternal? And I avow my faith that we are marching towards better days. Humanity will not be cast down. We are going on swinging bravely forward along the grand high road and already behind the distant mountains is the promise of the sun. – Winston Churchill

209. Your net worth to the world is usually determined by what remains after your bad habits are subtracted from your good ones. – Benjamin Franklin

210. Beware the Ides of March. – Shakespeare

211. The Chinese use two brush strokes to write the word 'crisis'. One brush stroke stands for danger, the other for opportunity. In a crisis, be aware of the danger – but recognize the opportunity. – Richard Nixon, 37th US President

212. All my life I've looked at words as though I were seeing them for the first time. – Ernest Hemingway

213. An eye for an eye makes the whole world blind. – Mahatma Gandhi

214. And whether you're an honest man, or whether you're a thief, depends on whose solicitor has given me my brief. – Benjamin Franklin

215. Believe nothing, no matter where you read it, or who said it, no matter if I have said it, unless it agrees with your own reason and your own common sense. – Buddha

216. But we know that freedom cannot be served by the devices of the

tyrant. As it is an ancient truth that freedom cannot be legislated into existence, so it is no less obvious that freedom cannot be censored into existence. And any who act as if freedom's defenses are to be found in suppression and suspicion and fear confess a doctrine that is alien to America. – Dwight D. Eisenhower

217. Do not fear mistakes. You will know failure. Continue to reach out. – Benjamin Franklin

218. Domestic animals revolutionized land transport. They also revolutionized agriculture, by letting one farmer plough and manure much more land than the farmer could till or manure by the farmer's own efforts. – Jared Diamond

219. Don't go around saying the world owes you a living. The world owes you nothing. It was here first. – Mark Twain

220. Few men have the virtue to withstand the highest bidder – George Washington, First US President

221. He who falls in love with himself will have no rivals. – Benjamin Franklin

222. Humans are not proud of their ancestors, and rarely invite them round to dinner. – Douglas Adams

223. I find television very educating. Every time somebody turns on the set, I go into the other room and read a book. – Groucho Marx

224. If one morning I walked on top of the water across the Potomac River, the headline that afternoon would read: 'President Can't Swim.' – Lyndon B. Johnson

225. If you would not be forgotten as soon as you are dead, either write something worth reading or do things worth writing. – Benjamin Franklin

226. Individual science fiction stories may seem as trivial as ever to the blinder critics and philosophers of today – but the core of science fiction, its essence has become crucial to our salvation if we are to be saved at all. – Isaac Asimov

227. Patience is the companion of wisdom. – Saint Augustine

228. The doorstep to the temple of wisdom is a knowledge of our own ignorance. – Benjamin Franklin

229. The idea is to try to give all the information to help others to judge the value of your contribution; not just the information that leads to judgment in one particular direction or another. – Richard Feynman

230. The rate of human invention is faster, and the rate of cultural loss is slower, in areas occupied by many competing societies with many individuals and in contact with societies elsewhere. – Jared Diamond

231. Life shrinks or expands in proportion to one's courage. – Anaïs Nin

232. The vote is the most powerful instrument ever devised by man for breaking down injustice and destroying the terrible walls which imprison men because they are different from other men. – Lyndon B. Johnson

233. Unlike presidential administrations, problems rarely have terminal dates. – Dwight D. Eisenhower

234. When a man dies they who survive him ask what property he has left behind. The angel who bends over the dying man asks what good deed he has sent before him. – Deeds, The Koran

235. When you teach your son, you teach your son's son. – The Talmud

236. At this moment I do not have a personal relationship with a

computer... it got so confusing, as to what was on the computer, what wasn't on the computer, what was on the hard drive, what was on the soft drive, that it made it easier for me to just do my work with pen and pencil. – Janet Reno, US Attorney General, 1998

237. The evolution of the human race will not be accomplished in the ten thousand years of tame animals, but in the million years of wild animals, because man is and will always be a wild animal. – Charles Darwin

238. Believers, Jews, Sabaeans or Christians – whoever believes in God and the Last Day and does what is right – shall have nothing to fear or regret – The Quran

239. I know you all, and will awhile uphold the unyoked humour of your idleness – Prince Henry IV, Shakespeare

240. A doubtful friend is worse than a certain enemy. Let a man be one thing or the other, and we then know how to meet him. – Aesop

241. A fanatic is one who can't change his mind and won't change the subject. – Winston Churchill

242. All good books have one thing in common – they are truer than if they had really happened. – Ernest Hemingway

243. Anyone who considers protocol unimportant has never dealt with a cat. – Robert A. Heinlein

244. By failing to prepare, you are preparing to fail. – Benjamin Franklin

245. Don't think you are going to conceal thoughts by concealing evidence that they ever existed. – Dwight D. Eisenhower, 34th US President

246. Early to bed and early to rise makes a man healthy, wealthy, and wise. – Benjamin Franklin

247. He that rises late must trot all day. – Benjamin Franklin

248. I feel like I just grabbed a big juicy worm with a right sharp hook in the middle of it. – Lyndon B. Johnson

249. I have sworn upon the altar of God, eternal hostility against every form of tyranny over the mind of man. – Thomas Jefferson, 3rd US President

250. If you gave me 10 million dollars, I wouldn't live any differently. Although nowadays I guess you'd have to raise that to 20 million to mean anything. – Jared Diamond

251. It is by the goodness of God that in our country we have those three unspeakably precious things: Freedom of speech, Freedom of conscience, and the prudence never to practice either of them. – Mark Twain

252. Life is pleasant. Death is peaceful. It's the transition that's troublesome. –Isaac Asimov

253. Misquote: Hell hath no fury like a woman scorned. Correct Quote: 'Heaven has no rage like love to hatred turned/ Nor hell a fury like a woman scorned.' by William Congreve – in The Mourning Bride of 1697.

254. Reading, after a certain age, diverts the mind too much from its creative pursuits. Any man who reads too much and uses his own brain too little falls into lazy habits of thinking. – Albert Einstein

255. Remember that credit is money. – Benjamin Franklin

256. The saddest aspect of life right now is that science gathers knowledge faster than society gathers wisdom. – Isaac Asimov

257. The truth is not always the same as the majority decision. – Pope John Paul II
258. You do not examine legislation in the light of the benefits it will convey if properly administered, but in the light of the wrongs it would do and the harms it would cause if improperly administered. – Lyndon B. Johnson
259. You must learn from the mistakes of others. You can't possibly live long enough to make them all yourself. – Sam Levenson
260. Endurance is one of the most difficult disciplines, but it is to the one who endures that the final victory comes. – Buddha
261. Children and animals are not possessions, but are people and creatures to be loved, cherished, and cared for. – Stephen Jason Griffith
262. 'I don't use drugs, my dreams are frightening enough.' – M. C. Escher
263. Be slow in choosing a friend, slower in changing. – Benjamin Franklin
264. Domesticated plants and animals yield far more calories per acre than do wild habitats, in which most species are inedible to humans. – Jared Diamond
265. For having lived long, I have experienced many instances of being obliged, by better information or fuller consideration, to change opinions, even on important subjects, which I once thought right but found to be otherwise. – Benjamin Franklin
266. Happy families are all alike; every unhappy family is unhappy in its own way. – Leo Tolstoy
267. He hoped and prayed that there wasn't an afterlife. Then he realized there was a contradiction involved here and merely hoped that there wasn't an afterlife. – Douglas Adams
268. Humanity has the stars in its future, and that future is too important to be lost under the burden of juvenile folly and ignorant superstition. – Isaac Asimov
269. Humility must always be the portion of any man who receives acclaim earned in the blood of his followers and the sacrifices of his friends. – Dwight D. Eisenhower
270. I don't know what it will take out there – 500 casualties maybe, maybe 500,000. It's the aughts that scare me. – Lyndon B. Johnson
271. I learned never to empty the well of my writing, but always to stop when there was still something there in the deep part of the well, and let it refill at night from the springs that fed it. – Ernest Hemingway
272. I saw few die of hunger; of eating, a hundred thousand. – Benjamin Franklin
273. I will do my best. That is all I can do. I ask for your help-and God's. –Lyndon B. Johnson
274. In those days spirits were brave, the stakes were high, men were real men, women were real women and small furry creatures from Alpha Centauri were real small furry creatures from Alpha Centauri. – Douglas Adams
275. It is far more important to be able to hit the target than it is to haggle over who makes a weapon or who pulls a trigger. – Dwight D. Eisenhower
276. It's a damn poor mind that can only think of one way to spell a word. – Andrew Jackson, 7th US President

277. Never worry about theory as long as the machinery does what it's supposed to do. – Robert A. Heinlein

278. One needs to be slow to form convictions, but once formed they must be defended against the heaviest odds. – Mahatma Gandhi

279. Poets say science takes away from the beauty of the stars – mere globs of gas atoms. I, too, can see the stars on a desert night, and feel them. But do I see less or more? – Richard P. Feynman

280. Simon Lynch: 'You are a stranger.' (Mercury Rising)

281. The English never draw a line without blurring it. – Winston Churchill

282. The test of leadership is not to put greatness into humanity, but to elicit it, for the greatness is already there. – James Buchanan, 15th US President

283. Things are more like they are now than they have ever been. – Gerald Ford, 38th US President

284. Until the end of the last Ice Age around 11,000 B.C., all humans on all continents were still living as Stone Age hunter/gatherers. – Jared Diamond

285. Some people die at 25 and aren't buried until 75. – Benjamin Franklin

286. We must, indeed, all hang together or, most assuredly, we shall all hang separately. – Benjamin Franklin

287. Rebellion against tyrants is obedience to God. – Benjamin Franklin

288. The discontented man finds no easy chair. – Benjamin Franklin

289. Creationists make it sound as though a 'theory' is something you dreamt up after being drunk all night. –Isaac Asimov

290. This prompted me to look at Kryptos from a slightly different perspective – not as simply an encrypted message, but also as a vehicle with which to deliver the key. This changes the task from one of cracking a code to one much more like solving a puzzle. – Gary Warzin

291. With a good script, a good director can produce a masterpiece. With the same script, a mediocre director can produce a passable film. But with a bad script even a good director can't possibly make a good film. For truly cinematic expression, the camera and the microphone must be able to cross both fire and water. The script must be something that has the power to do this. – Japanese director Akira Kurosawa

292. Faith is a continuum, and we each fall on that line where we may. By attempting to rigidly classify ethereal concepts like faith, we end up debating semantics to the point where we entirely miss the obvious- that is, that we are all trying to decipher life's big mysteries, and we're each following our own paths of enlightenment. – Dan Brown

293. To be prepared for war is one of the most effective means of preserving peace. – George Washington

294. Life is pretty simple: You do some stuff. Most fails. Some works. You do more of what works. If it works big, others quickly copy it. Then you do something else. The trick is the doing something else. – Leonardo da Vinci

295. War is an ugly thing, but not the ugliest of things. The decayed and degraded state of moral and patriotic feeling which thinks that nothing is worth war is much worse. The person who has nothing for

which he is willing to fight, nothing which is more important than his own personal safety, is a miserable creature and has no chance of being free unless made and kept so by the exertions of better men than himself. – John Stuart Mill (1806-1873)

296. If you're not failing every so often, then you're not trying hard enough. – Woody Allen

297. Stalked in the forest, too close to hide; I'll be upon you by the moonlight side – Lyric from 'Hungry like the Wolf' – Duran Duran

298. If you want to eat well in England, eat three breakfasts. – W. Somerset Maugham

299. Never give in-- never, never, never, never, in nothing great or small, large or petty, never give in except to convictions of honour and good sense. Never yield to force; never yield to the apparently overwhelming might of the enemy. – Winston Churchill

300. Behold the turtle. He makes progress only when he sticks his neck out. – James Bryant Conant, US chemist, diplomat, & educator

Pigpen Ciphers – page 358

1. Ask not what your country can do for you, ask what you can do for your country. – John F. Kennedy, 35th US President

2. The advance of liberty is the path to both a safer and better world. - George W. Bush speech to UN general assembly, September 21, 2004.

3. Every citizen should be a soldier. This was the case with the Greeks and Romans, and must be that of every free state. – Thomas Jefferson

Not So Easy – page 369

1. It is better to light a candle than curse the darkness. – Eleanor Roosevelt

2. Double double toil and trouble fire burn and cauldron bubble – Shakespeare

3. Sometimes one creates a dynamic impression by saying something, and sometimes one creates as significant an impression by remaining silent. – Dalai Lama XIV

4. It is a tale told by an idiot, full of sound and fury, signifying nothing. – Shakespeare from Macbeth

5. We can never obtain peace in the world if we neglect the inner world and don't make peace with ourselves. World peace must develop out of inner peace – Dalai Lama XIV

6. An old man, broken with the storms of state, Is come to lay his weary bones among ye: Give him a little earth for charity! – Shakespeare, Henry VIII [1491-1547]

7. I think it would be a good idea. – Mahatma Gandhi, when asked what he thought of Western Civilization

8. Seek first to understand, and then to be understood. – Stephen R. Covey

9. Attendance at religious services has risen a dramatic 39% in recent days. –Geraldo Rivera From the Movie Contact

10. Compassion and tolerance are not a sign of weakness, but a sign of strength. – Dalai Lama XIV

11. Go with me, like good angels, to my end; And, as the long divorce of steel falls on me, Make of your prayers one sweet sacrifice, And lift

my soul to heaven. – Shakespeare, Henry VIII [1491-1547]

12. Only two things are infinite, the universe and human stupidity, and I'm not sure about the former. – Albert Einstein

13. I believe that individuals can make a difference in society. Since periods of change such as the present one come so rarely in human history, it is up to each of us to make the best use of our time to help create a happier world. – Dalai Lama XIV

14. There was never a good war, or a bad peace. – Benjamin Franklin

15. If you want others to be happy, practice compassion. If you want to be happy, practice compassion. – Dalai Lama XIV

16. And so, my fellow Americans, ask not what your country can do for you; ask what you can do for your country. – John F. Kennedy, 35th US President

17. Freedom is not enough. – Lyndon B. Johnson

18. Remember that not getting what you want is sometimes a wonderful stroke of luck. – Dalai Lama XIV

19. A pint of sweat, saves a gallon of blood. – General George S. Patton.

20. Beneath the rule of men entirely great, the pen is mightier than the sword. – Edward Bulwer-Lytton

21. Beware the hobby that eats. – Benjamin Franklin

22. The basic sources of happiness are a good heart, compassion, and love. If we have these mental attitudes, even if we are surrounded by hostility, we feel little disturbance. On the other hand, if we lack compassion and our mental state is filled with anger or hatred we will not have peace. – Dalai Lama XIV

23. Variety is the spice of life. – Proverb

24. The roots of all goodness lie in the soil of appreciation for goodness. – Dalai Lama XIV

25. After all is said and done, more is said than done. – Aesop

26. We are not amused. – Queen Victoria [1819- 1901]

27. We cannot learn real patience and tolerance from a guru or a friend. They can be practiced only when we come in contact with someone who creates unpleasant experiences. According to Shantideva, enemies are really good for us as we can learn a lot from them and build our inner strength. – Dalai Lama XIV

28. 'I have found that the ability to think creatively needs to be cultivated, nourished, and even protected -- very much like a garden.' – Jay Wiseman

29. Now, naturally, in writing such a story as this, with its conditions as laid down in its Introduction, it is not surprising that an occasional 'rough spot' in composition is found. So I trust that a critical public will hold constantly in mind that I am voluntarily avoiding words containing that symbol which is, by far, of most common inclusion in writing our Anglo-Saxon as it is, today. Many of our most common words cannot show; so I must adopt synonyms; and so twist a thought around as to say what I wish with as much clarity as I can. – Ernest Vincent Wright, 'Gadsby'

31. People marched up to me, pointed accusing fingers, and shouted, 'I hate you!'. It was the ultimate compliment. Puzzle-addicted students hated me because they flunked their exams. Business professionals hated me because they arrived blurry-eyed on the job. Even some newlyweds hated me because I ruined their honeymoon. – Cliff

Johnson, creator of the computer game 'The Fool's Errand,' 1988

32. Going to Waterfall City might provide me with an opportunity to find out more about them. I agreed with Tok's suggestion that we have a guide for our journey, but I was not prepared to see the hog-parrot again. Tok pointed out that the creature is female. To be precise, her name is Bix, of the species Protoceratops multilinguous, an ambassador and translator, one of the few dinosaurs who can 'speak' human languages. She remembered me, and said, 'Breathe deep. Seek peace, Arthur Denison. No rock, I hope?' Evidently she has a sense of humor. – from Dinotopia by James Gurney

33. In less enlightened times, the best way to impress women was to own a hot car. But women wised up and realized it was better to buy their own hot cars so they wouldn't have to ride around with jerks. – Scott Adams

34. Always forgive your enemies. Nothing annoys them more.
– Oscar Wilde

35. The shadows are on your side; as soon as the lights go down; in the darkest place you can find; you belong to the hands of the night. – Duran Duran

36. 'I like circuit boards. They're easier to understand than relationships.' – Jeri Ellsworth

37. This is the heart of the main square of Wehnimer's Landing. The impromptu shops of the bazaar are clustered around this central gathering place, where townsfolk, travellers, and adventurers meet to talk, conspire or raise expeditions to the far-flung reaches of Elanith. At the north end of the space, an old well, with moss-covered stones and a craggy roof, is shaded by a strong, robust tree. The oak is tall and straight, and it is apparent that the roots run deep. – GemStone IV, Simutronics / play.net

38. The difference between theory and practice in theory is smaller than the difference between theory and practice in practice. – Quote made popular by Randal L. Schwartz (original source unknown)

39. If you cannot spot the sucker in the first half hour at the table, then you are the sucker. – Poker truism, source unknown

40. Strong cryptography is very powerful when it is done right, but it is not a panacea. Focusing on the cryptographic algorithms while ignoring other aspects of security is like defending your house not by building a fence around it, but by putting an immense stake into the ground and hoping that the adversary runs right into it. Smart attackers will just go around the algorithms. - Bruce Schneier

UUencoded Example – page 390
Under certain circumstances, profanity provides a relief denied even to prayer. Mark Twain

Challenging – page 391
1. An enemy can only control your message if they can find it. – Peter Wayner
2. I don't believe in personal immortality; the only way I expect to have some version of such a thing is through my books. – Isaac Asimov
3. I want to make a policy statement. I am unabashedly in favor of women. – Lyndon B. Johnson

4. If two men agree on everything, you may be sure that one of them is doing the thinking. – Lyndon B. Johnson

5. To conclude that women are unfitted to the task of our historic society seems to me the equivalent of closing male eyes to female facts. – Lyndon B. Johnson

6. What does not destroy me, makes me stronger. – Friedrich Nietzsche (Was mich nicht umbringt, macht mich starker.)

7. Artificial life is the study of man-made systems that exhibit behaviors characteristic of natural living systems. It complements the traditional biological sciences concerned with the analysis of living organisms by attempting to synthesize life-like behaviors within computers and other artificial media. By extending the empirical foundation upon which biology is based beyond the carbon-chain that has evolved on Earth, Artificial life can contribute to theoretical biology by locating life-as-we-know-it within the larger picture of life-as-it-could-be. – Chris Langton

8. With the MacArthur grant, I realized that people have high expectations of me, that they were placing me in this group of achievers. I compared what I'd actually achieved in my life with what I would like to achieve and what other people have achieved, and I found that comparison depressing. – Jared Diamond

9. Greater love hath no man than to attend the Episcopal Church with his wife. –Lyndon B. Johnson

10. He ran toward it for a few seconds longer, and then stopped. The sound of the machine had grown suddenly louder, changing from a whir to a roar. It had, obviously, shifted speed; an automatic switch somewhere in the building had turned it from low to high, and the air blowing past Justin came on so hard it made him gasp. He braced his feet against the metal and held on. In a minute, as suddenly as it had roared, the machine returned to a whisper. He looked around and realized he was lucky to have stopped; by the dim light from the sky he could see that he had reached a point where perhaps two dozen air shafts came together like branches into the trunk of a tree. If he had gone a few steps farther he would never have been able to distinguish which shaft was his. He turned in his tracks, and in a few minutes he rejoined his friends. – Mrs. Frisby and the Rats of NIMH by Robert C. O'Brien

11. I am not a speed reader. I am a speed understander. – Isaac Asimov

12. Jack was out kissing babies while I was out passing bills. Someone had to tend the store. – Lyndon B. Johnson

13. The New York Times is read by the people who run the country. The Washington Post is read by the people who think they run the country. The National Enquirer is read by the people who think Elvis is alive and running the country. – From the British TV series 'Yes, Prime Minister', translated from the original English into American by Robert J. Woodhead.

14. The separation of church and state is a source of strength, but the conscience of our nation does not call for separation between men of state and faith in the Supreme Being. – Lyndon B. Johnson

15. I saw the angel in the marble and carved until I set him free. – Michelangelo

16. Let us describe the education of our men. What then is the education

to be? Perhaps we could hardly find a better than that which the experience of the past has already discovered, which consists, I believe, in gymnastic, for the body, and music for the mind. – Plato

17. Experience has shown how deeply the seeds of war are planted by economic rivalry and social injustice. Harry S Truman [33rd President, 1945- 1953]

18. The presidency has made every man who occupied it, no matter how small, bigger than he was; and no matter how big, not big enough for its demands. – Lyndon B. Johnson

19. What we won when all of our people united must not be lost in suspicion and distrust and selfishness and politics. Accordingly, I shall not seek, and I will not accept, the nomination of my party for another term as president. – Lyndon B. Johnson

20. Lord, what fools these mortals be. – Shakespeare

21. No one can offend you without your permission. – Eleanor Roosevelt

22. The tide has turned. The free men of the world are marching together to victory. I have full confidence in your courage, devotion to duty, and skill in battle. We will accept nothing less than full victory. Good luck, and let us all beseech the blessings of almighty God upon this great and noble undertaking. – The D-Day Order – General Dwight D. Eisenhower (later 34th US President)

23. Until justice is blind to color, until education is unaware of race, until opportunity is unconcerned with the color of men's skins, emancipation will be a proclamation but not a fact. – Lyndon B. Johnson

24. When the burdens of the presidency seem unusually heavy, I always remind myself it could be worse. I could be a mayor. – Lyndon B. Johnson

25. I believe that this nation should commit itself to achieving the goal, before this decade is out, of landing a man on the moon and returning him safely to the Earth. – President John F. Kennedy

26. Falsehood is easy, truth so difficult. – George Eliot

27. We must believe in free will, we have no choice. – Isaac Bashevis Singer

28. For who would acquire a knowledge of the heavens, let him give up his days and nights to the marvels of Orion. Here may be found every conceivable variation of celestial phenomena: stars, giants and dwarfs; variables, doubles..triples..multiples; binaries visual and spectroscopic; clusters wide and condensed; mysterious rayless rifts and nebulae in boundless variety, with the supreme wonder of all supernal wonders at its heart – the Great Nebula – before which the learned and the laymen alike have stood silent in awe and reverence since the first lens unfolded to man's gaze its true vastness and intricacy, and which offers abundant field for all the geniuses of science, with their super-refinements of means and methods, for generations to come...' – Charles Edward Barnes

29. When things haven't gone well for you, call in a secretary or a staff man and chew him out. You will sleep better and they will appreciate the attention. – Lyndon B. Johnson

30. Scientific views end in awe and mystery, lost at the edge in uncertainty, but they appear to be so deep and so impressive that the theory that it is all arranged as a stage for God to watch man's

struggle for good and evil seems inadequate. – Richard P. Feynman

31. A rioter with a Molotov cocktail in his hands is not fighting for civil rights any more than a Klansman... They are both... lawbreakers, destroyers of constitutional rights and liberties and ultimately destroyers of a free America. –Lyndon B. Johnson

32. Education is not a problem. Education is an opportunity. – Lyndon B. Johnson

33. The Air Force comes in every morning and says, 'Bomb, bomb, bomb.' And then the State Department comes in and says, 'Not now, or not there, or too much, or not at all.' – Lyndon B. Johnson

34. The doctrines of religion are resolved into carefulness; carefulness into vigorousness; vigorousness into guiltlessness; guiltlessness into abstemiousness; abstemiousness into cleanliness; cleanliness into godliness. – The Talmud

35. [People constantly requesting government intervention] are casting their problems at society. And, you know, there's no such thing as society. There are individual men and women and there are families. And no government can do anything except through people, and people must look after themselves first. It is our duty to look after ourselves and then, also, to look after our neighbours. –– Margaret Thatcher

36. All your base are belong to us. – Infamous English (mis)translation of a line from the 1989 Japanese video game 'Zero Wing'.

37. Did you ever think that making a speech on economics is a lot like pissing down your leg? It seems hot to you, but it never does to anyone else. – Lyndon B. Johnson

38. Beauty and folly are old companions. – Benjamin Franklin

39. The men who have guided the destiny of the United States have found the strength for their tasks by going to their knees. This private unity of public men and their God is an enduring source of reassurance for the people of America. – Lyndon B. Johnson

40. All that Hubert needs over there is a gal to answer the phone and a pencil with an eraser on it. – Lyndon B. Johnson

41. Curtis Le May wants to bomb Hanoi and Haiphong. You know how he likes to go around bombing. – Lyndon B. Johnson

42. In the attitude of silence the soul finds the path in a clearer light, and what is elusive and deceptive resolves itself into crystal clearness. Our life is a long and arduous quest after Truth. – Mahatma Gandhi

43. Many forms of Government have been tried, and will be tried in this world of sin and woe. No one pretends that democracy is perfect or all-wise. Indeed, it has been said that democracy is the worst form of government except all those other forms that have been tried from time to time. – Winston Churchill

44. We live in a world that has narrowed into a neighborhood before it has broadened into a brotherhood. – Lyndon B. Johnson

45. There is a theory which states that if ever anybody discovers exactly what the Universe is for and why it is here, it will instantly disappear and be replaced by something even more bizarre and inexplicable. There is another theory which states that this has already happened. – Douglas Adams

46. I have learned that only two things are necessary to keep one's wife happy. First, let her think she's having her own way. And second, let

her have it. – Lyndon B. Johnson

47. Misdirected life force is the activity in disease process. Disease has no energy save what it borrows from the life of the organism. It is by adjusting the life force that healing must be brought about, and it is the sun as transformer and distributor of primal spiritual energy that must be utilized in this process, for life and the sun are so intimately connected. – The Kabbalah

48. Only two things are necessary to keep one's wife happy. One is to let her think she is having her own way, and the other is to let her have it. – Lyndon B. Johnson

49. Our society is illuminated by the spiritual insights of the Hebrew prophets. America and Israel have a common love of human freedom, and they have a common faith in a democratic way of life. – Lyndon B. Johnson

50. long since come to my attention that people of accomplishment rarely sat back and let things happen to them. They went out and happened to things. – Leonardo da Vinci

51. There are no favorites in my office. I treat them all with the same general inconsideration. – Lyndon B. Johnson

52. There is but one way for a president to deal with Congress, and that is continuously, incessantly, and without interruption. If it is really going to work, the relationship has got to be almost incestuous. – Lyndon B. Johnson

53. We the People of the United States, in order to form a more perfect Union, establish Justice, insure domestic tranquility, provide for the common defence, promote the general Welfare, and secure the Blessings of Liberty to ourselves and our Posterity, do ordain and establish this Constitution for the United States of America. – Preamble

54. What convinces is conviction. Believe in the argument you're advancing. If you don't you're as good as dead. The other person will sense that something isn't there, and no chain of reasoning, no matter how logical or elegant or brilliant, will win your case for you. – Lyndon B. Johnson

55. 'My Lord Bath, you and I are now as insignificant men as any in England.' – – Sir Robert Walpole 1721- 1742 Whig, to the Earl of Bath on their elevation to the House of Lords.

56. On the Duke of Newcastle: 'Sir, you have a right to speak, but the House has a right to judge whether they will hear you.' – Spencer Compton, Earl of Wilmington 1742-3 Whig

57. On the House of Lords: 'Let them alone; they make better speeches for us than we can make for ourselves.' – Henry Pelham 1743-54 Whig

58. I shall not... think the demands of the people a rule of conduct, nor shall I ever fear to incur their resentment in the prosecution of their interest. I shall never flatter their passions to obtain their favour, or gratify their revenge for fear of their contempt. – Thomas Pelham-Holles, Duke of Newcastle 1754-6 and 1757-62 Whig

59. Every King must make use of human means to attain human ends or his affairs will go to ruin. – William Cavendish, Duke of Devonshire 1756-7 Whig

60. During a debate on the cider tax: 'A noble duke knows the difficulty to

choose proper taxes.' – John Stuart, Earl of Bute 1762-3 Tory

61. A wise government knows how to enforce with temper, or to conciliate with dignity. – George Grenville 1763-5 Whig

62. Englishmen, whatever their local situation may be, know no obedience to any thing but the laws. – Charles Wentworth, Marquess of Rockingham 1765-6 1782 Whig

63. Wisdom is at no times more conspicuous, nor more amiable, than in the acknowledgement of error. – The Earl of Chatham, William Pitt 'The Elder' 1766-8 Whig

64. Unlimited power is apt to corrupt the minds of those who possess it. – Augustus Henry Fitzroy, Duke of Grafton 1767-70 Whig

65. Men may be popular without being ambitious, but there is hardly an ambitious man who does not try to be popular. – Lord North 1770-82 Tory

66. The sun of Great Britain will set whenever she acknowledges the independence of America – the independence of America would end in the ruin of England. – William Petty, Earl of Shelburne 1782-3 Whig

67. On accepting office for the second time: 'My fears are not that the attempt to perform this duty will shorten my life, but that I shall neither bodily nor mentally perform it as I should.' – William Bentinck, Duke of Portland 1783 and 1807-9 Whig

68. The deed is done and I am again a free man, and to you I may express what it would seem like affection to say to others, the infinite pleasure I derive from emancipation. – Henry Addington 1801-4 Tory

69. In youth, the absence of pleasure is pain, in old age the absence of pain is pleasure. – William Wyndam Grenville, Lord Grenville 1806-7 Whig

70. During a debate on corrupt electoral practices: 'I have nothing to say to the nothing that has been said.' – Spencer Perceval 1809-12 Tory

71. I consider the right of election as a public trust, granted not for the benefit of the individual, but for the public good. – Robert Banks Jenkinson, Earl of Liverpool 1812-27 Tory

72. The happiness of constant occupation is infinite. – George Canning 1827 Tory

73. There was no one good in this life that had not with it some concomitant evil. – Frederick Robinson, Viscount Goderich 1827-8 Tory

74. After his first Cabinet meeting as PM: 'An extraordinary affair. I gave them their orders and they wanted to stay and discuss them.' – Arthur Wellesley, Duke of Wellington 1828-30 Tory

75. The only way with newspaper attacks is, as the Irish say, 'to keep never minding'. This has been my practice through life. – Earl Grey 1830-34 Whig

76. It is impossible that anybody can feel the being out of Parliament more keenly for me than I feel it for myself. It is actually cutting my throat. It is depriving me of the great object of my life. – William Lamb, Viscount Melbourne 1834 and 1835-41 Whig

77. There seem to me to be very few facts, at least ascertainable facts, in politics. – Sir Robert Peel 1834-5 and 1841-6 Tory

78. I have made mistakes, but in all I did my object was the public good. – Earl Russell 1846-51 1865-6 Liberal

79. My Lords, I am now an old man, and like many of your lordships, I have already passed the three score years and ten. My official life is

entirely closed; my political life is nearly so; and, in the course of nature, my natural life cannot now be long. – The Earl of Derby 1852, 1858-9 and 1866-8, Conservative

80. I do not know how I shall bear being out of office. I have many resources and many objects of interest; but after being occupied with great affairs, it is not easy to subside to the level of common occupations. – Earl of Aberdeen 1852-5 Tory

81. The function of government is to calm, rather than to excite agitation. – Viscount Palmerston 1855-8 and 1859-65 Liberal

82. There are three kinds of lies: lies, damn lies and statistics. – Benjamin Disraeli 1868 and 1874-80 Conservative

83. The love of freedom itself is hardly stronger in England than the love of aristocracy. – William Ewart Gladstone 1868-74, 1880-85, 1886 and 1892-94 Liberal

84. English policy is to float lazily downstream, occasionally putting out a diplomatic boathook to avoid collisions. – Robert Gascoyne-Cecil, Marquess of Salisbury 1885-6, 1886-92 and 1895-1902 Conservative

85. There are two supreme pleasures in life. One is ideal, the other real. The ideal is when a man receives the seals of office from his Sovereign. The real pleasure comes when he hands them back. – The Earl of Rosebery 1894-5 Liberal

86. I am more or less happy when being praised, not very comfortable when being abused, but I have moments of uneasiness when being explained – Arthur James Balfour 1902-5 Conservative

87. On his own health regime: 'Personally I am an immense believer in bed, in constantly keeping horizontal: the heart and everything else goes slower, and the whole system is refreshed.' – Henry Campbell-Bannerman 1905-8 Liberal

88. Youth would be an ideal state if it came a little later in life. – Herbert Henry Asquith 1908-16 Liberal

89. On the House of Lords: '...a body of five hundred men chosen at random from amongst the unemployed' – David Lloyd George 1916-22 Liberal

90. If I am a great man, then a good many great men of history are frauds – Andrew Bonar Law 1922-3 Conservative

91. There never was a war before this, at any rate for our country, in which the whole people was engaged, directly or indirectly, and a war in which men went forth to fight in the full consciousness of what they did. Not a man whose name is commemorated on this tablet but went forth with a full knowledge that he was fighting for what he and his countrymen believed to be right for the liberties of the world, and those who fell in a belief – perhaps hardly uttered by themselves – that somehow or another their lives might be given to promote the betterment of this world. – Stanley Baldwin 1923, 1924-9, 1935-7 Conservative

92. We hear war called murder. It is not: it is suicide – James Ramsay MacDonald 1924 and 1929-35 Labour

93. This is the second time in our history that there has come back from Germany to Downing Street peace with honour. I believe it is peace for our time – Neville Chamberlain 1937-40 Conservative

94. On the RAF following victory in the Battle of Britain: 'Never in the field of human conflict was so much owed by so many to so few' – Sir

Winston Leonard Spencer Churchill 1940-5 and 1951-5 Conservative
95. Often the experts make the worst possible ministers in their own fields. In this country we prefer rule by amateurs – Clement Richard Attlee 1945-51 Labour
96. I thought and think that failure to act would have brought the worst of consequences just as I think the world would have suffered less if Hitler had been resisted on the Rhine – Anthony Eden 1955-7 Conservative
97. The wind of change is blowing through this continent and whether we like it or not, this growth of national consciousness is a political fact Harold Macmillan 1957-63 Conservative
98. There are two problems in my life. The political ones are insoluble and the economic ones are incomprehensible Sir Alec Douglas-Home 1963-4 Conservative
99. Whichever party is in office, the Treasury is in power – Harold Wilson, 1964-70 and 1974-6, Labour
100. If politicians lived on praise and thanks they'd be forced into some other line of business. – Edward Heath 1970-4 Conservative
101. A lie can be half-way around the world before truth has got its boots on. – James Callaghan 1976-9 Labour
102. It will be years before a woman either leads the Conservative Party or becomes prime minister. I don't see it happening in my time. – Margaret Thatcher, 1979-90, Conservative
103. Fifty years on from now, Britain will still be the country of long shadows on cricket grounds, warm beer, invincible green suburbs, dog lovers and pools fillers. – John Major, 1990-97, Conservative But let us unite in agreeing this: what happened in the United States on Tuesday was an act of wickedness for which there can never be justification. Whatever the cause, whatever the perversion of religious feeling, whatever the political belief, to inflict such terror on the world; to take the lives of so many innocent and defenceless men, women, and children, can never ever be justified. – Tony Charles Lynton Blair 1997-Present, Labor

Public Display of Encryption – page 418

1. 57=3*19, 551=19*29, 5063=61*83, 52961=211*251

2.

Solution to Question 2

3. The cycle is 3, 9, 27, 11, 33, 29, 17, 16, 13, 4, 12, 1, which has length 12. Note that the cycle length divides evenly into (5-1)(7-1) = 4*6 = 24.

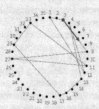

Solution to Question 3

4. By factoring n=55 deduce that p and q are 5 and 11, so (p−1)(q−1) is 40. This means that raising any number m to the power 41 and dividing by 55 yields the original number. The same thing happens if we raise m to the power 81, 121, 161, and so on, since the cycle has length 40. So in order for $(m^e)^d = m^{ed}$ to yield the original message number m, the product ed = 27d needs to be one more than a multiple of 40. If we write out multiples of 27, we quickly find that the 27*3 = 81 is one more than a multiple of 40, so d=3. Raising each of the enciphered numbers c to the third power and dividing by 55 we get the following deciphered numbers m. Each of the five deciphered numbers represents a position in the alphabet. The final answer is the word 'stone', as in 'keystone'.

C	m	Letter
24	19	S
15	20	T
5	15	O
9	14	N
25	5	E

Poe Challenge Cipher – page 420
Challenge Cipher 1 (method: Simple Substitution):

The soul secure in her existence smiles at the drawn dagger and defies its point. The stars shall fade away, the sun himself grow dim with age and nature sink in years, but thou shall flourish in immortal youth, unhurt amid the war of elements, the wreck of matter and the crush of worlds. Source: the 1713 play Cato, by Joseph Addison

Challenge Cipher 2 (method: homophonic substitution):

It was early spring, warm and sultry glowed the afternoon. The very breezes seemed to share the delicious langour of universal nature, are laden the various and mingled perfumes of the rose and the essaerne, the woodbine and its wildflower. They slowly wafted their fragrant offering to the open window where sat the lovers. The ardent sun shoot fell upon her blushing face and its gentle beauty was more like the creation of romance or the fair inspiration of a dream than the actual reality on earth. Tenderly her lover gazed upon her as the clusterous ringlets were edged (?) by amorous and sportive zephyrs and when he perceived (?) the rude intrusion of the sunlight he sprang to draw the curtain but softly she stayed him. 'No, no, dear Charles,' she softly said, 'much rather you'ld I have a little sun than no air at all.' – Source: Unknown

Fiendish – page 431
1. I tremble, my friends, when I reflect on the grievous sins which burden my conscience, and now, about to be summoned before the awful tribunal of God, I know not what I ought to do. I was bred to arms from my childhood, and am stained from the rivers of blood I have shed... It is out of my power to count all the injuries which I have caused during the sixty-four years of my troubled life. – William the Conqueror, 1087
2. The use of COBOL cripples the mind; its teaching should, therefore, be regarded as a criminal offense. – Edsger Dijkstra

3. A subtle thought that is in error may yet give rise to fruitful inquiry that can establish truths of great value. – Isaac Asimov

4. And so, my fellow Americans, ask not what your country can do for you; ask what you can do for your country. – John F. Kennedy

5. Lawyers are like other people—fools on the average; but it is easier for an ass to succeed in that trade than any other. – Samuel Clemens (Mark Twain)

6. Remind people that profit is the difference between revenue and expense. This makes you look smart. – Scott Adams

7. The cocks may crow, but it's the hen that lays the egg. – Margaret Thatcher

8. This is not the end. It is not even the beginning of the end. But it is, perhaps, the end of the beginning. – Winston Churchill

9. Whenever you have eliminated the impossible, whatever remains, however improbable, must be the truth. – Sir Arthur Conan Doyle

10. Actually, many years ago, we had a company-wide vote for our informal company-wide mascot, and the choices came down to the Boston tree fern, beef tape worm and a llama. And somehow the llama won the vote! – Will Wright, founder of Maxis, creator of 'The Sims'

11. I talk to him when I'm lonesome like, and I'm sure he understands. When he looks at me so attentively, and gently licks my hands; Then he rubs his nose on my tailored clothes, but I never say naught thereat, For the good Lord knows I can buy more clothes, but never a friend like that! – W. Dayton Wedgefarth

12. I thank God, we have not free schools nor printing; and I hope we shall not have these hundred years. For learning has brought disobedience, and heresy and sects into the world; and printing has divulged them and libels against the government. God keep us from both! – Sir William Berkeley

13. You see, wire telegraph is a kind of a very, very long cat. x You pull his tail in New York and his head is meowing in Los Angeles. X Do you understand this? Q And radio operates exactly the same way: you send signals here, they receive them there. X The only difference is that there is no cat. x – Albert Einstein

14. Being prime minister is a lonely job.... you cannot lead from the crowd. – Margaret Thatcher

15. During World War II the German armed forces top secret codes were broken at Bletchley Park, providing the allies with vital information towards their war effort. Situated 50 miles North-West of London, the site played host to a diverse group of code breakers, including Alan Turing and Dilly Knox. Among the ciphers that were broken were Enigma and Lorenz.
    Against seemingly insurmountable odds, the code breakers devised methods to allow them to successfully read enemy codes, often within a few hours of the messages being received by the outlying Y-stations. New technology was invented to automate the deciphering of messages. Colossus, the world's first semi-programmable computer was invented at Bletchley Park to aid the decoding of Lorenz ciphers, which were used by the German high command to send their most highly-classified and important communications. – Bletchley Park, Home of ENIGMA

16. For this is what America is all about. It is the uncrossed desert and the unclimbed ridge. It is the star that is not reached and the harvest that is sleeping in the unplowed ground. – Lyndon B. Johnson

17. If there are no stupid questions, then what kind of questions do stupid people ask? Do they get smart just in time to ask questions? – Scott Adams

18. Personally, I'm always ready to learn, although I do not always like being taught. – Winston Churchill

19. Let us see what has happened on the other side of the scales. The British nation and the British Empire, finding themselves alone, stood undismayed against disaster. No one flinched or wavered; nay, some who formerly thought of peace, now think only of war. Our people are united and resolved, as they have never been before. Death and ruin have become small things compared with the shame of defeat or failure in duty. We cannot tell what lies ahead. It may be that even greater ordeals lie before us. We shall face whatever is coming to us. We are sure of ourselves and of our cause, and that is the supreme fact which has emerged in these months of trial. – Winston Churchill

20. A mathematician is a device for turning coffee into theorems. – Paul Erdos (1913-1996)

21. Black holes are where God divided by zero. – Steven Wright

22. Liberals are like dogs: The liberal holds that he is true to the republic when he is true to himself. (It may not be as cozy an attitude as it sounds.) He greets with enthusiasm the fact of the journey, as a dog greets a man's invitation to take a walk. And he acts in the dog's way too, swinging wide, racing ahead, doubling back, covering many miles of territory that the man never traverses, all in the spirit of inquiry and the zest for truth. He leaves a crazy trail, but he ranges far beyond the genteel old party he walks with and he is usually in a better position to discover a skunk. – E. B. White

23. Every man has a right to a Saturday night bath. – Lyndon B. Johnson

24. Of course it's the same old story. Truth usually is the same old story.
– Margaret Thatcher

25. On subjects of which we know nothing, we both believe and disbelieve a hundred times an hour, which keeps believing nimble. – Emily Dickinson

26. To me, consensus seems to be the process of abandoning all beliefs, principles, values and policies. So it is something in which no one believes and to which no one objects. – Margaret Thatcher

27. We hold these truths to be self-evident, that all men are created equal, that they are endowed by their creator with certain unalienable rights, that among these are life, liberty, and the pursuit of happiness. (Declaration of Independence)

28. We have before us an ordeal of the most grievous kind, We have before us many, many long months of struggle and of suffering. You ask, what is our policy? I will say: It is to wage war, by sea, land and air, with all our might and with all the strength that God can give us: to wage war against a monstrous tyranny, never surpassed in the dark, lamentable catalogue of human crime. That is our policy. You ask, What is our aim? I can answer in one word: Victory – victory – at all costs, victory, in spite of all terror, victory, however long and hard the road may be; for without victory, there is no survival. Let that be

realised; no survival for the British Empire; no survival for all that the British Empire has stood for, no survival for the urge and impulse of the ages, that mankind will move forward towards its goal. But I take up my task with buoyancy and hope. I feel sure that our cause will not be suffered to fail among men. At this time I feel entitled to claim the aid of all, and I say, 'Come, then, let us go forward together with our united strength.' – Winston Churchill

29. And remember, where you have a concentration of power in a few hands, all too frequently men with the mentality of gangsters get control. History has proven that. All power corrupts; absolute power corrupts absolutely.– Lord Acton

30. In politics if you want anything said, ask a man. If you want anything done, ask a woman. – Margaret Thatcher

31. One of the things being in politics has taught is that men are not a reasoned or reasonable sex. –– Margaret Thatcher

32. Science without religion is lame, religion without science is blind. – Albert Einstein

33. The way to get started is to stop talking and begin doing. – Walt Disney

34. C makes it easy to shoot yourself in the foot; C++ makes it harder, but when you do, it blows away your whole leg. – Bjarne Stroustrup

35. Let us rise up and be thankful, for if we didn't learn a lot today, at least we learned a little, and if we didn't learn a little, at least we didn't get sick, and if we got sick, at least we didn't die; so, let us all be thankful. – Buddha

36. Politics is for the present... An equation is... for eternity. – Albert Einstein

37. I'm slowly becoming a convert to the principle that you can't motivate people to do things, you can only demotivate them. The primary job of the manager is not to empower but to remove obstacles. – Scott Adams

38. Of Man's first disobedience, and the fruit of that forbidden tree whose mortal taste brought death into the world, and all our woe. – Paradise Lost. Book i. Line 1. – John Milton

39. To wear your heart on your sleeve isn't a very good plan; you should wear it inside, where it functions best. – Margaret Thatcher

40. Never, never, never believe any war will be smooth and easy, or that anyone who embarks on the strange voyage can measure the tides and hurricanes he will encounter. The statesman who yields to war fever must realize that once the signal is given, he is no longer the master of policy but the slave of unforeseeable and uncontrollable events. – Sir Winston Churchill

41. It proved that Timothy's reading speed on new books of adult level varied from eight hundred to nine hundred fifty words a minute. The average murder mystery – he loved them – took him less than half an hour. A year's homework in history, Tim performed easily by reading his textbook through three or four times during the year. He apologized for that, but explained that he had to know what was in the book so as not to reveal in examinations too much that he had learned from other sources. – Wilmar H. Shiras, 'Children of the Atom'

42. 'One of the most frightening things about your true nerd, for many people, is not that he's socially inept – because everybody's been

there – but rather his complete lack of embarrassment about it.' – Neal Stephenson

43. 'You can always count on Americans to do the right thing – after they've tried everything else.' – Winston Churchill

44. The birth of a True Equilateral Triangle from Isosceles parents is the subject of rejoicing in our country for many furlongs around. After a strict examination conducted by the Sanitary and Social Board, the infant, if certified as Regular, is with solemn ceremonial admitted into the class of Equilaterals. – Edwin A. Abbott, 'Flatland'

45. To announce that there must be no criticism of the President, or that we are to stand by the President, right or wrong, is not only unpatriotic and servile, but is morally treasonable to the American public. -- Theodore Roosevelt

46. You need soldiers to fight soldiers, and you need hackers to fight hackers. You can't have some guy standing on a battlefield, getting shot at, saying, 'What's this? Small pieces of metal can be flung at high speed with deadly consequences? Since when was that possible?' The concept is no less ridiculous with network security. – Dan Kaminsky

Grab Bag – page 445

1. There is nothing more necessary than good intelligence to frustrate a designing enemy, and nothing requires greater pains to obtain. – George Washington, First US President

2. There is danger from all men. The only maxim of a free government ought to be to trust no man living with power to endanger the public liberty. – John Adams, 2nd US President

3. Banking establishments are more dangerous than standing armies. – Thomas Jefferson, 3rd US President

4. A pure democracy is a society consisting of a small number of citizens, who assemble and administer the government in person. – James Madison [fourth US president 1809-1817]

5. The American continents . . . are henceforth not to be considered as subjects for future colonization by any European powers. – James Monroe, 5th US President, 1817-1825

6. America does not go abroad in search of monsters to destroy. – John Quincy Adams [6th US President, 1825-1829]

7. It is to be regretted that the rich and powerful too often bend the acts of government to their own selfish purposes. – Andrew Jackson, 7th US President

8. I cannot expect to perform the task with equal ability and success. – Martin Van Buren, 8th US President, taking over from President Andrew Jackson in 1837

9. I believe and I say it is true democratic feeling, that all the measures of the government are directed to the purpose of making the rich richer and the poor poorer. – William Henry Harrison, 9th US President

10. Let it be henceforth proclaimed to the world that man's conscience was created free; that he is no longer accountable to his fellow man for his religious opinions, being responsible therefore only to his God. – John Tyler, 10th US President

11. Although... the Chief Magistrate must almost of necessity be chosen by a party and stand pledged to its principles and measures, yet in his

official action he should not be the President of a party only, but of the whole people of the United States. – James Polk, 11th US President

12. It would be judicious to act with magnanimity towards a prostrate foe. – Zachary Taylor, 12th US President

13. May God save the country, for it is evident that the people will not. – Millard Fillmore, 13th US President

14. A Republic without parties is a complete anomaly. The histories of all popular governments show absurd is the idea of their attempting to exist without parties. – Franklin Pierce, 14th US President

15. If you are as happy, my dear sir, on entering this house as I am in leaving it and returning home, you are the happiest man in this country. – James Buchanan, 15th US President

16. It is better, then, to save the work while it is begun. You have done the labor; maintain it – keep it. If men choose to serve you, go with them; but as you have made up your organization upon principle, stand by it; for, as surely as God reigns over you, and has inspired your mind, and given you a sense of propriety, and continues to give you hope, so surely will you still cling to these ideas, and you will at last come back after your wanderings, merely to do your work over again. – Abraham Lincoln, 16th US President

17. If the rabble were lopped off at one end and the aristocrat at the other, all would be well with the country. – Andrew Johnson, 17th US President

18. It is men who wait to be selected, and not those who seek, from whom we may expect the most efficient service. – Ulysses S. Grant, 18th US President

19. Coming in, I was denounced as a fraud by all the extreme men of the opposing party, and as an ingrate and a traitor by the same class of men in my own party. Going out, I have the good will, blessings, and approval of the best people of all parties. – Rutherford B. Hayes, 19th US President

20. Next in importance to freedom and justice is popular education, without which neither freedom nor justice can be permanently maintained. – James A Garfield, 20th US President

21. I may be president of the United States, but my private life is nobody's damned business. – Chester Arthur, 21st US President

22. A government for the people must depend for its success on the intelligence, the morality, the justice, and the interest of the people themselves. Grover Cleveland [22nd (and 24th) US President, 1885-1889]

23. I pity the man who wants a coat so cheap that the man or woman who produces the cloth will starve in the process. – Benjamin Harrison, 23rd US President

24. I have already transmitted to Congress the report of the naval court of inquiry on the destruction of the battleship Maine in the harbor of Havana during the night of the fifteenth of February. The destruction of that noble vessel has filled the national heart with inexpressible horror. Two hundred and fifty-eight brave sailors and marines and two officers of our Navy, reposing in the fancied security of a friendly harbor, have been hurled to death, grief and want brought to their homes and sorrow to the nation. – William McKinley, 25th US

President, 1898

25. Speak softly and carry a big stick; you will go far. – Theodore Roosevelt [26th US President, 1901-1909]

26. I have come to the conclusion that the major part of the work of a President is to increase the gate receipts of expositions and fairs and bring tourists to town. – William Howard Taft, 27th US President

27. No nation is fit to sit in judgement upon any other nation. – Woodrow Wilson, 28th US President

28. I have no trouble with my enemies. I can take care of my enemies in a fight. But my friends, my goddamned friends, they're the ones who keep me walking the floor at nights! – Warren Harding, 29th US President

29. Prosperity is only an instrument to be used, not a deity to be worshipped – Calvin Coolidge, 30th US President

30. Blessed are the young for they shall inherit the national debt. – Herbert Hoover, 31st US President

31. In the truest sense, freedom cannot be bestowed; it must be achieved. – Franklin D. Roosevelt, 32nd US President

32. A politician is a man who understands government and it takes a politician to run a government. A statesman is a politician who's been dead ten or fifteen years. – Harry Truman, 33rd US President

33. An atheist is a man who watches a Notre Dame – Southern Methodist University game and doesn't care who wins. – Dwight D. Eisenhower [34th US President, 1953-1961]

34. For of those to whom much is given, much is required. And when at some future date the high court of history sits in judgement on each of us, recording whether in our brief span of service we fulfilled our responsibilities to the state, our success or failure, in whatever office we hold, will be measured by the answers to four questions: First, were we truly men of courage? Second, were we truly men of judgement? Third, were we truly men of integrity? Finally were we truly men of dedication? – John F. Kennedy, 35th US President

35. Hell, it's just like the Alamo, and you damn well needed somebody. Well, by God, I'm going to go and thank the Lord that I've got men who want to go with me, from Secretary of Defense McNamara right on down to the littlest private who's carrying a gun. – Lyndon B. Johnson, 36th US President

36. My own view is that taping of conversations for historical purposes was a bad decision on the part of all the presidents. I don't think Kennedy should have done it. I don't think Johnson should have done it, and I don't think we should have done it. – Richard Nixon, 37th US President

37. Things are more like they are now than they have ever been. – Gerald R. Ford, 38th US President

38. We become not a melting pot but a beautiful mosaic. Different people, different beliefs, different yearnings, different hopes, different dreams. – Jimmy Carter [39th US President, 1977-1981]

39. Politics is supposed to be the second oldest profession. I have come to realize that it bears a very close resemblance to the first. – Ronald Reagan, 40th US President

40. Read my lips – No. New. Taxes. – George H. W. Bush, 41st US President

41. When I took office, only high energy physicists had ever heard of

what is called the Worldwide Web. . . Now even my cat has its own page. – Bill Clinton, 42nd US President

42. Do I forget the lessons of September 11th and take the word of a madman, or do I take action to defend our country? Faced with that choice, I will defend America every time. – George W. Bush, 43rd US President

Other Languages – page 455

French

1. Mais qu'est-ce que signifie 'éphémère'? répéta le petit prince qui, de sa vie, n'avait renoncé à une question, une fois qu'il l'avait posée. Ça signifie 'qui est menacé de disparition prochaine'. Le Petit Prince, Antoine de Saint-Exupéry

    Translation: 'But what does that mean, 'ephemeral'?' repeated the little prince, who never in his life had let go of a question, once he had asked it. 'It means, 'which is in danger of speedy disappearance." – The Little Prince, Antoine de Saint-Exupéry

Spanish

2. En un lugar de la Mancha, de cuyo nombre no quiero acordarme, no ha mucho tiempo que vivía un hidalgo de los de lanza en astillero, adarga antigua, rocín flaco y galgo corredor.

    Translation: Some place in la Mancha, the name of which I do not want to remember, not so long ago lived one of those gentlemen that keeps a retired lance, an ancient buckler, a skinny horse, and a racing greyhound. –'Don Quixote', Miguel de Cervantes

Russian

3. К сожалению, я пока не говорю по-русски.
    Translation: 'Unfortunately, I cannot yet speak Russian.'

4. В одно ухо вошло, из другого вышло.
    Translation: 'In one ear out the other.'

5. Чтобы я тебя больше не видел!
    Translation: 'May I never set eyes on you again!'

6. Легче приобрести плохую репутацию, чем узбавиться от неё.
    Translation: 'It is easier to acquire a bad reputation, than to get rid of it.'

Latin

7. A fronte praecipitivm a tergo lvpi.
    Translation: A precipice in front, wolves behind (between a rock and a hard place).

8. Braccae tvae aperivntvr.
    Translation. Your fly is open.

9. Certe, toto, sentio nos in kansate non iam adesse.
    Translation: You know, Toto, I have a feeling we're not in Kansas anymore.

10. Coniectvralem artem esse medicinam.
    Translation: Medicine is the art of guessing. (Aulus Cornelius Celsus)

11. Cvi peccare licet peccat minvs.
    Translation: One who is allowed to sin, sins less. (Ovid)

12. Conlige suspectos semper habitos.
    Translation: Round up the usual suspects

13. Da mihi sis cerevisiam dilutam.
    Translation: I'll have a light beer.

14. Da mihi sis crvstvm Etrvscvm cvm omnibvs in eo.
    Translation: I'll have a pizza with everything on it.

15. De gvstibvs non est dispvtandvm.
    Translation: There's no accounting for taste.
16. De nihilo nihil.
    Translation: Nothing comes from nothing. (Lucretius)
17. De dvobvs malis minvs est semper eligendvm.
    Translation: One must always choose the lesser of two evils. (Thomas a Kempis)
18. Dvm excvsare credis, accvsas.
    Translation: When you believe you are excusing yourself, you are accusing yourself. (St. Jerome)
19. Etiam capillvs vnvs habet vmbram.
    Translation: Even one hair has a shadow. (Publilius Syrus)
20. Age. Fac vt gavdeam
    Translation: Go ahead. Make my day!
21. Fas est et ab hoste doceri
    Translation: It's proper to learn even from an enemy. (Ovid)
22. Fortiter Fideliter Forsan Feliciter
    Translation: Bravely, faithfully, perhaps successfully
23. Gvtta cavat lapidem, non vi sed saepe cadendo
    Translation: The drop excavates the stone, not with force but by falling often. (Ovid)
24. Heu! Tintinnvntivs mevs sonat!
    Translation: Darn! There goes my beeper!
25. Horas non nvmero nisi serenas
    Translation: I count only the bright hours. (Inscription on ancient sundials.)
26. Illegitimis nil carborvndvm.
    Translation: Don't let the bastards grind you down.
27. Materiam svperabat opvs.
    Translation: The workmanship was better than the subject matter. (Ovid)
28. Nam et ipsa scientia potestas es.
    Translation: Knowledge is power. (Sir Francis Bacon)
29. Omnes vvlnerant, vltima necat
    Translation: All (hours) wound, the last kills. (inscription on solar clocks)
30: Perscriptio in manibvs tabellariorvm est
    Translation: The check is in the mail
31. Potes cvrrere sed te occvlere non potes.
    Translation: You can run, but you can't hide
32. Pvrgamentvm init, exit pvrgamentvm.
    Translation: Garbage in, garbage out.
33. Qvad nescivnt eos non interficiet.
    Translation: What they don't know won't kill them.
34. Qvid qvid latine dictvm sit, altvm videtvr.
    Translation: Anything said in Latin sounds profound.
35. Sativs est impvnitum relinqui facinvs nocentis, qvam innocentem damnari
    Translation: It is better that a crime is left unpunished than that an innocent man is punished. (Corpus Iuris Civilis)
36. Sed qvis custodiet ipsos custodes?
    Translation: Who watches the watchmen? (Juvenal)

37. Si fallatis officivm, quaestor infitias eat se qvicqvam scire de factis vestries.
   Translation: If you fail, the secretary will disavow all knowledge of your activities.
38. Si hoc legere scis nimivm ervditionis habes.
   Translation: Essentially it says, 'if you can read this, you're overeducated.'
39. Silent enim leges inter arma.
   Translation: Laws are silent in times of war. (Cicero)
40. Tempvs edax rervm.
   Translation: Time is the devourer of things (time flies)
41. Vltra posse nemo obligatvr.
   Translation: No one is obligated beyond what he is able to do.
42. Vt desint vires, tamen est lavdanda volvntas.
   Translation: Although the power is lacking, the will is commendable. (Ovid)
43. Veni, Vidi, volo in domvm redire.
   Translation: I came, I saw, I want to go home.
44. Verveces tvi similes pro ientacvlo mihi appositi svnt.
   Translation: I have jerks like you for breakfast
45. Vigilando, agendo, bene consvlendo, prospera omnia cedvnt.
   Translation: By watching, by doing, by counsulting well, these things yield all things prosperous. (Sallust)
46. Vinvm bellvm iucvnvmqve est, sed animo corporeqve caret.
   Translation: It's a nice little wine, but it lacks character and depth
47. Audio, video, disco.
   Translation: I hear, I see, I learn.
48. Vale, et pro piscibvs omnibvs grativs ago.
   Translation: So long, and thanks for all the fish.

Kryptos – page 501

1. BETWEEN SUBTLE SHADING AND THE ABSENCE OF LIGHT LIES THE NUANCE OF IQLUSION.
2. IT WAS TOTALLY INVISIBLE. HOW'S THAT POSSIBLE? THEY USED THE EARTH'S MAGNETIC FIELD. X THE INFORMATION WAS GATHERED AND TRANSMITTED UNDERGRUUND TO AN UNKNOWN LOCATION. X DOES LANGLEY KNOW ABOUT THIS? THEY SHOULD, IT'S BURIED OUT THERE SOMEWHERE. X WHO KNOWS THE EXACT LOCATION? ONLY WW. THIS WAS HIS LAST MESSAGE: X THIRTY EIGHT DEGREES FIFTY-SEVEN MINUTES SIX POINT FIVE SECONDS NORTH, SEVENTY SEVEN DEGREES EIGHT MINUTES FORTY-FOUR SECONDS WEST. ID BY ROWS
3. SLOWLY, DESPARATLY SLOWLY, THE REMAINS OF PASSAGE DEBRIS THAT ENCUMBERED THE LOWER PART OF THE DOORWAY WAS REMOVED. WITH TREMBLING HANDS I MADE A TINY BREACH IN THE UPPER LEFT-HAND CORNER AND THEN, WIDENING THE HOLE A LITTLE, I INSERTED THE CANDLE AND PEERED IN. THE HOT AIR ESCAPING FROM THE CHAMBER CAUSED THE FLAME TO FLICKER, BUT PRESENTLY DETAILS OF THE ROOM WITHIN EMERGED FROM THE MIST. X CAN YOU SEE ANYTHING Q?
   - Paraphrased extract from the diary of Howard Carter on November 26, 1922, the day he discovered King Tutankhamun's tomb

The Kryptos Morse
1. SOS
2. RQ
3. LUCID MEMORY
4. T IS YOUR POSITION
5. DIGETAL INTERPRETATU
6. VIRTUALLY INVISIBLE
7. SHADOW FORCES

Example – page 574

II.   Special Characteristics of Mr. Babbage's Analytical Engine.

1.   The mill. – The fundamental operation of Mr. Babbage's analytical engine is simple addition. This and the other elementary rules of subtraction, multiplication, and division, and all combinations of these, are performed in what is called 'the mill.' All the shifts which have to take place, such as changing addition into subtraction by throwing a reversing train into gear, or the shift of the decimal place, carrying and borrowing, and so forth, are effected by a system of rotating cams acting upon or actuated by bell-cranks, tangs, and other similar devices commonly used in shifting machinery, sometimes under the name of clutches or escapements. These clutches and bell cranks control the purely additive and carrying processes effected in the additive trains described in the note to § I., and, being themselves suitably directed, secure that the proper processes shall be performed upon the proper subject-matter of operation, and duly recorded, or used, as may be required.

2.   The store. – A series of columns, each containing a series of wheels, constitutes the store. This store, which may be in three or more dimensions, both receives the results of operations performed in the mill, and serves as a store for the numbers which are to be used in the mill, whether as original or as fresh subjects of operation in it. Each column in the store corresponds to a definite number, to which it is set either automatically or by hand, and the number of digits in this number is limited by the number of wheels carried on the shaft of the column. The wheels gear into a series of racks, which can be thrown into or out of gear by means of the cards.

3.   Variable cards. – All the numbers which are the subject of operation in the mill, whether they are the result of previous operations therein, or new numbers to be operated upon for the first time, are introduced to it in the form of Jacquard cards, such as are used in weaving. One set of wires or axes transfers the numbers on these cards to the subject of operation in the mill, exactly as similar cards direct which of the warp threads are to be pushed up, and which down, in the Jacquard loom. The mill itself punches such cards when required.

4.   Operation cards. – A different set of cards selects and prescribes the sequence of operations. These act, not upon the number wheels of the mill or store, but upon the cams and clutches which direct the gearing of these wheels and trains.

–   Extract from The Report of the Committee of the British Association for the Advancement of Science which, in 1878, recommended against constructing the Analytical Engine.

HELPFUL
REFERENCES

MORSE CODE TABLE

The Morse Code was developed by Samuel Morse (1791-1872), inventor of the telegraph. Samuel Morse assigned dots and dashes to the letters of the alphabet according to the frequency of their usage in the English language. The letters E and T, which are used frequently, each use only a single dot or dash, while the infrequently-used letters X and V are saddled with more dots and dashes:

A	.-	0	-----
B	-...	1	.----
C	-.-.	2	..---
D	-..	3	...--
E	.	4	....-
F	..-.	5	.....
G	--.	6	-....
H	....	7	--...
I	..	8	---..
J	.---	9	----.
K	-.-		
L	.-..	Fullstop	.-.-.-
M	--	Comma	--..--
N	-.	Query	..--..
O	---		
P	.--.		
Q	--.-		
R	.-.		
S	...		
T	-		
U	..-		
V	...-		
W	.--		
X	-..-		
Y	-.--		
Z	--..		

ENGLISH FREQUENCY TABLES

Most commonly used letters
1. E
2. T
3. A, O, N, R, I, S
4. H
5. D, L, F, C, M, U
6. G, Y, P, W, B
7. V, K, X, J, Q, Z

Bigrams (with different letters)
1. TH
2. HE
3. AN
4. RE
5. IN
6. ON
7. AT
8. ND
9. ST
10. ES
11. EN
12. OF
13. TE

Bigrams (with the same letter)
1. LL
2. EE
3. SS
4. OO
5. TT
6. FF
7. RR
8. NN
9. CC
10. MM
11. GG

Trigrams
1. THE
2. ING
3. CON
4. ENT
5. ERE
6. ERS
7. EVE
8. FOR
9. HER
10. TED
11. TER
12. TIO
13. VER

Letters which begin English words
1. T
2. A
3. S, I, O, W, H
4. B, M, F, C
5. D, P, L, N, R, E

Letters which end English words
1. E
2. D, S
3. T, N
4. R, Y
5. O, F
6. H, G, L, A

Repeated letters in the English language
1. LL
2. FF, SS
3. PP
4. EE
5. OO
6. ZZ, MM, RR, TT, CC, DD
7. GG
8. NN
9. BB

Most commonly used words in the English language, in order of frequency
1. the and to of a I in was he that
2. it his her you as had with for she not
3. at but be my on have him is said me
4. which by so this all from they no were if
5. would or when what there been one could very an
6. who them Mr we now more out do are up
7. their your will little than then some into any well
8. much about time know should man did like upon such
9. never only good how before other see must am own
10. come down say after think made might being Mrs again

Most common two-letter words
1. to of in he it
2. as at be my on
3. is me by so no
4. if or an we do
5. up am go us oh ye

A lengthy example is provided here, to aid with frequency analysis and the counting of bigrams and trigrams. For a hint (the key), check page 526. For the solution, go to page 569.

GG. Qmtlgaf Leapalrtpgqrglq ki Hp. Nannact'q Ajafxrglaf Tjcgjt.

1. Ret hgff.–Ret isjyahtjraf kmtpargkj ki Hp. Nannact'q ajafxrglaf tjcgjt gq qghmft ayygrgkj. Regq ajy ret kretp tfthtjrapx psftq ki qsnrpalrgkj, hsfrgmfglargkj, ajy ygugqgkj, ajy aff lkhngjargkjq ki retqt, apt mtpikphty gj vear gq laffty 'ret hgff.' Aff ret qegirq vegle eaut rk radt mfalt, qsle aq leajcgjc ayygrgkj gjrk qsnrpalrgkj nx repkvgjc a ptutpqgjc rpagj gjrk ctap, kp ret qegir ki ret ytlghaf mfalt, lappxgjc ajy nkppkvgjc, ajy qk ikpre, apt tiitlrty nx a qxqrth ki pkrargjc lahq alrgjc smkj kp alrsarty nx ntff-lpajdq, rajcq, ajy kretp qghgfap ytugltq lkhhkjfx sqty gj qegirgjc halegjtpx, qkhtrghtq sjytp ret jaht ki lfsrletq kp tqlamthtjrq. Retqt lfsrletq ajy ntff lpajdq lkjrpkf ret msptfx ayygrgut ajy

■ ■ ■ ■ 575 ■ ■ ■ ■

lappxgjc mpkltqqtq tiitlrty gj ret ayygrgut rpagjq ytqlpgnty gj ret jkrt rk § G., ajy, ntgjc rethqtfutq qsgranfx ygptlrty, qtlspt rear ret mpkmtp mpkltqqtq qeaff nt mtpikphty smkj ret mpkmtp qsnbtlr-harrtp ki kmtpargkj, ajy ysfx ptlkpyty, kp sqty, aq hax nt ptosgpty.

2. Ret qrkpt.–A qtpgtq ki lkfshjq, tale lkjragjgjc a qtpgtq ki vettfq, lkjqrgrsrtq ret qrkpt. Regq qrkpt, vegle hax nt gj reptt kp hkpt yghtjqgkjq, nkre ptltgutq ret ptqsfrq ki kmtpargkjq mtpikphty gj ret hgff, ajy qtputq aq a qrkpt ikp ret jshntpq vegle apt rk nt sqty gj ret hgff, vetretp aq kpgcgjaf kp aq iptqe qsnbtlrq ki kmtpargkj gj gr. Tale lkfshj gj ret qrkpt lkpptqmkjyq rk a ytigjgrt jshntp, rk vegle gr gq qtr tgretp asrkharglaffx kp nx eajy, ajy ret jshntp ki ygcgrq gj regq jshntp gq fghgrty nx ret jshntp ki vettfq lappgty kj ret qeair ki ret lkfshj. Ret vettfq ctap gjrk a qtpgtq ki paldq, vegle laj nt repkvj gjrk kp ksr ki ctap nx htajq ki ret lapyq.

3. Uapganft lapyq.–Aff ret jshntpq vegle apt ret qsnbtlr ki kmtpargkj gj ret hgff, vetretp retx apt ret ptqsfr ki mptugksq kmtpargkjq retptgj, kp jtv jshntpq rk nt kmtparty smkj ikp ret igpqr rght, apt gjrpkyslty rk gr gj ret ikph ki Balosapy lapyq, qsle aq apt sqty gj vtaugjc. Kjt qtr ki vgptq kp awtq rpajqitpq ret jshntpq kj retqt lapyq rk ret qsnbtlr ki kmtpargkj gj ret hgff, twalrfx aq qghgfap lapyq ygptlr vegle ki ret vapm reptayq apt rk nt msqety sm, ajy vegle ykvj, gj ret Balosapy fkkh. Ret hgff grqtfi msjletq qsle lapyq vetj ptosgpty.

4. Kmtpargkj lapyq.–A ygiitptjr qtr ki lapyq qtftlrq ajy mptqlpgntq ret qtostjlt ki kmtpargkjq. Retqt alr, jkr smkj ret jshntp vettfq ki ret hgff kp qrkpt, nsr smkj ret lahq ajy lfsrletq vegle ygptlr ret ctapgjc ki retqt vettfq ajy rpagjq.

–Twrpalr ipkh Ret Ptmkpr ki ret Lkhhgrrtt ki ret Npgrgqe Aqqklgargkj ikp ret Ayuajlthtjr ki Qlgtjlt vegle, gj 1878, ptlkhhtjyty acagjqr lkjqrpslrgjc ret Ajafxrglaf Tjcgjt.

XENOCRYPT FREQUENCY CHARTS

These charts show how letter frequency distribution differs between English, Spanish, French, Latin, and Russian.

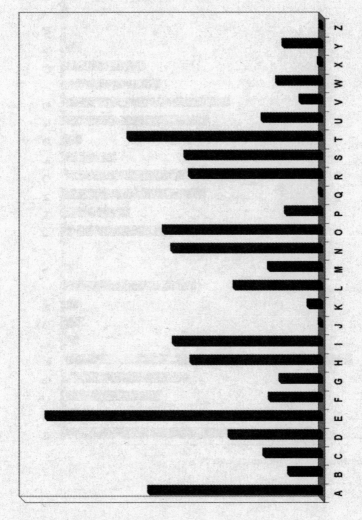

English letter frequency chart

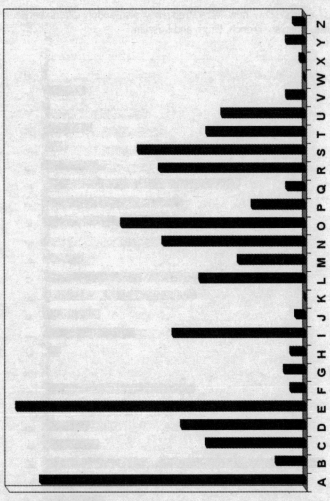

Spanish letter frequency chart

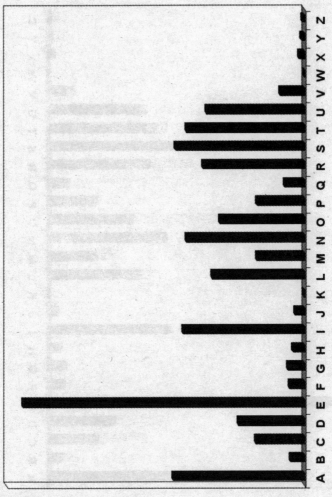

French letter frequency chart

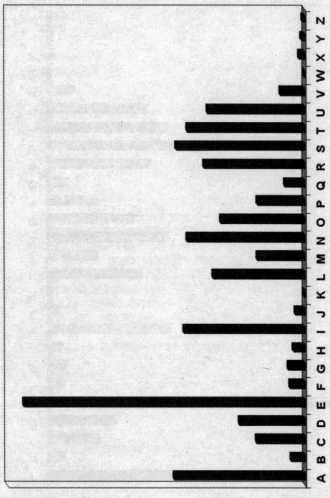

Latin letter frequency chart

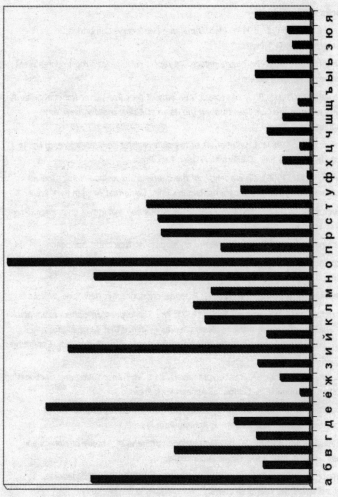

Russian letter frequency chart

RECOMMENDED READING

Books – Non-Fiction

Bach, E. & Shallit, J. (1996). *Algorithmic number theory*. Cambridge, Massachusetts: MIT Press.

Bamford, J. (1982). *The puzzle palace : a report on America's most secret agency*. New York: Penguin Books.

Bamford, J. (2001). *Body of secrets: Anatomy of the ultra-secret National Security Agency: From the Cold War through the dawn of a new century*. New York: Doubleday.

Barker, W. G. (1984). *Cryptanalysis of the shift register generated stream cipher systems*. Laguna Hills, California: Aegean Park Press.

Barker, W. G. (1996). *Cryptanalysis of the double transposition cipher: Includes problems and computer programs*. Laguna Hills, California: Aegean Park Press.

Bauer, F. L. (2002). *Decrypted secrets : methods and maxims of cryptology*. New York: Springer.

Buchmann, J. (2004). *Introduction to cryptography*. New York: Springer.

Denning, D. E. R. (1982). *Cryptography and data security*. Reading, Massachusetts: Addison-Wesley.

Ferguson, N. & Schneier, B. (2003). *Practical cryptography*. New York: Wiley.

Friedman, W. F. & Friedman, E. S. (1957). *The Shakespearean ciphers examined: An analysis of cryptographic systems used as evidence that some author other than William Shakespeare wrote the plays commonly attributed to him*. Cambridge: Cambridge University Press.

Friedman, W. (1993). *Military cryptanalysis, Part IV, Transposition and fractionating Systems*. Laguna Hills, California: Aegean Park Press.

Friedman, W. (1996). *Military cryptanalysis, Part I, Monoalphabetic substitution systems*. Laguna Hills, California: Aegean Park Press.

Gaines, Helen Fouché (1939). *Elementary cryptanalysis: A study of ciphers and their solution*. New York: Dover Publications.

Gannon, J. (2001). *Stealing secrets, telling lies: how spies and codebreakers helped shape the twentieth century*. Washington, D.C.: Brassey's.

Gardner, M. (1984). *Codes, ciphers, and secret writing*. New York: Dover Publications.

Goldreich, O. (1999). *Modern cryptography, probabilistic proofs, and pseudorandomness*. New York: Springer.

Goldreich, O. (2001). *Foundations of cryptography: Basic tools*. New York:

Cambridge University Press.

Graff, J. (2001) *Cryptography and e-commerce: A Wiley tech brief*. New York: Wiley.

Hershey, J. (2003). *Cryptography demystified*. New York: McGraw-Hill.

Kahn, David (1996). *The Codebreakers : The Story of Secret Writing. 2d ed.* New York: Scribner.

Knudsen, J. B. (1998). *Java cryptography*. Sebastopol, California: O'Reilly.

Koblitz, N. (1994). *A course in number theory and cryptography*. New York: Springer-Verlag.

Koblitz, B. (1998). *Algebraic aspects of cryptography*. New York: Springer.

Konheim, A. G. (1981). *Cryptography: A primer*. New York: Wiley.

Kozaczuk, W. (1984). *Enigma : How the German machine cipher was broken, and how it was read by the Allies in World War Two*. Frederick, Maryland: University Publications of America.

Kranakis, E. (1986). *Primality and cryptography*. New York: Wiley.

Kullback, S. (1976). *Statistical Methods in Cryptanalysis*. Laguna Hills, California: Aegean Park Press.

Levy, S. (2001). *Crypto: How the code rebels beat the government, saving privacy in the digital age*. New York: Viking.

Lewand, R. E. (2000). *Cryptological mathematics*. Washington, DC: Mathematical Association of America.

Luby, M. (1996). *Pseudorandomness and cryptographic applications*. Princeton, New Jersey: Princeton University Press.

Mao, W. (2003). *Modern cryptography: Theory and practice*. Upper Saddle River, New Jersey: Prentice Hall PTR.

Marks, L. (1998). *Between silk and cyanide: A codemaker's war*. New York: Free Press.

Menezes, A. J., Van OorSchot, P. C. & Vanstone, S. A. (1997). *Handbook of applied cryptography*. Boca Raton, Florida: CRC Press.

Meyer, C. H. & Matyas, S. M. (1982). *Cryptography : A new dimension in computer data security : A guide for the design and implementation of secure systems*. New York: Wiley.

Newton, D. E. (1997). *Encyclopedia of cryptology*. Santa Barbara, California: ABC-CLIO.

Owen, D. (1978). *Battle of wits : a history of psychology & deception in modern warfare*. London: Cooper.

Parker, H. (1916). *Manual for the solution of military ciphers*. Fort Leavenworth, Kansas: Press of the Army Service Schools.

Patterson, W. (1987). *Mathematical cryptology for computer scientists and mathematicians*. Totowa, New Jersey: Rowman & Littlefield.

Piper, F. & Murphy, S. (2002). *Cryptography: A very short introduction*. New York: Oxford University Press.

Prados, J. (1995). *Combined fleet decoded : the secret history of American intelligence and the Japanese Navy in World War II*. New York: Random House.

Salomaa, A. (1996). *Public-key cryptography*. New York: Springer.

Schneier, B. (1995). *Applied cryptography: Protocols, algorithms, and source code in C*. New York: Wiley.

Schneier, B., Kelsey, J., Whiting, D., Wagner, D. Hall, C. & Ferguson, N. (1999). *The twofish encryption algorithm: A 128-bit block cipher*. New York: Wiley.

Schneier, B. (2000). *Secrets and lies : Digital security in a networked world*. New York: Wiley.

Simmons, G. J. (ed.) (1992). *Contemporary cryptology : The science of information integrity*. Piscataway, New Jersey: IEEE Press.

Singh, Simon (1999). *The code book: The science of secrecy from ancient egypt to quantum cryptography*. New York: Anchor.

Sinkov, A. (1968). *Elementary cryptanalysis; A mathematical approach*. New York: Random House.

Smith, L. D. (1943). *Cryptography, the science of secret writing*. New York: W. W. Norton.

Stallings, W. (2003). *Cryptography and network security: Principles and practice*. Upper Saddle River, New Jersey: Prentice Hall.

Stinson, D. (2002). *Cryptography: Theory and practice*. Boca Raton, Florida: Chapman & Hall/CRC.

Van Tilborg, H. C. A. (1988). *An introduction to cryptology*. Boston: Kluwer Academic Publishers.

Wagstaff, S. S. (2003). *Cryptanalysis of number theoretic ciphers*. Boca Raton, Florida: Chapman & Hall/CRC.

Washington, L. C. (2003). *Elliptic curves : number theory and cryptography*. Boca Raton, Florida: Chapman & Hall/CRC.

Wayner, Peter (2002). *Disappearing cryptography: Information hiding: Steganography & watermarking*. Boston: Morgan Kaufmann Publishers.

Welsh, D. (1988). *Codes and cryptography*. New York: Oxford University Press.

Yardley, H. (1931). *The American black chamber*. London: Faber & Faber Ltd.

Books – Fiction

Brown, D. (2003). *The Da Vinci code: A novel*. New York: Doubleday.

Brown, D. (2004). *Digital fortress*. New York: Thomas Dune Books.

Doyle, A. C. (1997). *The adventure of the dancing men and other Sherlock Holmes stories*. New York: Dover Publications.

Harris, R. (1995). *Enigma*. New York: Random House.

Hill, T. (2003). *The cryptographer*. London: Faber & Faber.

Littell, R. (1981). *The amateur: A novel*. New York: Simon and Schuster.

Myers, K. (2000). *Code breaker*. Bend, Oregon; Salvo Press.

Passman, D. (2000). *Mirage*. New York: Warner Books.

Poe, E. A. (1991). *The gold-bug and other tales*. New York: Dover Publications.

Stephenson, N. (1999). *Cryptonomicon*. New York: Avon Press.

Web Resources

American Cryptogram Association (2005). *Resources*.
http://www.cryptogram.org/resources.html

Dunin, E. (2003). *Famous unsolved codes and ciphers*.
http://www.elonka.com/UnsolvedCodes.html

Dunin, E. (2005). *Recommended reading*.
http://elonka.com/kryptos/RecommendedCryptoReading.html

Kim, S. (2004). *Scott Kim, Puzzle Master*. http://scottkim.com/

Schneier, B. (2005). *Crypto-Gram newsletter*. http://www.schneier.com/crypto-gram.html

United States Department of the Army (1990). *Basic cryptanalysis* (Field manual 34-40-2). http://www.umich.edu/~umich/fm-34-40-2/

Wikipedia: Books on cryptography (2005).
http://en.wikipedia.org/wiki/Books_on_cryptography

ACKNOWLEDGEMENTS

Many people contributed to the puzzles within these pages, in a large international project that was coordinated via the internet over the course of a few months.

A few that I would like to thank individually are:

David Allen Wilson, who submitted dozens of unusual ciphers (including some in other languages!), and spent countless hours compiling glossary entries, writing up code tips, obsessing over proofreading, and testing hundreds of the other ciphers that came pouring in. David is a truly unique individual, whose skills and challenges have inspired me in my own quest for self-improvement. I am honoured to be able to call him a friend.

Edward 'Ted' Park for researching information on unsolved codes, and testing many puzzles throughout the book

Kurt J. Simmons II, author of the 'Caesarean Section', and several other puzzles

Scott Kim for his creative description of a pencil and paper way to understand asymmetric key cryptography

Andy Finkenstadt who set up the MediaWiki database that allowed for the coordination of this massive project

Thorne Kontos, who researched dozens of quotes from British Prime Ministers throughout the centuries, and helped test many of the harder ciphers

Guillermo Oscar 'Tordek' Freschi of Argentina and José Luis Saldías of Uruguay, who helped with the Spanish-language section of the book

Anatoly K. and Natalia Prokhorovich for testing the Russian ciphers

Elizabeth H. Banks, MLS, who worked on the bibliography, and answered countless other questions about formatting and indexing details

Kathryn Kaufman for researching many of the quotes to be encrypted, as well as helping to test several puzzles

Mike Combridge for cleaning up some of the historical cipher graphics, and supplying additional information about the Dorabella Cipher

Other thanks go to:

Everyone who helped create and test the puzzles that went into this book, especially Andrew J. Bromage, Larry McElhiney, Michael Madison, Richard L. Robinson, Tim Judkins, Dan 'Aestetix' McArdle, Rob Marston, and Jennifer Zipperer

Bryan Paschke for legal assistance and moral support

Pete Duncan at Constable & Robinson for convincing me to take on this project in the first place. And Les Dominey for his clever typesetting.

Bruce Schneier, Simon Singh, David Kahn, Jim Gillogly, the American Cryptogram Association, and Peter Wayner for their inspiring books and articles about cryptography

And many others who helped in many ways, both small and large, including:

Adam Vartanian, Aaron 'Baudburn' Kobayashi, Alisha Dean, Angela J. Slick, Ben Carter, Bill Gage, Billy Goto, Carrie Pritchard, Casey Hall, Chris 'Xenon' Hanson, Chris Speidel, Dan Kaminsky, Daniel Mallett, Dave Weinstein, David Halstead, David Whatley, Ed Gawrelak, Ed Scheidt, Evelyn Hirata, Graham Cox, Grant Guenter, Hannah Carter, Jackie Griffith, Jeff Gatlin, Jeri Ellsworth, Jim, Jonathan Tabor, John Wilson, Jonathan 'Giezr' McCloud, Kyle 'Deuce' Knight, Lane 'Thé' Whatley, Maxwell Zeuster, Michael Niemeyer, pixelfairy, Randal L. Schwartz, Rachel Carter, Rhoda Hall, Robin McLaughlin, T.J. Dunin Vine, Tim MacDonald, Tj Fallon, Tontin, Virgil G., Wilhelm M. Plotz, and Wendy Despain

Thank you all!

The following permissions to reproduce illustrations are also gratefully acknowledged: Edgar Allan Poe Challenge Ciphers and Edward Elgar's Cipher (Mike Combridge), used with permission of the Edgar Allan Poe Society of Baltimore, eapoe.org; Voynich Manuscript pages 19, 31, 67 and 94 (Takeshi Takahashi), used with permission of the Beinecke Rare Book and Manuscript Library, Yale University; decrypted text from Zodiac Killer message, unsolved Zodiac Killer message from 20 April 1970, and letter sent to the San Francisco Chronicle on 8 November 1969 (Tom Voigt), reprinted by permission of zodiackiller.com; Kryptos Sculpture (James Sanborn), used with permission; Phaistos Disk (Deniart Systems), used with permission of www.deniart.com; Russian letter frequency chart data, used courtesy of www.statsoft.ru.

As a final note: every cipher in this book was tested by at least two people, though some errors may have still crept in. It is worth remembering that nearly every 'real' historical cipher also had its own errors and typos. Sometimes encryption discrepancies were intentional, as a way of making a code more difficult to crack, but most had no better explanation than simple human error, especially when written under wartime conditions!

If you do discover any mistakes, please let me know, by writing to Elonka.Dunin@gmail.com. You can also find an 'Updates and Errata' page on the internet, at: www.elonka.com/mammoth

GLOSSARY

ADFGVX – A cipher originally created by a matrix of 5x5 (ADFGX x ADFGX) to include the alphabet, then 6x6 (ADFGVX x ADFGVX) to include the alphabet and 10 digits.

AES – A symmetric 128-bit block data encryption technique developed by Belgian cryptographers Joan Daemen and Vincent Rijmen.

Alice – The originator of a message. Other names used are Bob, Dave, Eve, Mallory, Trent, etc.

Amsco – Incomplete columnar transposition cipher

Anagram – A 'jumbled up' word or phrase.

Aristocrat – A simple substitution cipher, where the word divisions and or punctuation are still retained. See Patristocrat.

ASCII – American Standard Code for Information Interchange, a means of representing characters, numbers, and commands as numbers from 0 through 127 so they can be easily recognized on computers.

Asymmetric encryption – As opposed to symmetric encryption. This system is designed such that the key used for encryption is different from the key used for decryption. Furthermore, the decryption key cannot (at least in any reasonable amount of time) be calculated from the encryption key. This algorithm is also sometimes called 'public-key' because the encryption key can be made public. A complete stranger can use the encryption key to encrypt a message, but only a specific person with the corresponding decryption key can decrypt the message.

Atbash – A substitution cipher in which the last letter of the alphabet replaces the first: a = Z, b = Y, c = X, ... z = A.

Autokey – Any cipher that uses the text (either plaintext or ciphertext) as part of the encryption key.

Base64 – A binary-based block substitution, typically used by computers to encode 8-bit binary data into a printable subset of ASCII.

Bazeries cipher – A simple substitution and transposition cipher.

Beaufort cipher – A reciprocal substitution similar to the Vigenère cipher

Bifid – A fractionated cipher

Binary – A number system that is limited to exclusively 0 and 1

Bit – A 0 or a 1

Block cipher – Any algorithm that operates on plaintext in groups of symbols of fixed size.

Blowfish – A 64-bit block cipher with a variable length key.

Bob – The recipient of a message. See Alice.

Brute force method – To methodically eliminate incorrect solutions until the correct one, if it exists, is found.

Byte – Eight bits

Cadenus cipher – Columnar transposition.

Caesar cipher – This simple substitution technique is the replacing of the letters of the alphabet by those a preset number farther down. If no number is specified, it usually means a substitution of 3 (A = D, B = E, etc.)

Carol – A name tag given to a third, valid, participant in communications. See Alice.

Checkerboard – A cipher system devised by the Greek writer, Polybius

Cipher – A method of encrypting or decrypting. May also be used to refer to a ciphertext itself.

Cipher alphabet – The list of equivalents used to transform the plaintext into the encrypted form.

Ciphertext – The enciphered, unintelligible form of a message.

Cleartext – The plaintext.

Code – In the strict cryptological sense, this is an encryption system which, instead of using an algorithm that lets any type of message be encrypted, consists of potentially thousands of words, phrases, letters, and/or syllables with associated codewords or numbers. To decipher a code usually requires access to a 'codebook' with the equivalents. In another looser sense, the word 'code' may be used to refer to all types of ciphers and codes.

Coincidence analysis – Any statistical analysis of the ciphertext that involves counting 'coincidences': that is, letters that are the same. Examples include the Index of Coincidence, the Friedman test and the Kappa test.

Complete columnar transposition – The plaintext is written from left to right so that it entirely fills a square or rectangle. The text is then removed by columns, sometimes in order of a key.

Concealment cipher – A way of hiding a message in such a way that it is not immediately clear that there even is a hidden message. For example, invisible ink.

Cryptanalysis – The study of ciphers with the intent of solving cryptograms or cryptographic systems.

Cryptography – The concealment of information by means of a code or a cipher. From the Greek 'hidden writing'.

Cryptogram – An encrypted message.

Cryptology – The mathematical and/or scientific theory underlying both cryptography and cryptanalysis.

CT – See ciphertext

Cuneiform – A wedge-shaped writing invented by the Sumerians.

Dave – A name tag given to a fourth, valid, participant in communications. See Alice.

Decipher – The solving of cryptograms or cryptographic systems.

Decimal system – The base-10 number system, or, a number system that is based on ten digits.

DES, Triple DES – DES (Data Encryption Standard) is a widely used modern encryption algorithm that is a US and international standard. It is a symmetric algorithm, meaning that the same key is used for both encryption and decryption.

Diffie-Hellman algorithm – A revolutionary new way of generating keys that was invented in 1976. See Asymmetric encryption.

Digraph – A pair of letters.

Elliptic curve cryptography – An encryption method that is based on the mathematical properties of an ellipsis. Similar to the public key system, this system is also easier to encode than decode.

Encryption – The process of disguising a message in such a way as to hide its meaning

Enigma machine – A portable cipher machine widely used by the Germans during World War II. It was named after Sir Edward Elgar's musical composition, 'The Enigma Variations'.

Eve – An 'evesdropper', but who has no control over the data going between Alice and Bob. See Alice.

Feistel network – A method for creating a block cipher. They generally involve several combined methods such as bit-shuffling, substitutions, and other digital transformations (such as XOR).

Fibonacci cipher – A cipher based on the properties of the Fibonacci sequence.

Freemason cipher – Also known as the Pigpen cipher.

Friedman test – A means to estimate the key length of a Vigenère cipher.

Frequency analysis – A commonly used method to crack codes which involves counting the number of characters, bigrams, trigrams, and/or words and looking for those which are most common. This data can then be compared a standard frequency chart for the language in question, so that educated guesses can be made about which letter/word is which.

Goldbug cipher – A simple substitution cipher in Edgar Allan Poe's tale 'The Gold Bug'.

Grille cipher – A system that uses something like a piece of cardboard with holes cut into it to define which letters or words are used in a transposition-type system.

Gromark cipher – Transposition and substitution cipher.

Gronsfeld cipher – Polyalphabetic cipher, enciphered just like the Vigenère.

Hash – A hash (also called a 'digest') is a short fixed-length piece of data that represents the contents of a message. A mathematical function, which maps a message to a hash, is called a 'hash function'.

Hexadecimal – A number system that is base-16, instead of base-10 like the decimal system. It is commonly used to communicate digital data, because of the ease of converting from hexadecimal to binary.

Homophonic substitution – A complex substitution cipher where there are multiple possible ciphertext equivalents for each plaintext letter.

Incomplete columnar transposition – The plaintext is written from left to right such that it does not necessarily fill a square or rectangle. The text is then removed by columns, in order of a key.

Index of coincidence – Also known as 'IC'. It is used to determine whether or not two texts are written in the same language, by looking at what proportion of letter pairs are 'coincidences' (i.e. the same letter).

Jargon code – A way of hiding a message by talking around it in terms which are understandable to both sender and receiver, but may be incomprehensible (or unnoticed) by a third party observer.

Jefferson's wheel cipher – A complex substitution cipher by means of a cylinder with a series of wooden disks, each of which has a scrambled alphabet.

Kappa test – A means to estimate the key length of a Vigenère cipher.

Key – Also known as keyword, keyphrase, or key number, this is a way of modifying a particular cipher system. The key specifies such things as the arrangement of a cipher alphabet, or the pattern of a transposition.

Key length – The number of bits (letters, etc.) in an encryption algorithm's key; In general, the longer the key, the stronger the encryption.

Lipogram – A message that is constructed within certain constraints, such as a sentence that must be written without using the letter E.

Mallory – Mallory differs from Eve in that Mallory can disrupt, change, or alter the flow of information between Alice and Bob. See Alice.

Monoalphabetic – A simple substitution cipher, which uses only a single cipher alphabet.

Morbit cipher – A substitution cipher, which assigns numbers to Morse code values.

Morse code – A code specifically designed by Samuel Morse for communicating with the telegraph.

Myszkowski cipher – A variation of columnar transposition where the plaintext message is written into the tableau horizontally instead of vertically, and then the ciphertext is taken off by key order.

Nicodemus cipher – A transposition, followed by a polyalphabetic substitution, followed by a block cipher.

Nihilist substitution – A system whereby plaintext letters are replaced by their coordinates on a grid.

Null – Any letter or group of letters that is added to plaintext but is not part of the message.

Null cipher – A cipher in which the letters in the certain position of a string of words, not the words themselves, contain a meaning.

Octal – The base-8 number system.

One-time pad – Also known as OTP, this is a system in which a plaintext message is encrypted by applying it against a random set of characters, usually on a sheet of paper. After the message is encrypted, the page is 'torn off the pad' and never used again. The recipient has the same pad. The one-time pad, or OTP, is the only known 'perfect' encryption scheme, in the sense that any plaintext may map to any ciphertext with equal probability.

Patristocrat – An Aristocrat cipher broken into 5-letter groups, or otherwise modified such that the word length and/or punctuation information is removed.

Periodic Gromark – A transposition and substitution cipher.

PGP – A freeware electronic-mail security program, originally designed by Philip Zimmerman. It uses IDEA for data encryption, RSA (with keys up to 2047 bits) for key management and digital signatures, and MD5 as a one-way hash function.

Phi test – A means by which one can determine if a text has been enciphered with a monoalphabetic or polyalphabetic cipher.

Pig Latin – A simple form of manipulating speech by removing the first consonant of each word, placing it at the end of a word, and putting the sound -ay behind it. If a word begins with a vowel, add -yay instead.

Pigpen cipher – A simple substitution cipher which substitutes the shape of the grid in which the letter resides for the letter itself.

Plaintext – The unaltered, intelligible form of a text or information.

Playfair – A digraphic cipher, letters are encrypted and decrypted in pairs according to their location on a grid.

Pollux – A substitution cipher.

Polyalphabetic – A system that uses two or more cipher alphabets.

Polybius square – See checkerboard.

Private Key – The means by which a message is decrypted in asymmetric encryption.

PT – See Plaintext .

Progressive key – A type of cipher that has a steadily changing key as the encryption progresses through the message.

Public key – The means by which a message is encrypted in asymmetric encryption.

Public key cryptography – Public key cryptography differs from Symmetric key cryptography in that once a sender encrypts a message with another user's public key, only that recipient whose public key was used for the encryption of a message can decode the message by using that user's private key.

Quagmire variations – Variations on the Vigenère cipher.

Quantum cryptography – Cryptography that relies on the characteristics of quantum mechanics.

QWERTY – A standard layout of a typewriter keyboard. Taken from the order of the letters on the top left-hand row.

Ragbaby cipher – A substitution cipher.

Redefence cipher – A cipher in which the plaintext is written in a zigzag formation, and is then rewritten horizontally.

ROT-13 – A specific instance of the Caesar cipher whereby each letter is shifted 13 letters forward in the alphabet.

ROT-47 – A Caesar shift cipher that is similar to ROT-13, but, instead of shifting forward 13 spaces, shifts forward 47 spaces, and uses many printable ASCII characters instead of just A-Z.

Route cipher – A specific transposition cipher whereby the position of the letters are changed according to a path, or route.

RSA – RSA (named after its creators – Rivest, Shamir, and Adleman) is the most popular public-key algorithm.

SIGINT – Signals Intelligence – a department of the military whose function is intercepting and analyzing enemy communications.

Simple substitution – The consistent replacing of plaintext letters, numbers, and symbols, with other ciphertext letters, numbers, or symbols. Simple substitution always involves a direct one-to-one correspondence, as opposed to polyalphabetic or homophonic systems.

Skytale – A stick or rod used for transposition ciphers.

Slidefair cipher – A digraphic cipher.

Start/Skip transposition – The ciphertext is derived from the plaintext by 'skipping' a predetermined number of letters from a defined starting point.

Steganography – The embedding of information and images within other information and images such that the encipherment cannot be detected. See: Concealment cipher (and yes, there are secret messages in this book!)

Stream cipher – An algorithm that treats the plaintext as a stream of symbols.

Subkey – Part of a key.

Substitution – A class of ciphers where the the letters of the plaintext message are replaced by other letters, numbers or symbols

Symmetric key cryptography – An encryption scheme is considered to be symmetric if it uses the same key or method to encrypt a message, as it does to decrypt it.

Telephone dial code – A cipher based on the telephone dial.

Tetragraphic – A system of encryption that involves a set of equations in which the keys and plaintext letters have numerical values.

Transposition – A cipher system in which the order of the letters of the plaintext is changed, but the letters themselves are not changed.

Trifid – A fractionated cipher

Trigraph – A group of three successive letters.

Typewriter Code – A simple substitution code based on the layout of the typewriter keyboard.

UUencoding – A way of converting digital files into a series of printable ASCII characters that can be transmitted over the Internet.

Vigenère – A polyalphabetic cipher known as 'The Indecipherable Cipher' (Le Chiffre Indéchiffrable) in its day.

Xenocrypt – Any cipher which decrypts to a plaintext in a different language.

XOR – Exclusive-or operation. A way of modifying bits.

METAPUZZLE CLUES

There are dozens of metapuzzle hints hidden throughout the book. If you find any, you may wish to write them down here. It is also recommended that you write down *where* you found each clue (which page, which cipher/solution/key number), as that information may be important too. If you're not sure where to start, check the Introduction, and also read up on 'Concealment ciphers'.

INDEX